D1433369

LEARNING
AND ITS DISORDERS

Science and Behavior Books brings to those interested in the behavioral sciences important and timely books produced economically in durable vinyl covers. We solicit opinions and ideas from our readers.

THIS IS AN ORIGINAL EDITION

LEARNING
AND ITS DISORDERS

Edited by
I. N. Berlin, M.D. and S. A. Szurek, M.D.

The Langley Porter Child Psychiatry Series
Clinical Approaches to Problems of Childhood
Volume 1

SCIENCE AND BEHAVIOR BOOKS, INC.
577 College Avenue, Palo Alto, California 94306

Cover design by Deborah Sussman

Learning and Its Disorders

Third printing, July 1969

Library of Congress Card Catalogue Number: 66-18126

FOREWORD

Fritz Redl, Ph. D.

What a relief! At last perhaps we can get rid of the silly and wasteful controversy of "Learning Theory versus Psychiatry," into which so many writers seem to have clawed themselves so deeply that by now the whole field has trouble in disentangling itself.

It seems to me that we have been, for much too long a time, stuck in an entirely useless either-or trap. The idea that all learning can be reduced to what learning theorists have taught us about it, or that all teaching is but a matter of using the right techniques for catering to the cognitive needs of children, is as obsolete as, say, the concepts of aviation about the time of the Great Balloons. Of course, the naivete with which psychiatry seemed to look at this in years past—namely that all learning disturbances can be reduced to the problem of the kid who can't spell because the letter "F" reminds him of his drunken father, or that all that teachers have to worry about is to keep their "emotional-health" noses clean and to stop their neuroses from creeping into the countertransference to their students—is indeed equally obsolete.

We know better now. Of course, if I tried hard, I probably could still drum up a few individuals on either side of the fence who spend their time building straw-theories out of their opponent's blind spots, setting a match to them, and watching them go up in smoke. (By the way, I do not begrudge anybody that fun, for fun it is, indeed. I might even concede that some of these strawman-orgies have their use—who else could study anybody's blind spots as thoroughly as one who wants to use them for this kind of sport?) But it is time we put this learning-theory-versus-psychiatry issue where it belongs: into the museum of historically fascinating beginnings of a search for what really counts.

Even after we get rid of the above-mentioned naivete though, the real problem remains tougher than either side seems to realize. The roadblocks along the way are formidable. Among them I would give priority to these:

Teachers have a rough time gaining access to descriptions of what psychiatrists and other therapists really do when they say they are treating the "emotional components of learning disturbances." Such treatment processes are laborious, tedious; their description unavoidably involves, as any other medical or therapeutic operation would, strange concepts and even stranger procedures. Also, where would you find such descriptions? And if you did find them, how would you get the time to read them?

Psychiatrists or clinicians in general find themselves in an equally rough predicament. It is one thing to speculate on "Mental Health and the Teaching Profession" or to theorize about the "Neurotic Components of Learning Blocks": it is another to become familiar with the real issues involved in the complexity of the daily struggle of group life in a classroom. Materials which really shed light on the interwovenness, in learning as well as in teaching, of "cognitive" and related factors on the one hand, with the variables usually listed under headings like "Personality" or "Emotional disturbance or health" on the other, are still scarce.

The editors of this book—who also contribute in a major way to its contents—are among the few people thoroughly grounded in psychiatric lore, exceptionally experienced in clinical practice, and at the same time respectful of and conversant with the real life problems of both the child learner and the classroom teacher. It is this aspect which makes the volume unique.

Another virtue of this collection is shared by few publications in the field: it does not talk down or up to anybody. It does not attempt to simplify or make things seem "easy." This approach may sometimes be less comfortable for the reader, but, believe me, it is worth the cost ! It makes the volume more honest and more valuable, by bringing one closer to the complexity into which we are just beginning to penetrate....

PREFACE

This volume and those that follow result from the encouragement we received from our own students and graduates to make available to them our papers, published and unpublished, past and present. There has also been a continuing demand for reprints no longer available and in journals no longer in existence. In addition it is our hope that the materials we have found useful and appreciated in our own teaching might find sympathetic reading by, and be of use to, other professional persons concerned with children and their clinical problems.

We should like to take this opportunity to thank Mary Ann Esser for her excellent editorial assistance, as well as Sharon Brue, Patricia Olson, Sue Scobie, and Martha Lewis for their considerable help in preparation of the manuscripts.

We also wish to express our appreciation to friends and colleagues who contributed to the Child Psychiatry Fund of the University of California San Francisco Medical Center, helping to make publication of the series possible.

INTRODUCTION

The capacity to learn from experience, the ability to use symbols, and the development of a spoken and written language make it possible for man to deal more effectively with his environment, to communicate his experience to others, and to pass on what he has learned to the next generation. In the biological hierarchy man is the only species with a history communicable to his kind symbolically at a distance in space and time.

Those individuals born of human parents would seem infrahuman who would not learn from experience, who would be apparently unable to use symbols readied for them by their predecessors, who would not use speech to communicate nor give evidence of understanding what was spoken to them, and who would be unable to live in any community with others. Yet we see such children rather frequently, children with one or more of these failures in human learning.

Romulus of Roman mythological fame, or the Wolf Boy of Aveyron described by Itard (1), raised apparently without human contact, might reasonably be expected to be so disordered. However, we see such youngsters raised within their own families by intelligent, well-meaning, and concerned parents. In 1909 a pioneering psychologist, Lightner Witmer (2), described such a child whom he had treated and finally managed to bring from a state of animal-like savagery and inability to communicate, to a level of age-appropriate behavior, communication, and ability to learn and acquire knowledge.

To explain such failures in human learning and the many lesser degrees of learning difficulties that disable so many of our children in their living as productive citizens requires considerable investigation of the early conditions of living in the family.

Learning theorists and investigators (3) have described learning in terms of the stimuli impinging upon the organism, the state of receptivity of the organism to apprehend such stimuli, the frequent repetition of the stimuli, and the reinforcement of stimuli by reward or punishment, which makes for selection and retention or rejection of stimuli patterns and thus leads to learning. Pavlov, Skinner, and others have described such conditioning experiments with animals and human beings.

Freud and later psychoanalytic investigators have described the kinds of repetitive experiences in infancy and childhood that make for disorder (4). Piaget (5), Gesell (6), and many others have investigated the maturational sequences and readiness of the human organism for learning certain skills and for acquiring increasingly complex knowledge at certain stages and ages during childhood.

Recently ethologists like Lorenz (7) and Tinbergen (8) have described the complex social behavior of many species of birds, fish, etc. They have observed that certain so-called species-specific, instinctual, i.e., nonlearned, skills like nest-building can be interfered with artificially. Thus, when the materials for nest-building are removed from the normal environment so that these animals are unable to carry out such instinctual tasks at the normal time of nest-building prior to giving birth to young, they are later unable during pregnancy to carry out these functions even if the materials are then available. Lorenz (7) and others (9) have described the process of imprinting, which indicates that there are critical periods in a young animal's life when it follows any moving object, and it may thus learn to follow humans or other animals rather than the mother of its own species. Thereafter its behavior will be so indelibly modified that it will not recognize its own kind and will associate with and follow only humans or other subjects used in the imprinting process. Other experiments indicate that there may be critical periods in the infancy of many species for learning other essential adaptive behavior patterns. If such learning is interfered with at the critical time, the adaptive behavior may then never be learned.

Harlow (10,11) has shown that baby monkeys taken away from their mothers may be comforted, when placed under stress, by body contact with inanimate, soft, furry pneumatic figures. Subsequently these unmothered monkeys appear apathetic and withdrawn and have difficulty in learning to mate and to care for their young. While play and association with age-mates seems to reduce the "strange" behavior, the problems in mating and infant rearing remain.

Thus it is clear that infancy in all higher animals, but especially in the vulnerable human being with its prolonged interval between infancy and adulthood, is a critical period. It is critical for the development of traits, skills, and social behavior characteristic of its own species. The observations of Escalona and co-workers (12) that some infants seem to be constitutionally extremely sensitive to stimuli, together with the work of Richmond and Lustman (13,14) pointing to the great variability in the maturational state of the autonomic nervous system in infants, corroborate the probable greater vulnerability of some infants to early traumatic experiences. There may also be a correspondingly greater need in these vulnerable infants for more empathic and responsive nurturance by the mother.

The serious increase of emotional disturbances in young children in the last several decades is of great concern to educators and mental health professionals. While hereditary and congenital factors must be considered, it is probable that most failure to acquire knowledge in school, most antisocial and delinquent behavior, most psychosomatic disorders and psychotic disorders of childhood can be viewed as failures in the learning process with parents or parent figures early in life. Such early experiences result not only in failures in learning but also in such grave distortions in basic drives that there is a paradoxical aversion to learning. Each new situation arouses terror and panic instead of curious, eager exploration and pleasure in the novelty of new stimuli.

Our own almost eighteen years of investigation of childhood psychosis, described in several other volumes in this series, point up how difficult it is for the infant to develop and to learn with parents who themselves are troubled and in conflict. Such parents unwittingly are unable to provide the kind of nurturant medium that is required for the infant to take advantage of his inborn capacities to acquire certain skills as his maturation makes this possible.

In another volume in this series one of the editors (S. A. Szurek) describes how difficult it is for parents to help their children learn what they themselves have not learned in their experiences with their own parents. Further, the alliance of two troubled and conflicted adults who are unable to give to each other because of their own particular troubles and past experiences may find the drain of an infant's needs on their own emotional state so great that their child may be even more impoverished than his parents. The child may, therefore, experience a compounding of emotional deprivation that makes all learning well nigh impossible. We have seen this time and again with the sickest children and their parents whom we have studied and worked with psychotherapeutically.

We therefore look upon learning as an all-encompassing and vital process. We see education and the variety of special educational methods as vital therapeutic tools that may help a child to reduce some of the distortions of the learning processes acquired in his previous experiences. Each effort at teaching and learning provides the opportunity for the child to acquire new skills and thus new mastery, which reduces his fears of the world around him and makes it safer for him to investigate, to play, and to grow up.

This volume includes papers that deal with the early infant-parent relationship requisite for optimal learning and healthy living; the obstacles to learning, creativity, and integrated living in society; and the specific role of teachers in the vital learning experiences of children. We are also concerned with how the insights gained in child psychiatric practice, training, and research may be helpful to the educator and to others concerned with children and their learning difficulties.

REFERENCES

1. ITARD, Jean Marc Gaspard (1775-1838). The Wild Boy of Aveyron. Translated by George and Muriel Humphrey. New York: Appelton-Century-Crofts, 1962.

2. WITMER, Lightner. Orthogenic Cases, XIV. Don: a curable case of arrested development due to a fear psychosis the result of shock in a three-year-old infant. Psychol. Clin., 13:97-111, 1920. (Published originally in Ladies' Home Journal, April, 1919.)

3. HILGARD, Ernest R. Theories of Learning. 2d ed. New York: Appelton-Century-Crofts, 1956.

4. FREUD, Sigmund. Instincts and their vicissitudes. In Collected Papers, Standard Edition. London: Hogarth Press, 1957. Vol. 14, pp. 111-140.

5. PIAGET, Jean. Language and Thought of the Child. New York: Harcourt Brace, 1932.

6. GESELL, Arnold, and AMATRUDA, Catherine S. Developmental Diagnosis. New York: Paul B. Hoeber, 1941.

7. LORENZ, Konrad Z. King Solomon's Ring. New York: Thomas Y. Crowell Co., 1952.

8. TINBERGEN, N. The Herring Gull's World. New York: Basic Books, 1961.

9. HESS, E. H. Imprinting; an effect of early experience, imprinting determines later social behavior in animals. Science, 130:133-141, (July) 1959.

10. HARLOW, H. F. The nature of love. American Psychologist, 131:673-685, 1958.

11. HARLOW, H. F., and ZIMMERMAN, R. R. Affectional responses in the infant monkey. Science, 130:421-432, 1959.

12. BERGMAN, Paul, and ESCALONA, Sybille K. Unusual sensitivities in very young children. In Psychoanalytic Study of the Child. New York: International Universities Press, 1949. Vol. 3-4, pp. 333-352.

13. RICHMOND, J. B., and LIPTON, E. E. Some aspects of neurophysiology of the new born and their implications for child development. In L. Jessner and E. Pavenstedt (Eds.), Dynamic Psychopathology in Childhood. New York: Grune & Stratton, 1959, pp. 78-103.

14. RICHMOND, J. B., and LUSTMAN, S. L. Autonomic function in the neonate: I. Implications for psychosomatic theory. Psychosom. Med., 17:269-275, 1955.

CONTRIBUTORS

BERLIN, I. N. , M.D.
   Until March 31, 1965, Associate Clinical Professor of Psychiatry, University of California School of Medicine; Coordinator of Training, Children's Service, Langley Porter Neuropsychiatric Institute; and Psychiatric Consultant, Child Guidance Services, San Francisco Unified School District. Beginning April 1, 1965, Professor of Psychiatry and Head, Division of Child Psychiatry, University of Washington School of Medicine, Seattle.

FALSTEIN, Eugene I. , M.D.
   Clinical Professor of Psychiatry, Chicago Medical School; Attending Psychiatrist and Chief of Adolescent Care, Institute for Psychosomatic and Psychiatric Research and Training, Michael Reese Hospital and Medical Center, Chicago. Formerly Staff Psychiatrist, Institute for Juvenile Research, Chicago.

FORBING, Shirley E. , B.A.
   Formerly, teacher on Children's Service, Langley Porter Neuropsychiatric Institute.

HAGEE, Florence, M.S.W.
   Supervising Social Worker, Child Guidance Services, San Francisco Unified School District. Formerly, Social Work Consultant, Special Remedial Classes, San Francisco Unified School District.

HENRY, Alice C. , M.A.
   Supervisor, Child Guidance Services, San Francisco Unified School District.

JOHNSON, Adelaide M. , M.D.
   At the time of her death in 1960, Clinical Professor of Psychiatry, University of Minnesota. Previously, Staff Psychiatrist, Institute for Juvenile Research, Chicago, and staff member, Chicago Psychoanalytic Institute.

KAZANJIAN, Vard, M.A.
   Clinical Psychologist, Consultation Service, San Mateo County Mental Health Services. Formerly, Chief Psychologist, Child Guidance Services, San Francisco Unified School District.

KUHL, Marjorie A., M.S.W.
   School Social Worker, Everett Junior High School, San Francisco. Formerly, Social Work Consultant, Special Remedial Classes, San Francisco Unified School District.

MILLER, Dale D., M.A.
   Educational Psychologist, Children's Service, Langley Porter Neuropsychiatric Institute.

O'NEILL, Lena, M.A.
   Teacher, Presentation High School, Berkeley, California. Formerly, Assistant Principal and Dean of Girls, Mission High School, San Francisco.

OTT, John F., B.S.
   Teacher-Counselor, Sequoia Union High School District, San Mateo County, California. Formerly, Teacher-Counselor, Mission High School, San Francisco.

PHILIPS, Irving, M.D.
   Assistant Clinical Professor of Psychiatry, University of California School of Medicine, and Supervising Psychiatrist, Children's Service, Langley Porter Neuropsychiatric Institute.

ROYSTON, Clara, P.H.N.
   Formerly, Public Health Nurse, San Francisco Department of Public Health.

SUSSELMAN, Samuel, M.D.
   Associate Clinical Professor of Psychiatry, University of California School of Medicine, and Supervising Psychiatrist, Children's Service, Langley Porter Neuropsychiatric Institute.

SVENDSEN, Margaret, Ph.B. (Mrs. Margaret S. Davis)
   Staff Training Consultant, Children's Aid Society of Ottawa. Formerly, Social Worker, Institute for Juvenile Research, Chicago.

SZUREK, S. A., M.D.
   Professor of Psychiatry, University of California School of Medicine, and Director, Children's Service, Langley Porter Neuropsychiatric Institute. Formerly, Chief of Staff, Institute for Juvenile Research, Chicago.

CONTENTS

(Continued on next page)

SECTION SIX: THERAPEUTIC EFFORTS IN LEARNING DISTURBANCES

SECTION ONE:

BEGINNINGS OF LEARNING AND ITS DISTORTIONS

Introduction

The modern wonders of technology and the highest attainments in the arts and in science result from man's never-ending hunger for knowledge, his never-ceasing efforts to learn and to use the products of his learning. With his biological brethren of other species man also, from infancy on, is biologically driven and eager to learn, is insatiably curious, finds delight in exploration and satisfaction in emulation of his elders. What, then, alters this drive, dims this eagerness and curiosity, and produces problems in learning and in living? The following papers record some of our observations on the normal learning process and its distortions.

THE CHILD FROM TWO TO TEN

S. A. Szurek, M.D.

The years from early childhood to preadolescence is so broad a
subject that it is doubtful if in this discussion we can do more than
touch upon some of the highlights. There are many experts in this
field more qualified than I to talk about certain aspects of these
critical years of the human life span. For they are critical and
extremely important years, often not only determining the contentment and effectiveness of the adult's living with others but also, in
a way perhaps not fully realized, deciding how the next generation
will deal with its legacy of unsolved problems. We all know the
old aphorism, "As the twig is bent...," but under the pressures of
our now daily difficulties we find it very hard, with the most informed and most generous of intentions, to give the young human
sprouts those elements of care, protection, and emotional climate
that will foster the fullest development of the potentialities with
which they are born.

THE GROWTH PROCESS

These are the years when the human body with its intricate organization matures greatly, taking a long step towards completing its
inherent developmental plan. Not only do hand and eye and thumb
and fingers become able to perform fine and precise movements
and progressively more cunning manipulations, but the body as a
whole--good nutrition and absence of disease permitting--gradually
attains the buoyant and vigorous strength and capacity for that almost tireless activity that is sometimes so amazing, delightful, or
fatiguing to parents. But the growth process alone merely prepares
the body for its activities. The offer of toys and of opportunities
for play and games, encouragement and guidance to learn the skills,
to exercise the acquired coordinations, are of equal importance for
the attainment of the fullest possible physical development. This
developed physical strength and skill contribute a good deal to a
quiet sense of self-confidence and self-respect. It is cheering,
therefore, to notice an increasing change in our attitudes towards

2

the kind and amount of physical activity permitted and encouraged in girls. When the little girl and the later woman is physically as well developed and as skilled in games and sports as her brother, her boyfriend, or her husband, she is not only a more enjoyable playmate and companion and a healthier mother, but is able with calm self-assurance to further the fuller achievement of equality and democracy between all persons. Thus, future generations of women may be even better prepared to resolve the wasteful and harmful conflicts in the so-called "war of the sexes." Incidentally, such a woman rears children of both sexes with attitudes more likely to prevent in them conflicts about inferiority and the result-ant fears, envies, and hatreds all too frequent nowadays in both sexes.

These are the years, too, when intellectual activity grows greatly and is given its direction often for life. Here, too, whatever the endowed potentiality for learning, opportunities for study and stimu-lating teaching are essential for the fullest growth of that power in which the human being is pre-eminent among living things. It is a long and slow road each child travels from converting the vocal noises of infancy and early childhood into the more precise signals we call words, language, and all the other symbolic means the human race has developed for communicating with one another. Along with innumerable motor skills it is largely through master-ing verbal signs that the child acquires the cultural heritage of knowledge, of techniques, and of the ethics of his group. His lan-guage and developed capacity for abstraction permit him not only to learn how his ancestors dealt with problems and creatively to solve his own, but it is a tremendously important way of reducing his own sense of loneliness. He can tell his chum and others what he perceives, grasps, and feels, and he can learn that others share his experience and can confirm or correct his observations. The world expands enormously. But there is an ever present problem in education: how to keep alive and growing the spontaneous, eager curiosity of the child; how not to thwart its successful use, blunt its edge of effectiveness; and how not to divert its direction from cooperative creativeness with his fellow men.

However, both of these aspects of growth--the physical and intel-lectual--are the concern of specialties other than my own. Embry-ologists, physiologists, pediatricians, psychologists, educators, and specialists in physical training have all contributed much more than psychiatrists to the study, understanding, and precise measurement of the details of this maturation and to the methods of correction and treatment of its deviations. Psychiatrists interested in children naturally take a lively interest in the results of the work of these other specialists. Psychiatrists often collaborate with them in clinical work with individual children, since all aspects of a child's development affect or contribute to his personality growth and integration. But the special field of interest of child psychiatry are the feelings of the child, the attitudes he develops towards himself, and all those influences that help to mold them. For it is in these feelings, in the conscious and unconscious attitudes towards himself, that the child's emotional health resides. It is how he comes to feel about his body, its functions, his impulses and wishes, and how he will regard his own person that determine what degree of personality integration--mental health or disorder, if you please-- he attains. It is a well known truism that no one expresses attitudes towards other persons different from those he has towards himself, whether or not he is fully aware and conscious of these attitudes. It is therefore easy to understand that success in obtaining the satisfactions and the security we all need will depend a great deal on the qualities and characteristics of one's self attitudes. Since practically no satisfaction and no sense of security is obtainable except with and through other persons--that is the nature of the gregarious, interdependent human being--it is extremely important how other people feel and react towards oneself. And how others feel and react towards us is influenced, as we all know, in great measure by how we feel and behave towards them. One's personality, which is one's system of interpersonal attitudes, since personality has no meaning apart from oneself in relation to other persons, is then one's chief instrument for or obstacle to achieving satisfactory, happy, and productive living.

EXPERIENCES IN EARLY INFANCY

For these reasons, all of us, psychiatrists in particular, are very much interested in knowing how we come to feel the way we do about ourselves, what makes us <u>tick</u> the way we do when we are adults. A large part of the answer comes from the experiences during the critical years before adolescence.

Although I understand that the topic of this seminar does not include the earliest and most helpless months of infancy, I cannot forego touching upon a few matters concerning this period. Modern psychiatric theory considers as extremely important for later mental health not only the experiences of the period when the young child

begins to talk and show more clearly the rudiments of mental functioning, but also those of the period before he walks, including the
first weeks of nursing and the birth experience itself. There are
even psychiatrists who push their inquiry into the causes of mental
disorders into the period prior to birth, into the attitudes of the
parents towards the expected child and their emotional health and
maturity. However, time permits only one comment to be made
about this phase of a child's experience and emotional development.

There is need to underscore the central importance of the infant's
extreme helplessness and utter dependence upon the human adult
environment for meeting his every need. This dependence includes
not only his special nutritional requirements and need for protection
from injury, from infection, from extremes of temperature, and
from sudden, intense sensory overstimulation, but also his equally
important needs for tenderness and soothing stimulation, especially
from the mother. The effect of the mothering adult's feelings and
attitudes towards the infant has, because of this helplessness and
dependence, a tremendous effect upon its state of being, physiological and emotional. Students of this period of life emphasize how
important for the establishment of sucking, for good nutrition, res-
piration, circulation--in short, for all of the physiological processes which lead to health and growth--is the quality of emotional contact between child and the mothering adult. It is surprising how
often adults regard the infant and the young child as, on the one
hand, a peculiarly mindless creature, that is to say, a rather in-
sentient automaton, and, on the other hand and at the same time,
an autocrat whose impulses and behavior require early curbing,
regulation, and control. The overwhelming fear of such persons,
it seems, is the terrible danger of "spoiling" the child. His unique
and individual physiological rhythms in these early weeks and
months of eating, sleeping, and elimination must be routinized and
subjugated or else his parents will be enslaved by them. And when
violations of his rhythms bring in their train as a direct consequence
(in addition to bodily disorders) rage, anxious irritability, or compensatory self-stimulation in the mouth or other bodily regions,
these, too, must be promptly and forcefully combatted.

It matters little whether or not the parent carries out such training and discipline with what seems to him an attitude free of anger.
The underlying anxiety and fear get through to the infant and child
by means of an empathy between the helpless, dependent one and
the all-powerful giant authority who is at the same time the dis-

penser of good things: all the good things that not only allay the tormenting inner cravings of bodily needs, but also provide those inner states of comfort and well-being when the parent is pleased, happy, and free of tension.

RELATION OF CULTURE TO DEVELOPMENT

What does matter is just <u>when</u> culture thus invades physiology-- whether development and growth have reached a point where "it can take it"--and with what intensity and persistence such blocking and thwarting of biological rhythms and needs occurs. In other words, if biological processes are interfered with too early and too strongly, that is, with strong feeling on the part of the parental culture bearer to which the immature human organism is so extremely susceptible, the stage is set for trouble--trouble with not only immediate reactions of disordered physiology in one or another system of the body, but trouble later with fearful or rebellious subjective states, with uncertain, divided attitudes towards oneself and others.

These few and inadequate comments upon the earliest months and years must suffice. They may make somewhat more comprehensible the statement that how the child who now walks well, who has been partially domesticated, and who has begun the struggle to master language, reacts, learns, and feels during the next seven or eight years depends a great deal upon what his experience with people has been up to this point in his career.

LEARNING TO LOVE

From the psychiatrist's point of view the critical years prior to pubescence determine fairly definitely the child's and the future adult's capacity to love. I am aware that this word "love" is difficult to define, perhaps because each of us has a different complex of feelings we call by this word. It may be difficult to define also because it is in the present phase of human history still an ideal achieved in any notable measure by only a few of us. The character of current interpersonal and international relations leaves little doubt that much remains to be desired in this direction. Nevertheless, the degree to which each of us achieves prior to adolescence the actual, generous capacity to obtain as great a satisfaction from the satisfactions of another person as from our own--which is what we here call love--the more closely we reach a fully human estate, the greater and stronger is our personality integration, and the better our mental health. Let me repeat, the

chief emotional goal of the preadolescent years is to attain a firm
integration of the self, the hallmark of which is a genuine ability
to love. And by love we mean to feel as full a satisfaction and
pleasure in the satisfaction of another as in one's own satisfactions.

Careful consideration of this statement will reveal that it includes
a great deal. It presupposes a fairly thorough acceptance of one's
own body and its dominant needs, firmly grounded self-respect
based on achieved abilities, coupled with tolerance of one's limitations. It precludes the shaky self-esteem that requires an exces-
sive constant approval of others to bolster it and to reduce the
readiness to self-contempt or to hatred of others, however restrained in expression, or however disguised from the self and
others. Such capacity to love includes a genuine love of the self--
and by this we do not mean the anxious concern about the self so
often misnamed self-love. Such love of the self requires no submission from, or enslavement of others, nor does it countenance
domination from others. Content with its own abilities and desires,
such a self vigorously pursues its needs and exercises its capacities in reality, without seeking to harm others thereby, and is,
therefore, relatively free of anxieties about retaliation and so is
free of crippling inhibitions. Delays to its satisfaction, actual
losses, deprivations, and blows to its prestige can be tolerated
without a catastrophic or devastating degree of emotional disequi-
librium--that is, without severe anxiety or major loss of self-
confidence. This does not mean it is immune to the tragic sense
of life, nor indifferent to setbacks; but a sturdy, realistic optimism permits it aggressively to do as much as reality allows to
rectify errors and to seek to compensate for losses. Thus out of
its own fullness such a self radiates a benign atmosphere about it
and feels the happiness it helps to bring to others.

THE CHILD'S WORLD

Briefly thus to characterize the goal of the emotional development
of the childhood years points out the long and arduous path both the
child and its parents need to travel to attain it. For if there is one
characteristic of the young child of two or three years that im-
presses a psychiatrist most, it is his almost complete egocentri-
city. It is no news to anyone that the child wants what he wants
when he wants it, of course without much regard for any obstacles
or for anyone else's wishes, satisfaction, or peace of mind. He
is the center of his universe. Not only must the adult give him
immediately the food, the sweets, the toys and care he desires,

and the affection he needs to reduce his sense of impotence and loneliness, but generally also no two adults in his presence can have too much to do with one another, at least not for very long. Other children are apt for some time to be interlopers and rivals for the exclusive affection of the parents. He has, depending on his prior experience, little feeling of disgust for his bodily products or uncleanliness; not much shame about any parts of his person, and probably no guilt about the destructive, revengeful rage which follows promptly upon the thwarting of any of his wishes. He knows only that most of his bodily functions feel good; that some parts of his body surface feel better than others; and that anything or anyone interfering with the impulse of the moment is hateful. What he sees and wishes to touch and manipulate belongs to him by the divine right of all kings and by the omnipotent power of his desire and of his cry.

THE CHILD LEARNS ABOUT THE ADULT WORLD

The exercise of all his senses and muscles is delightful except when for totally incomprehensible reasons mother or father become tense with anger, or with uncertainty and anxiety. Gradually he comes upon the strange and equally incomprehensible fact that some gestures and words that these big and powerful adults call "love," or hugs, or smiles, or politeness, may be absolutely necessary preliminaries to get what he wants, or that these words and gestures are magically powerful in making the adults pleased, appeased, or delighted, which always makes him feel better. In any case, such magical gestures and words of ingratiation, or others that these adults call "apology" and that they sometimes enforce unremittingly after he has been "bad," make these adults much more manageable to his own ends. Further, through countless repetitions he gradually learns, again quite arbitrarily and incomprehensibly, that certain things he wants, or does, make mother or father tense, and that always makes him extremely uncomfortable and anxious. At first this happens only in their presence; later, much later, and only gradually, this uncomfortable feeling comes even when they are not around during the act, and then eventually even when he has only briefly wished to do such a thing. Finally, it may happen that he is very uncomfortable and very unhappy without even knowing exactly why.

INTEGRATIVE LEARNING EXPERIENCES IN CHILDHOOD

Naturally there may be in early life many of the opposite and happier experiences. The parents who are relatively secure and content with themselves and with each other are probably people who are generally pleased, delighted with, and affectionate towards the child. His needs and wishes receive consistently gentle, kindly indulgence whenever possible, and consoling sympathy when this is impossible. Spontaneous tenderness flows from them towards the child without his having to earn it by being "good." His rights as a member of the family are treated with consideration and full justice between him and his siblings; his possessions and person are regarded with respect. The necessary disciplines that lead to control of sphincters, general cleanliness, and self-care are imposed gradually, when and as he is able to learn them, and with calm firmness but much praise and pleasure at each of his positive achievements. His helplessness, weakness, or beginning ineptness at any skill is never derided or ridiculed. Instead, help and encouragement towards any independent strivings come readily and consistently. No part of his body or any of its functions is labeled "bad" or "nasty," and none of the various self-gratifying manipulations evokes disgust, anxiety, or anger from his parents. There are no secrets about life, and all curiosity about human biology is satisfied simply and directly with no uneasy evasiveness but with frank acknowledgment that people do not like to talk about and do some things in public. Instead of demanding that the child be polite, grateful, or generous, such parents themselves feel and behave thus towards the child with almost infinite patience. They do so not as a way to "manage" or to "handle" the child, but because their own self-regard permits them to act in no other way. Their firm self-respect demands no menial ingratiation nor resentful submission from the child. Their self-confidence is reflected in their steady optimism that this weak, small, impulsive creature will grow strong and self-reliant if given opportunity and warmth, if his strong urges are guided and directed rather than crushed, and if no depreciation greets his stumbling trials at learning. Above all, since their secure self-esteem makes unnecessary any shame or anxiety about their own feelings, and since, therefore, they do not deceive themselves about them, such parents are frank and honest about their own feelings with the child, and rarely, if ever, consciously or unconsciously deceive him.

Now the time allotted to me is gone, and no one of you is more clearly aware than I how little I have said about many things important in the experience of the pre-adolescent child. I have talked as much about parents as about the child. I believe that is inevitable from the nature of things. I have said nothing about what teachers, grandparents, and other adults, and what brothers, sisters, and playmates may contribute to the growth of the self. All of these are important, although from a psychiatrist's point of view somewhat less important than the primary relatives upon whom the child chiefly depends throughout most of his bodily, economic, and emotional immaturity. It is from these primary relations that he develops his basic and fundamental feelings about himself. It is with his mother's and father's feelings about him and his impulses that, as we say in psychiatric jargon, he identifies. That is, he tends to adopt towards himself their individual and several and composite attitudes towards him. Having adopted these attitudes, and many psychiatrists believe this identification or incorporation of parental attitudes into the self-organization is achieved in the main by the fifth or sixth year, the child then tends to act towards others outside of the family in the light of them. In other words, he treats others as he now treats himself, which is as he was treated. This does not mean that changes in the feelings about himself cannot be brought about by any different feelings towards him of others outside of his home; otherwise psychiatrists could not practice psychotherapy. But these at best may be slow in coming unless a strong and prolonged emotional tie between child and such another adult develops.

Finally, perhaps all I have said was more briefly and more wittily put when a humorist quipped, "No matter what we teach our children, they insist on acting like we do."

Reprinted by permission of the National Society of Children's Nurseries (London) from the Nursery Journal, June-July 1948.

ASPECTS OF CREATIVITY
AND THE LEARNING PROCESS

I. N. Berlin, M.D.

The obstacles to creativity in students of the arts and sciences are the concern of many teachers. Some teachers have been fortunate enough not to have had many obstacles to overcome themselves. Others have been helped by their teachers to greater creativity.

As one of the latter, I have been interested in trying to understand how I've been aided and to make the methods explicit in the process of working with my own students. I'm sure all teachers have experienced feelings of frustration as promising students give one glimpses of creativity that never matures or is never fully realized. For the purposes of this discussion, I have defined creativity as that kind of self-expression in one's own medium that results in constant growth and synthesis of experiences essential to the continual production of new and original work.

While I have been concerned primarily with the creativity that produces original thinking in my own specialty of psychiatry, and while my attention to the obstacles to creativity has been centered on my own students who show promise, I've also had the opportunity as a psychotherapist to work with several writers, painters, sculptors, and photographers, where these obstacles have been of primary concern in the treatment. My own avocation of photography has widened my horizons further and provided additional opportunities to see other teachers in another field try to deal with the same problems in their students.

These efforts to crystallize some of my thoughts of the past few years in writing are the result of reading two papers. The first is Walter Rosenblum's "Teaching Photography," published in Aperture, Vol. 3, 1956. The second is Irving Sarnoff's "Some Psychological Problems of the Incipient Artist," published in Mental

<u>Hygiene</u>, July 1956. Both articles stimulated trains of thought that had not quite crystallized and helped me make these thoughts more explicit.

Sarnoff in his paper reviews his experiences as a psychotherapist in a university health service with a number of promising students in the arts. He discusses three fears that prevent creativity. The first is the fear of assuming a position of authority that permits the artist to place the stamp of his perceptions on the world. In my own words, this means to accept one's role as a mature adult who can assert his ideas authoritatively and is thus the equal of others in the same field and especially the equal of authoritative persons from one's childhood, one's parents. The second fear is the fear of talent, the anxiety about committing oneself to the unremitting work of developing one's creative capacities, to bearing the frustrations, hard work and responsibility of seeking self-fulfillment. Sarnoff points out that many young artists are dismayed when they do discover glimpses of their talent. They would rather continue to be promising aspirants in their fields than be committed to the development of clearly evidenced talents. The third fear Sarnoff mentions is the fear of inner emptiness or the anxiety that there are few inner resources, that they will soon run dry and leave the artist without any foundation for further work. In Sarnoff's clinical examples, the artistic production is felt as a loss of substance by students who still feel the need for continual gratification from others.

My own point of view on creativity and the hindrances to its realization is in large part the result of training, research, teaching, and practice of child psychiatry, or, more accurately, family psychiatry. My particular research interest in childhood schizophrenia has provided opportunities to work with children whose creativity is almost nonexistent, whose capacities for learning are stunted, and with their parents who in several instances were talented people with creative potential never fully realized. It was in such a setting that the problems around creativity, and the inhibiting factors that result from the child's experiences with the adults in his life, became vivid to me.

Perhaps the conflict most evident in the schizophrenic child can be seen in his very attitude, the stiff awkward movements, the frozen demeanor, the paucity of speech, and the general inhibition of emotion except for destructive rages. As one works with such children and their parents, one becomes aware of the dovetailing conflicts in the parents about their unconscious need to repress many feelings. Conscious and verbal awareness of feelings gives one the conscious choice about how any feelings could be expressed non-destructively. These parents feel it dangerous to experience freely and fully many emotions. One usually learns that in their childhood such feelings as anger, hate, acute disappointment, childlike feelings of wanting to be cuddled, as well as sensual and sexual feelings, were forbidden verbal expressions. From some parents we learned that such suppression aroused much anxiety since there was always increased possibility of imminent discharge of these feelings into destructive or forbidden behavior. One parent described the feeling as "sitting on a powder keg of feelings." Thus these parents who were talented and even successful in earning their living in graphic arts, writing, etc., were usually unable consciously to feel emotions, so that their work failed to breathe of life. They tended to do acceptable, fairly stereotyped, not very imaginative work from which they made their livelihood. In their therapy they described the absence of feelings of self-fulfillment. In the course of psychotherapeutic work with the children and their parents, it became clear that the unconscious conflicts that result in repression of feelings consumed a tremendous amount of energy. Thus they were constantly fatigued, their productivity was reduced, and even their perceptivity was markedly diminished.

Obviously there are many other aspects of conflict that inhibit creativity and were evidenced in these children and their parents. Another aspect of the conflicts that resulted in the massive inhibition of feeling were those conflicts that centered around learning. In the child learning such things as self-care and later learning in school often were markedly inhibited. All aspects of learning at every developmental stage can be viewed as preparation for the fullest living and learning in the next stage of development. Thus, as an adult one functions as an individual with other persons but is not parasitically dependent upon them for one's being able to live. The schizophrenic child, especially, evidences a great fear about learning. Learning seems to mean to him to "grow up," that is, to cease being a helplessly dependent child and thus to preclude forever obtaining the gratifications he has not yet received. It is clear that in this area these children have not had the experience of participating with their parents in the mutual pleasures of infancy around feeding, daily care, playing and learning. The parental conflicts reduced markedly the parents' tender assistance to the infant and child in learning and in physical and emotional development. These conflicts resulting from their own unmet needs in childhood greatly diminish the parents' enjoyment and thus their ability to behave as parents with their child. In their living as adults some of these parents seek satisfactions from other adults, not as co-equals, but as helpless dependent children whose needs often must be met, so that they can continue to function as adults in other aspects of their living. Thus when parents have not been helped by their own parents to mature through their childhood experiences they are not free to explore the resources within themselves and in the world around them. By their conflicts from childhood they are inhibited and restricted from freedom in thinking and feeling. To both parents and the child independence continues to portend the loss of satisfactions from others.

These observations are similar to those described by Sarnoff of his art student patients. The three fears of assuming a position of authority, committing oneself to the development of one's talent, and anxiety that one will be drained dry by each piece of work, can be understood in terms of conflicts resulting from early life experiences with conflictful parents. Quantitatively these conflicts are less severe in most art students than they are in schizophrenic children or their parents. I'm convinced that qualitatively they are similar. Thus conflicts stemming from the oral stage of psychosexual development, from experiences with tense and conflictful mothers, are reflected in the constant yearning for gratification from someone and an inability to find satisfaction in one's own work. Coupled with this are those conflicts from later stages of development where the child has not been helped to enjoy learning and mastery of his environmental tasks through perseverance. He therefore feels continual frustration and inability to complete his work. When he does come close to finishing a piece of work, he risks again the loss of sustenance from others if he is successful and the anxiety of successfully competing with his parent that stems from unresolved oedipal conflicts.

For many potentially creative people, only prolonged psychotherapy will give them the necessary personal experience that their own work can be satisfying, that they do not lose gratification from others in the process, and that their parents continue to survive and even enjoy their success.

The following three brief case histories illustrate the increased freedom and creativity that may result from the resolution of some conflicts through psychotherapy. The first case is that of an adult whose conflicts inhibited his creative work but did not obliterate it. The second case describes work with the mother of a schizophrenic boy. Her intense conflicts were responsible at least in part for the schizophrenia of her child and certainly for her markedly diminished creativity. The third case summarizes psychotherapeutic work with a schizophrenic child who was gradually helped to greater freedom as he was helped to learn.

CASE #1:

A successful commercial photographer consulted me because of recurrent tension headaches, continuous feelings of hate and anger with frequent explosive rages that stopped just short of physical violence. His feelings and behavior inhibited his effectiveness with clients, marred his relations with co-workers, and threatened his marriage. The recurrent severe headaches and a constant tired feeling also markedly reduced his productivity, and each job was completed with great effort. Since he was aware of my interest in photography he occasionally brought in examples of his work. These were invariably well thought out, meticulously executed advertising photographs of the same caliber as those found in current magazines. It was only after many months of work together that he began to describe his impulses in each job to make photographs that expressed more fully his ideas and feelings. At such times he experienced massive anxiety. He felt that such departures from the usual commercial work would be deprecated and rejected by his clients and thus might call forth his uncontrollable rages. He felt safest, although tense, unhappy, discontented and unfulfilled, when he made the "slick, run-of-the-mill" photographs. At such times he also had severe and almost intractable headaches. During this period of our work, he began to bring in occasional "Sunday" photographs. These gave hints of his creative ideas and feelings, but they gave me a sense of being inhibited and restricted as if on Sundays he were trying desperately to make up for his week-day dissatisfactions. My patient expressed his continued dissatisfactions with these pictures too. In addition, it became clear that Sunday photography added to the tensions of his already strained relationship with his wife.

In time he began to work through some of his problems,
which centered around his very prosperous and domineering
father, who, although financially successful, failed to
achieve the eminence and recognition he felt was due him
for his professional achievement. His father violently
disapproved of his early leanings towards art and of his
eventual decision to seek training in photography. My
patient had vivid memories of the many times in childhood
that he brought his pictures to his parents only to face his
father's scorn and ridicule and his mother's extravagant
praises and idolization. These conflicting attitudes and
their effect on him were a recurring theme in our work.
Gradually he was able to dissociate his clients from his
feelings about his parents, his fear of their scorn and hope
for their adulation and praise. At the same time he began
to see his wife in a new perspective. He had seen her
originally as the person he hoped would sustain him with
admiration, uncritical praise, and constant attention to his
needs. Thus her often valid and constructive evaluations of
his work my patient felt as his father's scorn and depreca-
tion. When she voiced her needs in their relationship he
could only feel hate and rage at being asked to "give" when
he was in such dire need himself.

In time he began, first in a few instances, to present clients
with both the standard photographs and those that expressed
his own creative ideas. To his surprise and satisfaction,
a few clients preferred his creative ideas. Thus encouraged
he began to present more freely his own ideas, to follow his
own creative urges with increasing success and contentment.
His relationship with his wife improved, his headaches were
markedly reduced and his rages were more and more infrequent. The "Sunday" photographs he brought reflected his
increasing freedom of seeing and feeling.

As my patient gained more perspective about himself as an
adult and felt easier about himself and his relations with
people, he was able to show his father some of the photographs that were most satisfying to him. To his surprise
his father expressed admiration and appreciation of the
work he was able to do.

CASE #2:

A thirty-five-year-old art teacher, the mother of a twelve-year-old schizophrenic boy patient of mine, sought treatment for herself after I had worked with her son about a year. She had begun to notice that her son was becoming less frozen and that on a few occasions he evidenced a kind of spontaneity that was new to him. In each instance she had suddenly felt that she rarely experienced such spontaneity herself. The past 12 years teaching art in high schools and making extra money by illustrating children's books had left her feeling constantly dissatisfied with herself. An unhappy marriage and subsequent divorce when her son was age five resulted in her having to care for her child by herself. She solved this by living with her parents, who took care of him. In this household of rigid, reserved, and isolated elderly grandparents, the boy became increasingly withdrawn. The mother spent little time at home. The boy did fairly well in school and was not a behavior problem either at school or at home. Thus no one was concerned until at age ten he began to talk about feeling strange. He was not sure his hands or feet belonged to him, his head felt enormous and felt as if it were about to float away. He described odd sensations of being encased in cotton. He also saw people as having large heads and felt he was being looked at by everyone.

In the course of the boy's first year of work with me, these bizarre symptoms abated and he became more sociable, he made a few friends, and his school work improved markedly. His mother said she occasionally noticed an animation that was new to him and that she realized she had never experienced herself.

During the three years of weekly interviews, the mother would bring in her paintings. She had discovered when she was anxious, depressed, full of rage or of yearning, that in painting she found at least temporary relief. Her professional painting had always been objective and representational. She enjoyed mostly the precise, detailed illustrations she made for children's books. Her first paintings during psychotherapy disturbed and delighted her. They were the first non-objective paintings she had

ever done. They were very precise, tidy, well-balanced
triangles, circles, squares in pastel colors. She interpreted them as expressing her feelings of fury at her
husband and parents. Gradually these paintings became
less precise, freer. There was more movement, tensions
were more clearly expressed in intense, vibrant colors and
in less constricted form.

She began to work through some of her rage, first at her
husband, whose demands that he be taken care of and
catered to created so much rage that she had little feeling
for her infant. She was only glad he was a good, quiet baby
who seemed to accept without complaint the succession of
housekeepers who cared for him while the mother and father
continued to work. After her divorce she found herself still
tied to her parents and son, unable to find friends, resenting
her teaching, and fearful of men. Her sexual experiences
found her cold and resenting another demand from her husband.

During this period she painted many vivid, violent pictures
but the forms were still geometric. Later she began to
work through many of her childhood experiences, especially
her own acute affectional deprivation. Her mother was
unable to give or receive affection or permit any display of
emotion. Her father was only slightly less restricted.
Early her talents in dancing and her beauty led her mother
to enroll her in dancing school. Her mother kept her
practicing and performing so that she had almost no playmates and few childhood activities. My patient's interest
in art was in part at least a rebellion at mother's demands
that she continue her dancing.

During the next period in her psychotherapeutic work, her
paintings lost all of their precise qualities, and both form
and color were used freely without constriction. She found
herself delighted with her increasing freedom.

At the end of the second year of therapy, she gave up
teaching to spend full time in illustrating and painting.
Oddly enough, as her oil paintings became freer, her
illustrations became rather fragile and exquisite, but
there was much more emotion expressed. For the first
time, too, she was able to draw animals in whom one could

get a sense of movement and character. Her illustrating
became so successful that she was able to live comfortably
and to find time for painting regularly. In her last year
of therapy she found herself with many friends, several
men friends proposed marriage, and an affair with one of
them found her enjoying sex for the first time in her life.
During this period she was able to take her son to live
with her and found the relationship at times difficult, but
quite congenial. She also began to take classes in modern
dance and was delighted with a new-found freedom of movement and balance unknown to her since pre-adolescence
when she gave up ballet.

Her work with me ended after three years when she moved
to another state to accept a better job in illustration. By
that time her oils had aroused favorable comments from
several art critics. She had had a successful one-man show
and her paintings were beginning to sell. I have seen her
and her son almost every year, and they both continue to
do well. The mother has engaged in several relationships
with men, all of them sexually satisfying, but they end
because she seems to select men who are not able to live
with her in her intellectual and artistic world. Her son,
now in his late teens, has exhibited considerable talent in
writing and is about to matriculate in the School of Journal-
ism in their state college.

CASE #3:

Barney, at age four, was a stiff, tense boy with a stony,
expressionless face. Since the birth of a baby sister when
he was aged two and one-half, he had stopped saying the
few words he knew. Since that time, too, his silent, withdrawn behavior alternated with destructive rages during
which he broke and tore any household articles within reach.
He attacked his baby sister and his mother whenever he was
near them. He was better behaved with his father, but he
remained stiff and isolated from him. The father was a
precise, dapper industrial designer who wanted everything
spic and span. He deprecated his wife's helplessness in
care of the home and adroitly managed all the household
accounts and the household help, decorated the home, and
even planned the menus. The mother was a pretty, child-

like woman whose helpless appearance seemed to get others
to do everything for her. She related in treatment her
great fear of men and boys, especially their genitals.
She had left Barney almost entirely to the care of nurses
since his birth. At the birth of a girl, the mother came to
life and found herself able to nurse and care for the baby
where this had been impossible with her son. She made
every effort to have her son cared for by the maids.

In the three-times-weekly sessions, Barney was at first
either completely isolated, standing or sitting staring into
space, or in a screaming, kicking rage because he had
been brought to the playroom against his will. After the
first few weeks he responded to my rolling the toy cars
in his direction by tentatively rolling them back to me.
After three months of such tentative contacts, he reacted
to my continual naming of each toy I picked up or used by
whispering the names of a few toys after me. Shortly
thereafter, he accepted my suggestion that his rage at
being brought down to the interview against his will could
be expressed by hitting the pegs on the pounding board.
After a few tentative swipes my encouraging vocal "slam
bang!" seemed to make it possible for him to begin to hit
the pegs harder until he was smashing them and yelling,
"Slam!" "Bang!" at the top of his lungs. This was the
turning point in our work and he began to repeat more
words after me and to want to learn to do things. He began
to build with blocks, after I used his hands to show him how.
Later I drew with chalk, crayons, and finger paints, using
his hands, until very slowly he took over and began to use
the materials, at first in a restricted, cramped fashion
and finally with freedom. One day as he was crayoning
indifferently he looked at the piece of clay I had picked
up and was molding into an animal. I had been doing this
for weeks during those periods in our interviews when
Barney would cease his activities and would look blankly
and vaguely around him. This was done in preparation for
the moment when he might want to use this material as a
means of self-expression and working out his problems.
By this time he said my name, used nouns freely but no
pronouns and only a few verbs. On this day while absently
drawing with crayons and mechanically making heavily
crayoned strips of blue, red, and brown, he suddenly put

out his hand for the clay in my hand. I put the partially
completed cat in his hand, he looked at it intently, and
then looking guardedly at me he crushed it into a ball. I
suggested we try to make a cat together and he looked
sullen and angry, shook his head, pinched and worked the
clay a bit, looked at the shapeless mass and angrily threw
it down. I picked it up, began to work it as he looked at
me, and carefully drew one end of the clay into a snout.
I took another piece and asked him if he would like me to
show him how to do this. He stood rigidly but permitted
me to put the clay into his limp hands, and to use his hands
to slowly make a snout. It appeared as if his hands and body
did not belong to each other, his eyes and face evidenced no
interest in what his limp hands were doing. In this fashion
we made five or six snouts until I felt his hands come alive
in mine. I relaxed my hands, still surrounding his, as he
fashioned a very good snout. For the first time his eyes
seemed to see what was going on. After another snout he
removed his hands from mine and made several, each one
better than the next. This began the use of clay and his very
skillfully learning to make not only clay animals, but also
human figures. He later began to talk and play out conflicts
in the form of phantasies with his mother, father, and baby
sister. This process of making it possible for Barney to
learn, helping him to learn by doing things with him until
he was free to do them alone, was paralleled in the home
environment where slowly he was helped to learn self-
care, dressing of himself, eating, and finally, after almost
two years, some reading. This boy, at the end of two years,
evidenced much talent in handling art materials. His increasing freedom and pleasure in his activities were delightful to see. These were mirrored in all phases of his living
as he finally entered school and engaged in games and school
activities with other children. He began to express himself
with ease verbally and after a time to use "I" and "me"
correctly instead of referring to himself by "you" as he had
done when he began to talk. In the last months of our work
together, he would sometimes ask me to make the same clay
animal that he was making. When mine turned out not to be
as good as his, he would deftly show me how it could be
improved. On those occasions when my clay animal was
better than his, he'd cluck and nod approvingly and try to
reshape his own so that it would be better.

THE TEACHER'S ROLE

How then can the teacher help those students who show promise of creativity and, to some degree and in various proportions, some of the inhibiting factors just mentioned? First, the teacher must be aware that he may not be able to be helpful to some students no matter how hard he tries. Their obstacles to creativity are of such degree that another kind of help, as just illustrated, may be necessary. But he can be of much assistance to many students.

Walter Rosenblum in his beautiful article gives a clear example of how a teacher may behave in such a way with his pupils that they identify with his attitudes towards his work and towards life. It is both through the process of identification and through the teacher's consistent help to the student in achieving mastery of the subject that new learning occurs and some of the old conflicts and fears are somewhat resolved. To quote Rosenblum, "Through past experience I have learned that the teacher cannot push, he cannot provide pat answers, he cannot anticipate problems before they arise, . . . The guidance must be gentle and never hurrying. This development can only proceed under self-propulsion."

Here, I feel Rosenblum is saying that he is behaving with his students not as parents may behave, parents who want the child to succeed for the sake of the parents' own lack of achievement to make up for their own frustrations. The parents, in living through the child, may prevent the child from developing his resources for his own satisfactions. Thus patience, the absence of an attitude that says I know all the answers, helps the student gradually to begin to find them within himself and for himself.

Rosenblum's emphasis on helping the student to become aware of the emotional impact of his environment bespeaks his own freedom to react freely without shame with his own feelings to everything about him. He thus provides a model for the student groping toward self-expression.

I'm particularly struck by the succinct and beautiful way in which Rosenblum points to the heart of the teaching relationship. That is, helping the photography student become consciously aware of his world. The emphasis on conscious awareness is indeed the touchstone, as he points out. "The word conscious is the key word, for if his feelings remain on an unconscious level, it then becomes impossible for him to grow, on the basis of his past experience."

Rosenblum thus makes the effort to help the student verbalize his feelings, hunches, and ideas. I'm certain that Rosenblum himself must give evidence to his students that it can be done and thus help them to feel free to put into words nebulous feelings, ideas, presentiments until they become crystallized. The atmosphere provided by the teacher must make this possible. In addition, the teacher must provide a model for the student of what can be done by this means. He must himself be a creative practitioner of his art. The atmosphere of respect for the individual humanness and potentialities of his pupils is an absolutely essential ingredient of the teacher's attitudes. This attitude is implicit in the writings of Rosenblum.

I had a recent experience with another great artist and teacher of photography that further crystallized my thinking about the teacher's role. In a recent workshop with Ansel Adams, the students were of varied capabilities, talent, maturity, and even basic photographic knowledge. My first feeling was how much could be done with so variegated a group. I was interested to see that Adams' belief that they could all be helped to take a further step, no matter where they were in their development, his basic respect for the individual and his potential, was perceived by everyone and was an important factor in promoting their learning of material difficult for many to grasp. His attendant enthusiasm and endless patience, his willingness to repeat material, to give examples until the student was clear, were also factors important to the student's learning. Another important factor was the completely honest but gentle criticism of the student's work. Helping the student face the reality of his present state of development and the work necessary to proceed to realize the self further is an absolute essential in freeing students to be more creative. They are helped to divorce themselves from pretenses and self-deceptions that permit them to go on without self-realization. Such self-deceptions have often been fostered by parents, husbands, or wives who themselves have never been able to face the realities of both their present accomplishments and the work necessary to really satisfy themselves. Such parents often dissemble with their children about their school work, art, writing, music, etc., fearing to hurt the child. They are aware of how they too would feel if the actual truth about their own accomplishments were told them and a course of work laid out. Parents who have not learned to work for themselves regularly and persistently can't believe that it can be done by others, and they often know of no solution but unreal deception of the child. Thus the teacher who has achieved his creative stature by just such regular, persistent work and self-exploration can honestly face the student with his present status. He can at the same time express his confidence in the student's potential and his readiness to be of help. His own example that it can be done is a vital factor in the learning of the student.

The teacher's attention to all the small and seemingly minute details of the student's work is often protested against and felt as unfair by the student. He often believes the teacher is failing to recognize the worth of the idea or general concept. However, such attention to small details, the teacher knows, is essential for the student's complete mastery of his medium and for his self-mastery. Sloppy work and unfinished details bespeak the old conflicts about doing work with all one's energies and to one's own complete satisfaction. It indicates the tendency to start many times with ideas that are then left in a state of incomplete fruition. The student may thus deceive himself and others about the worth of the work. The readiness to do a complete piece of work also bespeaks one's readiness to do the work alone without the overseeing of a teacher or parent, which is a final evidence of creative maturity.

The meticulous attention by a master like Adams to small details, even of matting a print and the lighting of a finished photograph, was a constant source of wonderment and delight to many of his pupils.

The process of learning through identification is basic to all learning. The child begins to learn through identification with his parents' attitudes. The student learns much through his identification with his teacher. Such learning when coupled with the complete mastery of subject material is not imitation, it is the integration of attitudes about the self, about how one finds self-satisfaction and self-fulfillment; it is the integration of a philosophy of growth and creativity that permits one to explore one's own potential rather than imitate others. One can often see in the students the attitudes of the teachers. Thus in the issue of <u>Aperture</u> in which Rosenblum's article appeared, there was another article with similar breadth of approach to the philosophy, teaching, and learning of photography; and I was not surprised to find that the author was a student of Rosenblum's. Although I know Minor White (the Assistant Curator of Eastman House) only through his photographs and writing, I often have been able to guess correctly who his students were because their attitudes revealed in their work conveyed some of his general philosophy towards life and towards creative seeing. This is true of students of Ansel Adams, who give evidence of a particular kind of perception, perhaps best demonstrated by their efforts to unify the elements in a photograph to present a beautiful and cohesive whole, whether the subject be macrocosmic or microcosmic. They also have his basic respect for people and their work. This is also true for the students of my own teacher and I hope of my own students. In conclusion I'd like to quote from The Prophet by Kahlil Gibran a quotation we inscribed in a compilation of my teacher's writings presented to him at an anniversary of his work with us. "The teacher . . . if he be indeed wise, does not bid you enter the house of his wisdom, but rather leads you to the threshold of your own mind."

Reprinted by permission from The American Imago, 17:83-99, 1960.

EMOTIONAL FACTORS IN THE USE OF AUTHORITY

S. A. Szurek, M.D.

There is perhaps no more troublesome problem than that of the use of authority, not only in all kinds of interpersonal situations where two or a few more persons have relations with one other, but also in those where larger groups of people--especially nations--interact. It is not necessary here to say much to substantiate this statement. Such words and phrases as "civil rights," "dictatorship," "democracy," "totalitarianism," "police state," "the sovereignty of a nation," "freedom"--to name only a few--will recall the manifold problems of authority that acutely beset us today in the world, and that probably beset every generation in human history.

Some might object that such problems are far removed from the purpose of our meetings here in these two weeks. These are political problems, one might say, or problems in philosophy or in political science or in law, or at best they are the phenomena of human historical processes. Certainly, such an objector could maintain, the problem of authority has only a tangential relation to science, to medicine, or to one of its specialties, psychiatry. Nevertheless, if our discussions together have succeeded in suggesting to you that psychiatry has something to do with the problems of people living together, with their influence upon one another, even with their effect upon one another's health and bodily functions, then it will be quite obvious to you all that no medical man can be unconcerned about the problem of authority. Whether or not the doctor is clearly aware of the problem, he is constantly involved in its implications. This is true simply because he himself is vested with a certain authority. He is vested with this authority not only by virtue of his medical license and degree, but also by virtue of the feelings of his patients toward him. And in public health work special, legally established responsibilities of the medical officer invest him with an authority in certain situations that differs in its nature and problems from that of the physician in private practice.

How he exercises this authority is of tremendous importance for
the effectiveness of his work and for his own satisfaction in it.

I shall probably never forget a bit of autobiography one of my teachers in medical school shared with us. He said it took him ten years
in private practice to unlearn what he had acquired in his work with
charity patients during his internship in a county hospital. During
those first ten years of practice he examined conscientiously, studied thoroughly, and prescribed sometimes minutely for his patients.
If a patient returned some months later no better for his ministra-
tions and occasionally worse off, and if he learned that the patient
had taken one of his prescriptions but failed even to have another
prescription filled, he became angry and offended. He ordered the
patient to leave and seek another physician's help. Gradually it
dawned on him that the motto of the salesman, "The customer is
always right," was equally applicable to the practice of medicine.
If the patient had asked, received, and paid for a doctor's advice,
he really had the right to do with it what he wished, which, of
course, included the right to disregard it. After he had learned the
lesson it took him a decade of medical practice to acquire, my
teacher thereafter, with regretful but more sympathetic patience,
tried to unravel the again-tangled threads of his patient's illness.

This story illustrates very dramatically for me many of the problems with regard to authority involved in the physician-patient
relationship. It suggests some sources of our difficulties with
effective medical practice. It describes a too frequent attitude that
complicates work with patients and generally diminishes therapeutic
influence. An older colleague of mine, himself a psychiatrist, once
humorously described a psychiatrist as a doctor who could rarely,
if ever, be insulted. The wisecrack has an important half-truth in it.

Another illustration of the same kind of difficulty, a personal experience from my own early efforts at psychotherapy, comes to mind.
It was in the days when I hoped that I had learned enough of psychotherapy from reading and lectures to be able to seem useful, and
certainly informed, to patients. One patient in particular continued
to come to see me for a much longer time than the circumstances
seemed to warrant. I listened for many sessions with a studied,
and to me quite frequently strained, silence until an explanation of
his behavior, a mechanism--as we were then prone to call it--
dawned on me. With insufficiently restrained enthusiasm, if not
glee, I pronounced an interpretation to the patient. He listened

politely and again effectively reduced me to strained silence by the brief reply, "So what!" Although I was not clear about it then, I later realized that my patient and I were struggling about authority. The interpretation meant nothing to him subjectively and yet I expected him to accept it wholeheartedly on my say-so.

Many years later, after I had undergone considerable discipline during training for psychoanalytic therapy, a patient of Central European origin listened with obvious uneasiness to the note of annoyance and impatience in my voice as I commented on what he was saying for the twentieth or more time. He interposed with anxious amazement that I sounded very angry. After I promptly acknowledged that I was annoyed and told him why, he said with evident relief, but persistent astonishment, that he had the impression from previous European experience that Analytikers did not have, much less did they display, any feelings toward their patients. This patient had had problems of authority and was still struggling with them in vain, but at this time I felt much less uneasy about mine.

I would like to add one more illustrative anecdote. This was a personal experience during my first month as an intern with a ward patient who gave me my first, startlingly unexpected experience and minor success in psychotherapy. After a gynecological laparotomy this woman was placed in a quiet room. Her own surgery was uncomplicated, her course post-operatively was expected to be smooth. As junior intern it was my duty to make daily urinalyses until the post-operative acidosis disappeared. On a busy service it became a bit troublesome as well as a matter of considerable concern when the acetone and diacetic acid tests remained four plus on the third and fourth days. I investigated and learned from the nurses that the patient was afraid to drink and eat because her roommate, who had eviscerated following her first intake of fluids by mouth about a week before, lay distended in the other bed still in acute discomfort with a stomach tube protruding from her lips. I tried more or less gently to reassure the first patient that nothing like that threatened her, that her wound was healing well, that her general condition was excellent and would improve if only she would begin to take fluids. On the fifth and sixth days the acidosis was practically undiminished; the patient continued to be uneasy about fluid intake. The pressure of my work increased, as did my concern for the patient. I spoke again to the patient, this time with more annoyance than I wished, telling her I saw no need for her attitude and behavior, that there were reasons for her roommate's condition other than the intake of fluids post-operatively. On the following day the acidosis had completely disappeared.

For my part, I was a bit ashamed of my assumption of a paternal tone toward a woman a decade or more my senior. I avoided her somewhat for my remaining few days on the service and on the last day was quite uneasy about saying goodbye to her, as I did to all the other patients on the ward. However, in spite of my discomfort, I did say goodbye and tried to turn away quickly. I was amazed to find that one of my hands was suddenly grasped by both of hers and kissed. With tears in her eyes and with quite obviously genuine gratitude, the woman thanked me and said that I had done more for her than anyone else in the hospital! This was my first clinical lesson in the therapeutic power of authority. Apparently the patient was more impressed with my interest and concern for her welfare than resentful of the impatience of which I had been so ashamed.

What are some of the elements common to all these situations? Is there more than one kind of authority? Are all situations involving authority equally unpleasant and likely to cause difficulty for both the person in authority and the subordinate? Are these difficulties inevitable? Or are there tendencies on both sides that may spell the difference between a mutually happy and effective relation and one that is full of trouble and discomfort?

Merely to ask these questions is to suggest some of the answers from our experience. We all know that despite the frequency of trouble in the relations between a superior and a subordinate there are instances in which all kinds of authority are effectively exercised with willing and happy cooperation on the part of subordinates. Now and then we also see some peculiar relationships. We ask ourselves then how a person can take such attitudes from the so-and-so. Or we wonder how someone can be so mean. Yet both parties may not only appear content, but each may actually defend or even extol the situation or the other person. It is easy for most of us to understand why the dominant one might be satisfied in such peculiar relationships. It is more difficult to comprehend what the apparent underdog, who seems happy, gets out of it, or how he got that way.

Suggestions have been made and explanations have been given regarding these same problems in other contexts, so that some of what I say now will be repetitious. But perhaps this repetition may not be altogether useless.

It is possible--according to Erich Fromm (1)--to distinguish two general types of interpersonal situations in which authority plays a role. Only rarely do we meet either type in pure culture, especially in this country with its traditions and ethics. These two types are polar opposites. They may be the limits along a scale of variation never actually reached, like the asymptotes of a hyperbola. In other words, we may be making a distinction between the absolute good and the absolute bad, the angel and the devil, and hence may not be describing reality, actually occurring interpersonal integrations. Nevertheless, I have found the conceptions of these two types of authority situations useful in my thinking and practice, provided I also remember to define how much of each type is present in any actual instance.

These two types of authority-subordinate relationships can be distinguished by several criteria: the mode of operation, the basic purpose, and the predominant results or usual outcome.

In one type of relationship--which might be called authoritarian-- coercive power, whatever its nature, is exercised by the dominant person primarily for his own rather than the subordinate's immediate gain. The power is exercised to the end that the status quo of the relation in these terms be continued forever, or for as long as possible. In simpler terms it is an enslavement, an effort by the dominant person to maintain control of the slave's services, deference, admiration, or whatever is demanded. Only such care is given, only such concessions or attention to the inferior person's welfare and needs are made by the dominant one as will enhance or assure the continuation of the benefits and profit to the latter. Certainly there is no concern or interest in the development of the inferior's potential abilities or strength, for this might endanger the relationship or lead to freedom for the inferior. On the contrary, there is positive hostility and fear of such a possibility, often on the part of both persons. What is little realized is that personal stultification is inevitable for both persons. As one writer puts it, every dictator is slavish and every slave dictatorial. There are other describable results of this type of relationship, such as ruthless cruelty, mutual suspicions, hostilities, rebelliousness, with retaliatory anxieties and general chronic tensions that produce great anxiety about prestige, brittle rigidity of attitudes, and a narrow pessimistic outlook.

In the other type of authority-subordinate relation, the polar opposite, which might be called democratic, or more truly, and from our point of view, legitimately _authoritative_, the converse is observed in all these characteristics. Coercion is absent. The authority derives from superior competence and skill. As in the best teacher-student or ideal parent-child relations, the purpose of both persons in the situation is to promote and foster the acquisition by the subordinate of the competence and skill of the authority. Their common effort is to grow more alike in respect to the power that the competence brings and eventually to achieve equality and genuine freedom of each other. Admiration and deep respect is mutual. Confidence, optimism, a benign expansiveness of outlook, readiness for experimentation and risk, and a tolerance for thwarting, frustrating obstacles as well as a capacity for more enthusiastically productive work are characteristic qualities generated in such relations. Rather than envy, the good teacher or ideal parent manifests genuine delight if the student or child approaches or even begins to surpass his own competerce. Sympathy without any trace of contemptuous pity and mutually affectionate warmth without anxious oversolicitude permeate the relationship. Flexibility of attitudes coupled with firm consistency is gradually transmitted from the authority to the subordinate.

There are many other contrasts between these two extremes of authority relations. What has been called spiritual anthropophagia of the first or authoritarian type is replaced by anthropophilia of the second or authoritative type. This is, of course, a polysyllabic way of saying that destructive, emotional swallowing of man by man is supplanted by genuine love of man. This brings one to make some very necessary distinctions between varieties of "love."

Many relations essentially of the dictator-slave variety are called "love" even, perhaps especially, by the participants. When sexual activities occur in these situations, one may be certain that they will belong to the sado-masochistic category, regardless of what bodily zones or orifices are stimulated and regardless of the sex of both persons. The fact that jealousy and exclusive possessiveness, as well as depressions, panics, or impulses to murder or suicide on threatened separations are so widely accepted as natural concomitants of "love" is no justification to perpetuate the unconscious self-deception that mutual enslavement has anything in common with a mature, genuine love. Mature love, it has been said, has no need to be blind. When one loves maturely one loves the other person in spite of the qualities one dislikes in him. Emotional maturity capable of such love is an expression of a self-love that is clear-eyed and tolerant of the limitations within oneself, the while it is contentedly and securely proud of one's assets. Such self-love cannot be mistaken for the deeply anxious concern about the self that must disguise its self-destructive sense of terrible inferiority and weakness either with a brittle and aloof conceit and an exaggerated appearance of superiority or with an ingratiatingly submissive self-abnegation and an assumed false modesty.

Incidentally, it is probably this strong feeling of inferiority and weakness, however hidden from others or unconscious to the self, that is the source of, and chief motivational energy behind, the compensatory drive for power over others that leads to the dictatorial enslaving types of relationships. A genuine and solid self-love cannot be depleted by love of another. On the contrary, it is enhanced, and sacrifices or services to the other flow from relatively inexhaustible reserves of strength and plenty. Such self-respect neither countenances domination nor requires submission from another. In other words, there is neither masochism nor sadism, neither slavishness nor tyranny. By its nature it fosters the growth of the potentialities of the other and revels in the give and take between equals. By its very nature and its needs it cannot behave otherwise. Hence, without strain or effort on the part of such a person, all others who come in contact with such qualities of personality are attracted and so affected as to make even some tiny steps toward maturity and freedom themselves.

Maturity is not at all immune to a tragic sense of life. It is not, for instance, immune to genuine and deep grief and mourning for the loss of a friend or a beloved person through death. It is not, however, subject to the likelihood of the severe depressions or agitatedly depressive reactions of the authoritarian-dependent character in the event of the death of, or temporary separation from, the person with whom it is enmeshed. In these depressive reactions, of course, exaggerated fears about one's future, fears of loneliness, and guilt about one's hostilities toward the other person are prominent. In both types of character there is an identification with the other and an incorporation of the other into one's own ego or self. But the treatment of this incorporated object, and in turn, the effect of the incorporated object upon the self, are quite opposite and the resultant feelings differ markedly. Instead of panic or anxiety or the repression and splitting off of these emotions, there is ready expression of sadness, grief, and longing. Instead of the schizoid absence of feeling in consciousness resulting from a repression of panic and anxiety, with its attendant sense of impoverishment of the self and unbearable loneliness, helplessness, and futility, there is a fullness of feeling, however painful, and with its full expression there comes a calm enrichment within the self with positively toned memories of the other.

Thus, in the case of the mature person there is no panicky sense of loss or abandonment when the other is temporarily absent. He still has contact with the other through pleasant memories and through continuing affectionate feelings despite great geographical separation and despite infrequent communication. In other words, the mature person has a feeling of wholeness and no sense of diminution of his power or strength. With the immature person, however, the opposite is the case. There is a kind of fragmentation of the self with an inevitable increase in the inability to deal with the reality of his own actual assets and potentialities and with the reality of the friendliness of other persons remaining about him.

The mature person has no Pollyanna quality in his recovering optimism. He has, instead, a capacity for realistic discrimination of the possibilities in the actual situation after his loss. The bereaved, genuinely loving person carries on. The slavish-dictatorial person tends to collapse, to reduce his activities in the real world of remaining persons. At least his hedonism or enjoyment is reduced. He senses within himself a futility and a gloom. An uncanny world of terrors and unnamed threats frequently obscures the actual world of other persons and the possibilities for personal satisfaction. The one retains or rapidly regains possession of himself; the other tends to "lose his grip on himself," "goes to pieces," feels a progressive sense of unreality, and sometimes progresses to a state of depersonalization. In such circumstances the mature person actually requires solitude; but even at other times he serenely enjoys his own companionship. The immature, the authoritarian person, on the other hand, carries within him a deep sense of estrangement from himself--the result, if you please, in psychoanalytic terms of the hateful tension between the superego and the ego--such a sense of constant loneliness and bereavement that solitude is intolerable.

Another difference between these extremely opposite personalities is that the genuinely friendly, mature person, unlike the other, has no need for exclusiveness in his affectionate ties with people. Feeling a good deal of warmth and tenderness for several persons in no way diminishes the intensity of his feeling for a few intimate friends or for the especially beloved person of the opposite sex. The immature personality, however, compulsively attaches himself to one other person with such tremendous, all-consuming force that relations with others are rarely as intense and are generally incompatible with it. Automatically and rather helplessly, he puts all his eggs in one basket, hence any slight threat to this basket tends to precipitate feelings of impending cosmic disaster.

One could go on and on through the whole gamut of variations in human psychopathology to show that the personality traits of the participants--that is, the emotional factors in the relationship-- determine the quality of any authority exercised. Perhaps, however, I have indicated enough of the background to bring into focus the problems suggested by the title of this lecture.

Conflict between persons generally occurs whenever any egocentric impulse of one person meets opposition to its gratification from another person in authority. The impulse may be for some necessary bodily satisfaction or for some more psychological (emotional) need for security, prestige, affection, approval, or the like. The opposition to gratification may be motivated by various factors, perhaps most often by an inability to supply the need; anxiety about being deprived or hurt by the demand; or ideally, as in the case of a parent in regard to a child's impulse, by genuine interest in the person's immediate safety or future welfare. This latter problem-- the concern of the person in authority for the immediate and future welfare of the subordinate--is, of course, part of a much wider problem, the satisfactory adjustment of the quite individual needs of each person and his welfare to the welfare and needs of the group of which he is a part. In guiding individual persons toward ways of gratifying their egocentric impulses that will be either least destructive or more in consonance with the welfare of the entire group, one has something of the parent's problem of inculcating durable personality traits in the child that will fit him to live happily and responsibly within his culture.

In any case, whenever such opposition to egocentric impulses is encountered and for whatever reasons, anger is the inevitable and biologically adequate reaction. Under such circumstances a healthy organism, human or not, reacts not only with rage but also with efforts to circumvent or remove the obstacles to its satisfactions. If this is impossible, there is a revengeful attack upon the

opposing organism. Whether this rage or attack is direct or in-
direct, frank or disguised, and whether or not it is persistent depends, of course, on many factors, not the least of which is the
relative strength and power of the two persons involved. Another
factor of great importance to the eventual issue of such a conflict
is the firmness of the person in authority. This firmness is frequently a crucial factor in the manner in which the conflict is
solved. It frequently determines whether the subordinate learns
how to get satisfactions in ways that are non-destructive to himself
and others, or whether he remains rebelliously set in seeking his
own satisfactions quite egocentrically, disregarding the welfare of
others. In the latter case he may also remain distrustful of all
authority, with a suspicious, hostile readiness to react defensively
and often self-destructively to any suggestions from others. He
then remains unintegrated with the group, in effect isolated from
it, perhaps maintaining an exaggerated self-assertiveness that further estranges him from others and that estranges others still further from him.

For these reasons the quality of firmness in the authoritative person is important and requires more detailed examination. In the
first place, firmness needs to be distinguished from dictatorial or
sadistic suppression, deprivation, or complete denial of any gratification to the subordinate. In brief, the authority does not assert
himself in the conflict situation merely for the sake of an egocentric satisfaction in his own power and prestige. His primary purpose is not to deny all satisfaction to the subordinate's impulse,
but to guide him in obtaining it in ways that are non-destructive to
the interests of others and to his own other self-interests. His
purpose is to indicate ways that ultimately will gain for the subordinate deeper satisfaction, since they will tend to integrate him
with the social group whose approval enhances his self-esteem.
Such firmness on the part of the authority, then, is possible when,
and only when, the authoritative person's conscience is clear as to
his motives in regard to the welfare of the subordinate. If he has
no need to deprive the subordinate, if he has no egocentric (compensatory) power drives or exaggerated prestige needs of his own,
if he has no wish to enslave the other or hurt him revengefully, he
will be free of retaliatory anxieties. He can then remain calmly
and quietly firm in opposition, not to the impulse of the subordinate, but to the manner or circumstances of its satisfaction.

There are other describable and essential elements that contribute to the quality of firmness of an authority. Perhaps the chief one of these is that the authoritative person himself is integrated, is wholehearted in his own attitude with regard to the impulse active in the subordinate. In other words, it appears to me necessary that the authority, himself, has actually learned and acquired ways of gratifying such an impulse in accordance with his self-esteem and the mores and ethics of the social group. This again presupposes what one might call emotional maturity, a mastery of similar impulses within himself. By mastery of impulses I do not imply simply a constantly uncertain, although sometimes fanatically rigid, self-restraint, a compensatory reaction formation. Such compensatory attitudes, opposite in direction to the given impulse, generally signify that the conflict is active and persistent. In situations affording temptation or the possibility of gratification, the balance of forces within the self remains precarious. In these circumstances of unresolved conflict--even though the conflict is largely or wholly unconscious--within the personality of the authoritative person, the pressure or the demand of the impulse of the subordinate often increases the conflict. The authority is usually uneasy and tends to vacillate within himself about prohibiting another from doing what he himself is either tempted or actually permits himself to do.

Such anxiety tends to cloud the issue with the subordinate and often leads the authority to irrational behavior in order to deal with his own anxiety: he is either doubtful and hesitant or defensively authoritarian and suppressive. Neither type of reaction can be called firmness. If the authority vacillates, the tendency of the subordinate is to gratify his impulse even though surreptitiously. If the authority is defensively suppressive and dictatorial, defiant self-assertiveness is likely to be aroused in the subordinate. Whether the subordinate responds to either attitude in these ways or in some other manner depends, of course, on _his_ character, on his previous experience with authority and the patterns of behavior he has previously acquired in these experiences, as well as on other possibilities in the current situation. In any case, the subordinate is likely to experience anxiety in reaction to the anxiety of the authority. Anxiety in a serious degree in any person tends to fog his perception of the realities of the situation and of his own self-interest.

Another element in the quality of firmness is patience. The person who has matured emotionally, who has genuinely resolved the conflicts of his earlier life, is not only convinced through his own experience that it is quite often possible to gratify one's selfish impulses non-destructively, but is also convinced through such personal experience that it takes time to achieve such solutions. He has learned among other things that emergencies are relatively rare in peacetime, that most problems are capable of solution, that even though he may not see how to meet a threat to his satisfactions at a given moment, a solution may appear later. He has learned that no miracles are necessary in such instances but that a "miraculous" clarification of the situation and of his own feelings can occur if only he grants himself time first to see how he feels about the dilemma and to examine more closely what real possibilities exist. He realizes that his own rage at the threatened thwarting need not be destructive to anyone, since he has learned solidly that he can control the form of its expression. He has learned finally that his whole happiness never depends upon the loss of any one satisfaction and that he can survive it. To him the whole world of other persons rarely appears as totally hostile, unjust, or oppressive. At the same time, having lived through such anxieties, impatience, greediness, and subjective cosmic calamities in his own progress toward maturing, he appreciates sympathetically what the subordinate is experiencing. This sympathetic appreciation permits him to wait patiently, but none the less firmly, for the subordinate to make alternative choices of action. His quiet confidence, reflecting his own achievement, is then a positive, constructive aid to the subordinate, who psychologically and often unconsciously imbibes of it.

I have been discussing the problems and difficulties of the person in authority. This is in many respects the converse of the "what is wrong with the patient" type of discussion that is more usual in discourses on psychopathology. This discussion does not mean that I feel that all the difficulty in authority-subordinate relationships resides on one side of such relationships, nor that if the person in authority were only more thoroughly integrated emotionally and more mature, all problems would end. The role of the patient or subordinate in these relationship difficulties is considerable; it has been implied and touched upon here and in other lectures. The entire range of immature tendencies--the regressive attitudes of helplessness; the demand for protection, for care, for relief from all responsibilities; the slavish ingratiation used to obtain gratification; and many other attitudes--are here involved. But I have been interested in making two points, first, that immaturity does not by itself progress to maturity but requires mature help, guidance, and firmness from another, and second, that the difficulties between two people rarely stem from the immaturities of only one of them.

This latter point brings me to the final topic of this lecture. I have already suggested that the critically important factor is how much immaturity remains and how much maturity has been achieved by any one of us at a given period of his life. The dynamic balance between these two constitutes our total self-organization or personality. Whether or not we are aware of our immature tendencies, whether or not we are conscious either of the regressive trends or of our defenses against them makes little difference. If they constitute an important fraction of our total attitudes toward ourselves, they will be evident in certain interpersonal situations. They will be stirred up or intensified to disturb us and the other person. Our tendencies to irrational behavior, our anxieties and underlying conflicts are particularly likely to be aroused in situations involving authority and in love relationships. In the case of those relations where authority is involved, our conflicts may be equally heightened in either the position of authority or that of subordinate.

From this point of view it is obvious that periods of neurotic illness and disorder may be precipitated in our patients, and in ourselves, by situations involving persons in authority, persons with whom the patient is currently "in love," or both types of persons. It is then that people become our patients whether or not we are psychiatrists.

This is not the place to review in detail what the therapy consists of, whether it be in a psychiatrist's office or in the office of the non-psychiatric medical practitioner. However, one may mention a few of the steps that one hopes will occur.

The first phase of such interaction is the establishment of working rapport--the transference--a relationship between patient and doctor with therapeutic potentialities. This has many rather technical problems. One is the time such a transference may require and another is the basic attitude of the doctor, leaving out of consideration the character of the patient. Both of these are variable from patient to patient and from physician to physician. That is, the time required generally varies inversely with the skill, experience, the basic attitude of the doctor. The greater his skill, experience, and maturity, the shorter the time required, other things being equal, namely, such things as the frequency of visits, age, and the character problem of the patients.

There follows, with no sharp line of demarcation from the first phase, the phase of "working through." This is a repetition of the inevitable struggles of the patient both to re-establish and maintain a relationship characteristic of his degree of immaturity and to resolve the conflict between the immature and mature portions of his total self. The result or outcome of this phase varies, of course, and depends on many factors. Certainly, even in the most intensive efforts at psychotherapy, namely, in psychoanalytic treatment, no perfectionistically ideal goals are attainable or necessary. Although in this form of therapy the hope is that the character of the patient, the total self or personality, may undergo a rather basic reorganization, a great deal has been accomplished if at least some firm steps are taken in this direction. If only a few limitations to growth are removed or even just loosened, much has been achieved. The only factor I wish to emphasize again is the attitude, the actual maturity, the competence of the doctor. If his authority is based on such competence and if it is infused with at least a measure of the parental desire to help and to allow the patient to grow, then movement toward the common goal of doctor and patient may occur.

We do not have much time left to examine the specific problem of the utilization of authority in the situation of an executive or director and his staff. There is perhaps time to make only one or two comments. Although some of the same processes may occur, although some of the same dynamics may be present in this situation as in the therapeutic relationship, there are a few obvious differences. For one thing, the complexity in executive-staff relations is obviously greater. One enters the sphere of larger social integrations, of group psychology, and of leadership. The interrelations and the problems between the subordinates as equals or between levels of a hierarchy of authority are present. Mutual envies and competitions, as well as sibling types of collaboration, are present. In this collaboration, interidentifications, which in effect are identification with the leader for the purpose of the organization's work, occur. Nevertheless interidentifications for mutual support in rebellion against the leader may at times be predominant or coexist with the whole collaborative attitude. Problems of delegation of responsibility and authority always exist. The degree of freedom of choice granted the subordinate and the encouragement of his independent decisions within the limits of the delegated authority are obviously important.

The problem frequently arises of how to avoid making punitive changes in general policy that affect all members of the staff when only one member fails to act responsibly. Questions of group morale occur. These are frequently questions of the nature of the leadership and the type of authority exercised by the director. His attention to reward by approval, appreciation, or promotion is as important as his promptness of censure and disapproval. Perhaps of even greater importance are the leader's actual competence in all phases of the organization's work and his willingness to risk being wrong. The latter quality frequently relieves much anxiety in the subordinates about their inadequacies, inexperience, and incompetence. It may release whatever growth potential exists in them.

Finally, the leader's readiness to accept specific competences of a subordinate that may be superior to his own is of great importance. For the leader to accept a subordinate who has grown and matured in skill as an equal and as a colleague and for the leader always deeply and spontaneously to respect the subordinate's personality remain the most effective incentives for each subordinate and provide the integrating power for the entire staff as a unit. Such authority so exercised is likely to be utilized with a minimum of interference from complicating or obstructing emotional factors.

REFERENCES

1. FROMM, Erich. Escape from Freedom. New York: Rinehart, 1941.

Reprinted by permission of the publishers and The Commonwealth Fund from Ethel L. Ginsburg (Ed.), Public Health Is People. Cambridge, Mass.: Harvard University Press, Copyright 1950 by The Commonwealth Fund.

SECTION TWO:

THE TEACHER'S ROLE AND HIS PROBLEMS

An honorable and respected profession since the ancient civilizations, teaching the young has in recent years become increasingly arduous, unsatisfying, and difficult for many teachers. Social and cultural developments have fostered more learning difficulties in the young. More of the impossible is expected from teachers, with fewer of the previous rewards of recognition, honor, and adequate remuneration. The following papers record some experiences and observations about the changing role of both teacher and student in our highly mobile and unstable society.

TEACHERS' SELF-EXPECTATIONS: HOW REALISTIC ARE THEY?

I. N. Berlin, M.D.

I vividly recall a young teacher who could not control a group of defiant high-school boys. He had been teaching only a few months, but already he was convinced that he was a dismal failure. No one must know the dark despair and the hatred that welled up within him, this teacher told himself. He was on the verge of resigning from his position when an intuitive administrator sensed the churning emotions that the teacher was trying to hide. With sympathetic understanding the administrator helped this man stay on the job. The administrator did more: he helped his despairing staff member develop into an extremely competent teacher.

Many teachers, like this one, hold themselves to expectations that are unrealistic, expectations that can be a source of dissatisfaction and constant strain in the classroom. Some teachers, for example, think that they should love their students unfailingly and, in turn, be unfailingly loved by them. These teachers believe that their administrators expect to see signs of this unfaltering love whenever they step into a classroom. The evidence demanded is a quiet, orderly room. Hence the teachers strive to avoid the slightest disturbance, since even minor breaks in order carry the risk of disapproval. Other teachers have the idea that the personality of the student is so fragile that firmness, anger, or insistence on study may produce trauma. These teachers make it a cardinal rule to treat students with utmost gentleness.

There is another dubious notion abroad. Teachers are being told that they should be experts on child-rearing, prepared to instruct parents on how to be better parents. To live up to the requirement, teachers often feel impelled to give mothers and fathers explicit and detailed instruction on how they can help their children. When the advice fails repeatedly, the teacher feels more inadequate than ever, and at this point he may begin to think of easier ways of earning a living.

I have consulted with many teachers who studied at many colleges
(1). In working with these men and women, I have tried to learn
what led to the unrealistic expectations these teachers had of themselves, what produced their self-defeating attitudes toward children
and their parents. To find an explanation I studied the professional
preparation required of teachers. As I have come to understand it,
most of the attitudes of the student teacher are not explicitly taught.
Rather they are caught. The student teacher's ideas of how a good
teacher should behave and feel reflect his instructors' ideas. I
discovered also that schools of education seem to pay little attention to the difficulties, strains, and burdens of classroom teaching.
Professors emphasize the elements of good discipline in a classroom, but professors rarely, if ever, talk about the feelings of the
teacher who is confronted with problems in discipline. The advice
that professors give their students on such problems often makes
the solution seem very simple indeed, but instead of helping the
student teacher, the advice leaves the troubled trainee feeling more
estranged and uneasy than ever over the emotions he finds within
himself. Students seldom learn from their professors what feelings difficult classroom experiences may normally engender in
the teacher. Most trainees are under the impression that only
calm, kind, loving, and patient emotions are worthy of a teacher
and that all ungentle emotions are frowned upon, as indeed they
often are, by professors and administrators. When these trainees
move into their profession, they continue to cling to these beliefs.
Like the high school faculty member who was about to resign, they
think that they should have no unpleasant emotions. If, in spite of
themselves, unpleasant emotions do well up, teachers seem to
think that their feelings must be hidden.

I remember several conferences at which teachers recounted their
difficulties with hostile, aggressive students. At these sessions I
told the teachers that in their place I might feel angry and hateful
toward a student. Whenever I make this admission teachers glance
anxiously at the administrator, if he happens to be in the room.
When the administrator agrees with me, the teachers sigh in relief, and I can see strained facial muscles relax. The transforma-
tion is unmistakable. It takes place as soon as it is clear that at
times anger and hatred are not reprehensible but quite understandable and human.

It is essential to help trainees understand and accept the wide-
ranging emotions they may encounter in themselves in the class-

room. Only as teachers accept their feelings and dare to speak of them can they avoid the anxiety that their emotions may erupt into sadistic, revengeful behavior. The experienced teacher well knows that eruptions of pent-up emotions can be harmful to the child and disruptive to the teacher-child relationship. However, a distinction must be made between being aware of feelings, hostile or otherwise, and acting on them irrationally. The purpose of becoming aware of all one's feelings and not repressing them--and the warning bears repeating--is to avoid the wear and tear of tension and repression as well as the possibility that, under the guise of kindness and firmness, sadistic and retaliatory feelings may find expression.

The subject, of course, has a bearing on mental health. It would certainly be a boon to the mental hygiene of the prospective teacher to feel that his professors understood the emotions that he might encounter in himself as he taught in the classroom. By exploring these emotions with students, understanding professors can give beginning teachers insights that can safeguard emotional health. Forthright, honest, experienced teachers can make a valuable contribution by sharing their feelings and experiences with student teachers. Throughout practice teaching, it is customary for students to meet to discuss teaching techniques. At these sessions, a way might be opened for student teachers to discuss their emotions, especially emotions that may take hold when a young teacher is confronted by a hostile, provocative, stubbornly negativistic student or by a placidly indifferent one. If student teachers came to feel that their emotions were understood and accepted by their professors, less of the teachers' energy would be expended in repressing turbulent, forbidden emotions and more energy would be available for working with difficult children.

If I seem to labor the point, I do so because of my own experiences with teachers whom I have tried to help. At times, they cannot hear what I have to say that might help them in their work. Before a troubled teacher can listen to me, I have to demonstrate to him that the emotions difficult children may set off are understandable and not shameful. The teachers' emotions, unpleasant as they may be, are a reality that must be faced frankly. The teacher who recognizes his emotions and handles them wisely has come to grips with a common source of classroom stress.

One way, then, to help the teacher function within the realities of the classroom is to help him understand himself. Another way is to help him understand the role he plays in the child's growth and development. We have recently added to our knowledge of how personality evolves. During the past ten years, especially, we have come to appreciate the need to understand the child's experiences with meaningful adults in his life, adults who have a powerful influence in determining his personality (3). Parents, of course, are among these adults. It has become clearer to us that certain parental conflicts, and attitudes that stem from these conflicts, can cause distortions in personality development. By the age of six, these distortions can be quite marked and difficult to modify. The last point deserves to be stressed, since teachers are being made to feel responsible for changing the personality of disturbed students. Teachers, as we have already pointed out, are expected to take on the work of counseling children and parents. Those who would give teachers this responsibility seem to be unaware that trained psychotherapists may work with a family for years before they can detect any change in attitudes.

Parents, of course, wield the earliest influence on the child. What kind of influence do they have on personality? In what kind of home can we expect the most wholesome development of personality? Certainly, a home where both parents are, first of all, relatively free of conflict and, beyond this, a home where both parents are fully aware of their own feelings and can speak of them openly. In the home that favors healthy growth, the mother enjoys nurturing her infant. Yet she does not need to deny her occasional weariness, her feelings of irritation and momentary longings to be free of the responsibilities of motherhood. She can share her feelings of annoyance with her husband, and he, too, does not feel that he has to repress his resentment at being tied down, tired, and sleepy. Both parents can indulge each other's feelings of wanting to be babied, and, at stressful times, both husband and wife feel free to ask themselves: "Are children worth all this trouble?" In such an emotional climate, parents are able to love each other--as well as the child--freely.
What does a child learn about emotions in a home where feelings are not repressed, in an atmosphere where the adults about him feel free to express emotions whether they are pleasant or hateful? Whether they are appropriately mature or infantile? From his parents' example, the child learns how feelings can be expressed fully in ways that are not destructive to him, to others, or to the things around him.

As the child in that home learns to talk, he finds that he may say what he feels. All emotions--even hateful, angry emotions--can be put into words without jeopardy. His outbursts do not provoke his parents into emotional withdrawal or hostility and thus set off in him fantasies of peril to those he loves. On the contrary, the prompt ventilation of emotion leaves the child free to play or make excursions into the world around him.

When the child in this home becomes curious about his surroundings, his mother and father encourage his explorations. As part of their encouragement, they place firm limits on activities that might endanger him. The limits reduce conflict yet leave the child free to explore areas that are reasonably safe. As the child grows, he becomes more and more eager to put his capacities to full use. The helpless dependency of infancy is often pictured as an idyllic state that the child gives up only with the greatest reluctance. On the contrary, the satisfactions and pleasures that learning brings the child at each stage of growth make him eager to continue to learn and grow without regret for the gradual loss of the pleasures of dependency. Satisfactions from learning, from mastering tasks, and from creativity are universal, the inevitable product of wholesome growth.

At times, however, neurotic conflict interferes with children's development. The child who has conflicts about learning may show his distress by hostility, anger, sullenness, or indifference. Usually his parents also have conflicts about learning, conflicts that probably date back to childhood and make the mother and father tense, helpless, and dependent on others. Their lives are marked by the inevitable disappointment that comes to those who expect others to fulfill old, unmet yearnings. Such parents are unable to help their child experience the pleasure of learning. In such a home, little constructive learning takes place, and understanding acceptance of emotions is highly unlikely.

If the child does not see acceptance demonstrated at home, where can he experience acceptance? Here the teacher can make an invaluable contribution to the child's emotional development. The teacher can demonstrate behavior the child has never known. The teacher may be the first person the child has ever met who can accept a hostile outburst without withdrawing emotionally or without becoming angry or defensive. But before the teacher can accept the child and his hostility, the teacher will have to face his own emotions and do so without feeling helpless before them. The teacher himself will have to know the pleasure that comes from learning, the satisfaction that comes from mastery over self and environment. The task calls for a teacher who is fairly free of pretense about himself.

The teacher may be able to help the child learn only very little, but by dint of firm, insistent expectancy, the teacher can gradually add to the child's store of skills and knowledge. No experienced teacher or administrator needs to be reminded what it can mean to help a stubborn, hostile, or indifferent child learn even the smallest skill or achieve even the most minute scholastic success. The slightest achievement can help the child feel entirely different about himself and the world around him. This kind of teaching, it seems to me, is the greatest contribution the teacher can make to the mental health of his students. The teacher may try to counsel children or their parents. But his efforts in counseling cannot compare with the effect of persistence and firmness in helping a child learn and make a start, however small, toward measuring up to his capacities.

Again, I may seem to belabor the obvious. I dwell on the point because recent efforts to make teachers counselors rather than better teachers seem to me to ignore insights gained from recent studies in ego psychology (3). Many teachers have told me that their slow, constant insistence that work be done--their firmness in the face of tantrums, illness, and excuses--finally paid off as the child began to learn. Such beginnings seem to reduce the child's fears of the world about him. As the world seems less hostile, the child, in turn, feels less hostile, and, in time, less afraid and less helpless as well; and as the child feels the mastery that comes from learning, his hostility and fear and helplessness fall away even more.

In this connection, I might add that teachers who have worked with seriously disturbed children--psychotic youngsters--have also discovered that the same emphasis on helping them to learn, however slowly, over a long period of time is important in their groping toward health.

A recent conference on inpatient psychiatric settings for children disclosed that few teachers are prepared to work with children who have serious emotional ills. There is an ever increasing need for qualified teachers in this expanding field. There is also a need for teachers who can face difficult emotional problems in programs for the mentally retarded. For this work teachers need preparation that helps them accept and understand their own feelings plus additional practical experience on children's wards in a hospital like the Langley Porter Neuropsychiatric Institute. The problems of supervising and integrating trainees in a psychiatric setting would have to be worked out carefully. However, a core of teachers who have had experience with seriously disturbed children could help prepare other teachers for such work and contribute greatly to all facets of teacher education. Psychotic children are unusually sensitive to pretense. Their teachers must have self-awareness, and they must be honest in expressing their feelings. Principles learned from working with our most disturbed children could probably be adapted for work with children in our regular school program. It is my hope that some of the most mature teacher candidates will be encouraged to explore and pioneer in this field, where much remains to be done in developing teaching methods.

Somewhere in their preparation, teachers who work with disturbed children should be helped to understand that their real job with parents is to listen uncritically to their troubles. The teacher's suggestions, if they are needed, should center on ways of improving the child's schoolwork. Here, also, concentration on schoolwork has often helped parents who want to help their children. The teacher can point out to parents that firm insistence on learning in school and, where necessary, at home, can be helpful. Again, the teacher gives his help by way of educational problems, not the neurotic troubles of the parent and the child. The teacher cannot hope to modify emotional difficulties a great deal. By working on school problems, an area where the teacher is competent, he can best help parents deal with their child in an area where they can be competent--responsible parenthood.

Now for my last point: the role of the administrator. Many teachers have personal problems that make it difficult for them to enjoy teaching, to feel at ease in the classroom, free of conflict and able to be firm. In my experience as a consultant, I have met administrators who, through long experience plus an intuitive feeling for people, have unconsciously become the kind of administrator I am about to describe. They behave with their teachers as they hope their teachers will behave with their students. These administrators are available to hear teachers' troubles. These administrators relieve teachers of the feeling, often imbued in school staffs, that they should be able to do their job by themselves. These administrators want no teacher in their school to feel that he is carrying a burden alone. Yet the administrators I am describing are honest about their limitations. They do not pretend to know everything or to be able to solve all problems. By their readiness to admit that some difficulties are beyond them, by their willingness to admit defeat at times, they help the teacher feel less guilty about his own difficulties and often spur him to try again.

Although the administrator listens to his teachers' troubles, he firmly but sympathetically insists that each teacher do his own job. The administrator does not permit the teacher to abdicate his role to the administrator, for he knows that the teacher can be happier and more content with himself only as he learns to teach more effectively. The administrator does not hide his own feelings from himself, nor does he suppress his disappointment or even anger with teachers who continue to be helpless. However, he takes care to impart to his staff his certainty about the value of his work and shares with them what he has learned about achieving satisfaction in it. Unconsciously the staff emulates him.

The more troubled and anxious a teacher is in his work, the more important it is that he be helped to do his job better. One way of working toward better teaching performance is to set high standards for every aspect of the job. Tardiness, slovenliness, and inaccuracy, if overlooked, lead to ever increasing difficulties, accompanied by increasing anxiety about holding the position. Thus, the more troubled the teacher, the more attentive the administrator must be to details. The administrator's constant insistence on better performance and his willingness to accept the teacher's anger without retaliation eventually result in a better job and increased pleasure in teaching. Above all, the administrator who concentrates on getting the best possible teaching can afford to ignore personality problems and quirks that do not stand in the way of competent teaching. He can feel secure that his helpful vigilance in requiring good teaching can be an aid to his teachers' well-being.

I am aware that in every teachers college there are a few professors, supervisors, and seminar leaders who explore the subject of teachers' feelings (2). I also know administrators who help their teachers immeasurably by blending firmness and sympathetic understanding. It is my hope that more and more student teachers will be given the opportunity to explore the realm of emotions and that more and more teachers will be able to count on the support that the right blend of understanding and firmness in an administrator can bring a school staff.

REFERENCES

1. BERLIN, I.N. Some learning experiences as psychiatric consultant in the schools. Mental Hygiene, 40:215-236, 1956.

2. STEWART, Robert S., and WORKMAN, Arthur D. Children and Other People. New York: Dryden Press, 1956.

3. SZUREK, S.A. and BERLIN, I.N. Elements of psychotherapeutics with the schizophrenic child and his parents. Psychiatry, 19:1-9, 1956.

Reprinted by permission of The University of Chicago Press from The School Review, Summer 1958.

EMOTIONAL FACTORS
IN THE TEACHER EDUCATION PROCESS

I. N. Berlin, M.D.

The emotional stability of classroom teachers has been a growing concern of school administrators. Simultaneously educators in teachers colleges have become increasingly aware of the need for careful selection of teacher candidates to obtain the most mature trainees. The emotional stresses upon the student teacher resulting from difficult classroom situations, or, conversely, from practice teaching under ideal circumstances, only to face trying classroom settings after receiving his credentials, seems to be of less concern to educators.

SELECTING TEACHERS

My own experiences, both in psychotherapeutic work with children and in psychiatric consultation with teachers and school administrators, have increased my awareness and aroused my interest in some of these problems of school people. My effort to clarify my thinking about these problems has resulted in the point of view that is presented here. In trying to think through the problems attendant on teacher selection, I speculated about the qualities necessary for the well adjusted teacher. I became aware that these were qualities of personality that would make a good doctor, nurse, social worker, psychologist, or any other professional person who works with people as individuals or in groups--the difference being the teacher's preference for teaching as a satisfying way of earning his livelihood. In speculating about any special qualities that might be necessary for work with children, I could not be sure what these special qualities would be.

The concern of personnel officers in teachers colleges and school systems with how one can be certain that one has selected good teachers is shared by people responsible for selection of trainees in psychiatry, child psychiatry, psychoanalysis, psychology, or social work. It may be reassuring to personnel people to find that

those who know most about personality from their daily psychotherapeutic work, the psychiatrist and the psychoanalyst, are also dissatisfied with their selection methods and with their failures in candidate selection. Since 1948 there has been a research project at the
Menninger Foundation on the selection of psychiatric residents. A
summary of the findings to date has been published recently (1). The
findings show that single interviews with experienced psychiatrists
and psychoanalysts have little predictive value, that a single psychological test, like the Rorschach, T.A.T., etc., is even less helpful predictively. The most valuable information could be gathered
from examining the actual performance of candidates in the same or
similar work. Past performance gave a more accurate estimate of
what could be expected in the future than any other single method
It is of interest that the analysis of data from interviews and psychological tests revealed that interviews often failed to perceive the
degree of psychopathology present; on the other hand, psychological
tests revealed much of the psychopathology but little of the integrative and adaptive aspects of the personality.

Walker, Botha and Barbato, in a recent paper entitled "The Psychiatric Interview and Teacher Training," (2) wrote that the good
teacher, like the good parent, should be a warm and firm person.
They concluded their paper by saying, "We are convinced that our
present level of knowledge does not permit us to predict accurately
whether or not an individual may be a successful teacher." These
psychiatrists suggested the use of a psychiatric interview early in
the college experience of prospective teachers so that the obviously
disturbed students could be helped to choose another profession.
They also felt that in the course of the survey they could help the
students who had neurotic manifestations that might interfere with
their teaching, to accept psychotherapy. The survey was used to
help both psychiatrist and student assess the student. It covered
the areas of motivation--why the student was interested in teaching
--and an effort was made to evaluate such positive aspects, as good
identifications with parents and respected teachers, previous successful work with children in scouts, campfire girls, etc., and
those negative aspects that indicated the student's need to live out
in his pupils his own unrealized emotional experiences. The authors speculated that the student who looked on teaching as a way
of earning a living to make possible creative work such as art or
writing might, despite "poor" motivation, be a better teacher and
less neurotic that the teacher who "just loved children." The psychiatrist explored the psychosomatic illness in the student's life-

time, and tried to evaluate his current living with respect to school, work, marital and sexual adjustment, financial independence, family relations, and social activities. Past work, school, and military history were reviewed. In addition, the interviewer tried to get some feeling of the student's tendency to extreme mood swings and how he characteristically reacted to stress. As previously mentioned, these psychiatrists felt they could not predict from their data which students would make successful teachers. It seems to me easier to determine those who would not do well in teaching. Thus, the student who appears to prefer teaching because he feels it is safer, i.e., less threatening, to work with small children than with adults, will usually give some history of severe and painful experiences with adults in his own childhood and a consequent life of isolation from peers, lack of participation in class and school activities, and withdrawal from most interpersonal relationships. When such a candidate reaches practice teaching he is made very anxious by any hostility or aggression in children and either withdraws or is anxiously punitive. In general, lack of spontaneity, rigidity and frozenness, obsessive attention to detail, may indicate defenses against the eruption of hostile, aggressive, and infantile feelings. To candidates who have such massive defenses the classroom may be a very threatening situation.

Candidates who have varied interests, friends, and social activities are less likely to live out unsatisfied needs through their students. A realistic appraisal by the candidate of the advantages and the disadvantages of teaching, considering security and vacations in contrast to low pay and heavy emotional demands, gives one a feeling of the maturity of the candidate. The past school and work history gives one clues about the student's ability to follow through and complete a job. Warmth and spontaneity in relating to people and a feeling of respect for self and children are not easy to evaluate except in an actual teaching situation or through continued contact with the student. It seems to me important to differentiate between the presence of any neurotic traits and the presence of those neurotic traits that are likely to interfere with teaching. Some psychopathology can usually be uncovered, but one must evaluate such findings in the context of the individual's total integration.

It occurred to me, after this discussion of problems of teacher selection, that in the light of inadequate salaries and the current teacher shortage, even if we develop criteria for selecting teachers, the choice may not be very great. It may thus be necessary for administrators to learn how to help individuals not so well suited to the job to develop into adequate teachers.

WEAKNESSES IN TRAINING

In my work with new teachers I have heard frequent complaints about the disparity between the practice teaching situation and the realities of classroom teaching (3). Teachers often wonder aloud why the principles of good pedagogy that were so vivid, clear, and logical as enunciated by the professors and demonstrated by master teachers seemed not to work in the classroom, why discipline problems in the flesh seemed not to yield to the tenets and methods taught in the teachers college. I also tried to understand why some new teachers were having problems in the classroom and other new teachers seemed to have less difficulty in their job.

DIFFERENCES BETWEEN
"SUCCESSFUL" AND "UNSUCCESSFUL" TRAINEES

In the course of some seven or eight years of consultation with teachers, it became clear to me that the new teachers who did well in difficult classroom situations tended to be direct, firm, and honest with their pupils. They seemed to be task-oriented; their job was to teach these youngsters. Often they "appeared" to be insensitive to the emotional problems of their students, not to be concerned with counseling them, not to be interested in whether the pupils liked them as teachers. They were interested primarily in helping their students learn. Paradoxically, their students said both that these teachers were disliked because they were so tough, severe, and demanding of performance, and, in retrospect, that they liked these classes because they learned in them. I discovered that these successful new teachers often had had prolonged experiences with children prior to teaching. They had worked in child care, in scouts, campfire girls, summer camping, or came from large families. In contrast, the new teachers with troubles in the classroom were relying primarily on what they had learned in teacher training. Certain concepts about child development and discipline learned in courses in psychology and educational methods were swallowed whole and not tempered by much direct experience. Thus they seemed to be afraid of hurting, damaging, or stunting in some way the psyches of their students. They seemed to have absorbed from their professors that a goal of successful teaching was love for their students. Implied in this goal was that the teacher's love would be reciprocated, and learning would then go on blissfully in such an atmosphere. These teachers were therefore dismayed to find how difficult it was to "love" certain students, and they reported how frightened and secretive they were about the kinds of feelings they discovered within themselves. This emphasis on how good teachers "ought" to feel in contrast to the human feelings discovered within one's self in the process of classroom teaching of difficult, defiant, and negativistic students seemed to me to be a major factor in the teacher's difficulties in the classroom. Further investigation with these teachers and subsequently with student teachers revealed that in most teacher-training curriculums there is little if any emphasis on helping the trainee anticipate, understand, and evaluate the feelings that may be aroused in him in trying situations. The attitudes the teacher has about himself and how he should feel are conditioned largely by the attitudes of his professors. He thus comes to believe that to have angry, thwarted, hateful feelings is pathological and means that there is something wrong with him as a person. He feels he must hide the knowledge of such feelings from others else he will be thought to be "bad," not fit for his job. Thus the absence of discussion and attention to all the human feelings aroused in a teacher by the difficult classroom situations so common in our culture, tends to undermine the teacher's feelings about his own worth as a human being, and thus his effectiveness as an instructor.

When these beginning teachers heard from the psychiatric consultant, administrators, and experienced teachers that feelings of rage, impotence, anger, etc., were understandable human feelings, that such emotions could and needed to be shared with others, they felt less burdened and less alone with their problems and functioned more effectively in the classroom (3).

TRAINEES NEED EMOTIONAL INSIGHT

From these repeated experiences, I came to feel rather strongly that a regular part of all teacher training should be devoted to helping the trainee become aware of and understand his human emotions. His professors need to demonstrate that they too have experienced certain disagreeable feelings of impotent rage, anger, disgust, and frustration while teaching. The professor's verbalization of his feelings and experiences would give the trainee the feeling that such emotions could be discussed and assessed with colleagues and administrators. He would learn that these feelings can be dealt with in an integrative manner. The risk of not understanding and working through such feelings is not only that efforts at repression increase tensions and anxiety so that the work is difficult, but also that such feelings may erupt around trivial incidents into hostile, retaliatory, irrational behavior harmful to the student-teacher relationship and damaging to the teacher's self-esteem. Our experience is that new teachers who are helped to accept, understand, and work with their own turbulent feelings, teach better, i.e., with less strain, and become effective teachers, whereas previously in the same school system we understood they often quit teaching, feeling that the emotional drain was too great.

PERSONALITY STRUCTURE NOT FRAGILE

Another factor in the student teacher's feeling about himself often stems from the emphasis in child development courses on the effects of psychological traumata on the child's personality.

This emphasis does not take into account the clear evidence in recent years that the personalities of children are not easily modified after their pre-school years. Also, not a single traumatic event alone, but the totality of the child's relationship with parents and parent figures is responsible for his character structure (4). Further, where the child's early experiences with adults have resulted in personality problems, the child needs to find in his teachers a steady attention to the tasks to be done that will help him learn to learn (5).

Personality problems in children that are manifested in learning difficulties and antisocial behavior usually stem from experiences with troubled parents, parents who have difficulty in deriving pleasure from learning and gratification from their own accomplishments. They seem to need to have their satisfactions in living provided for them by others. Thus the child has never experienced any steady consistent help in learning or any continued expectations of integrative behavior. Parents who, because of their own neurotic troubles, have not been able to help their child find satisfaction in the accomplishment of tasks consistent with the child's maturing capacities seem alternately to expect more and to accept less than the child can actually do. The child's resulting dissatisfactions and disappointments often are seen in rages, temper tantrums, or sullen withdrawal. The child often mirrors the parents' unpredictable behavior, uncontrolled anger, or apathetic resignation in the face of tasks to be done. Thus, the teacher's steady focus on the learning to be done and the satisfactions to be obtained from successful learning is a new and integrative experience for the child.

As teacher trainees become more consciously aware of their own feelings they feel less frightened by and estranged from the feelings expressed by their difficult students. The teacher can be more helpful to the student when the student's behavior evokes neither anxiety, hostility, or withdrawal. The student can then be helped to focus on the job to be done in the classroom and can learn that with satisfaction in the mastery of subject matter, he feels better about himself, less hostile, friendlier, and thus literally more lovable and more loved. The student may thus experience with his teacher the most important lesson to be imparted in school. He may learn that by working on the tasks at hand he feels better about himself.

Mental hygiene for teachers logically begins in the teachers colleges. There the attitudes of professors that might help trainees accept and understand their own feelings as teachers need emphasis and clarification. The focus on the self-understanding of teacher trainees could be useful in helping the trainees better understand their role with emotionally disturbed students. The trainees' awareness that the most effective help they can give an emotionally upset pupil is to help the pupil experience the satisfactions resulting from learning and mastery of subject matter, is good mental hygiene for both the pupil and the teacher.

REFERENCES

1. HOLT, Robert R., and LUBORSKY, Lester. The selection of candidates for psychoanalytic training. J. Am. Psychoan. Assn., 3:666-681, 1955.

2. WALKER, Warren; BOTHA, Eleanor; and BARBATO, Lewis. The psychiatric interview and teacher training. Mental Hygiene, 40:406-412, 1956.

3. BERLIN, I.N. Some learning experiences as psychiatric consultant in the schools. Mental Hygiene, 40:215-236, 1956.

4. SZUREK, S.A., and BERLIN, I.N. Elements of psychotherapeutics with the schizophrenic child and his parents. Psychiatry, 19:1-9, 1956.

58

5. STEWART, Robert S., and WORKMAN, Arthur D. Children and Other People. New York: Dryden Press Publications in Psychology, 1956.

Reprinted by permission from Calif. J. Secondary Education, 33:7-12, 1958.

FROM TEACHERS' PROBLEMS TO PROBLEM TEACHERS

I. N. Berlin, M.D.

Psychiatric consultation with several school systems has convinced me that most problem teachers become so as the result of certain pressures and practices that seem inherent in many school systems. I rarely have seen a teacher in consultation whose difficulties resulted only from her own personality problems. I have many times worked with teachers whose evident character disorders would seem to preclude their effectiveness as teachers, and yet with wise management and assistance from alert, intuitive administrators these disturbed teachers were doing good jobs in the classroom. Other psychiatric consultants have confirmed my impressions that neurotic disturbances among teachers are not more frequent than among other professionals who work with people. Problem teachers seem to result from the same juxtaposition of forces that makes for neurotic disability in all human beings --namely, the severity of the stresses, their duration, and the susceptibility or predisposition of the individual.

The stresses that impinge on the teacher can be divided into two large categories--the external stresses and the internalized ones.

The external stresses are becoming more and more severe. They seem to be unremitting and pose serious problems for the mental health of even the most stable teachers. These increasing stresses result from the ever-larger numbers of children with little motivation to learn, little curiosity in the world about them, and very little ability to derive satisfaction from working or mastering a task. Teachers are being faced in their classrooms with growing numbers of indifferent children who have little desire to learn to read or to learn at all.

With these ever-larger groups of nonreaders and nonlearners comes an increase in behavior problems. Since these children ob-

tain few if any satisfactions from learning and since they have not
been helped by their parents to learn to master environmental problems by regular, continued, and steady effort, these children feel
constantly dissatisfied, disgruntled, and tense. These feelings are
expressed in acting out, aggressive, hostile, tantrum behavior.

Such disruptive behavior occupies more and more of the teacher's
time. She has less and less time to teach the few children who
want to learn. The teacher's satisfactions from teaching consequently are being steadily reduced. Added to these stresses are
the unreal demands upon the teacher of both school administrations
and the communities.

In the face of these growing problems many school administrators
have been demanding that teachers counsel disturbed children and
their parents. Thus, to the burdens of attempting to teach unwilling
pupils are added the burdens of attempting to counsel troubled parents and children whose hopeless and helpless feelings are often
manifested in hostile, defiant, indifferent, and demanding attitudes.

The teacher is therefore doubly frustrated and defeated. She is
not trained in psychotherapeutic techniques, her efforts to help
disturbed children and their parents often backfire, and even skilled,
well adjusted teachers begin to feel helpless and ineffectual.

From many communities there are increasing demands, tacitly
accepted by some school administrators, that the school instill
discipline, the desire to learn, cooperative interpersonal attitudes,
respect for authority, good work habits, etc. Many parents in our
society seem to be desperately looking to others, since they seem
unable to look to themselves, to exercise the parental roles. Under
such pressures more school administrations accept these roles.
The evidence accumulated in the last few years is quite clear: it is
extremely difficult if not impossible, except in rare individual instances, for teachers to assume the parental responsibilities. The
educator faces an almost impossible task with those children who
have not been helped to enjoy learning, to delight in the quest for
knowledge, and to feel the satisfactions that come from mastery of
self and the environment.

The pathetic paradox is that all of these increasing demands and
expectations are placed on the shoulders of teachers who are ill-
paid and yet are expected unselfishly to devote all their time to

work that not only has little monetary reward but carries ever-
fewer satisfactions in actual teaching.

In addition to these external stresses teachers are subject to a
traditional indoctrination in most teachers colleges that tends to
deny the teacher the right to feel and to express human feelings.
Teacher trainees usually are given to understand by their instructors that good teachers feel only love and compassion for their students, and that no matter what the provocation they must never feel
hostile, angry, frustrated, and hopeless. Teachers who find themselves in difficult teaching situations often feel they have nowhere
to turn, no one to whom they can ventilate and relieve themselves
of the burdens of suppressed feelings. How often I've heard administrators say, "We just don't get angry. We help all our children
with love and patience, don't we?"--this to a teacher beside herself with tension and fury because her best efforts have been thwarted by an indifferent, defiant student. In many schools a teacher
knows that any admission of how she feels will cause her to be la-
belled a poor teacher. In my own experience this burden alone
has caused teachers to feel that the strains of teaching were too
difficult to endure, and they have consequently left teaching.

Thus, there are increasing demands on teachers to instruct more
and more unwilling, rebellious pupils. In addition, they are expected to take over not only the parental job towards the children
but in many instances to be parents to the parents, or at least to
be their psychotherapists. Finally, there are the unreal internal
stresses that deny teachers the recognition that their feelings in
difficult classroom situations are human, acceptable, and must,
for the sake of their own mental health, be ventilated and communicated to others.

All these teachers' problems tend to produce problem teachers.

The problem teacher is usually one whose psychological makeup
results in a particular equilibrium that is necessary for his functioning but is maladaptive and discordant in the school setting.

As I have tried to understand the problems of the teachers with
whom I have worked, I have come to feel that those with learning
problems of their own seem to react to stress with the most maladaptive behavior. I have no way of knowing the frequency with
which these particular patterns occur in schools.

I have been most interested in these problem teachers who appear to derive little satisfaction from learning. Since they themselves have not acquired the capacity to obtain pleasure and satisfaction from learning, from working effectively and mastering their job, they seem to be especially vulnerable in situations in which their students manifest similar problems of the same or greater severity. Thus, they are trying to help others do what they themselves cannot do. Many of them turned to teaching in the hope that they could get by with little effort or knowledge, only to find themselves increasingly disorganized, harried, frantic, and unable to control their classes. If the administrator tries to help by making the job easier, by expecting less of the teacher or doing some of it for the teacher, the problems usually are compounded. These teachers tend to regress the more their work is done for them. They are most difficult for administrators, and I feel they are their most troublesome problems.

For such teachers classroom control is extremely difficult. They often lose their tempers and resort to corporal punishment in a desperate effort to maintain some control of their pupils. The substitution of force for teaching skills and knowledge occurs frequently with these teachers and presents recurrent problems to the administrator.

Certainly any severe neurotic conflicts that reduce the teacher's feelings of self-esteem and worth will result in teaching problems. These may be seen either in overindulgent seductive behavior or punitive harsh actions with pupils. Both extremes are designed to maintain control of their pupils in the face of violent internal conflicts.

I have been impressed repeatedly with the way those administrators who focus on the job of teaching to be done are able to reverse the process from problem teachers to teachers' problems. Their ability to listen to teachers with concern and to expect and insist on a good job of teaching has helped teachers to work more effectively to their own increased satisfaction. In turn, as teachers do more teaching they begin to expect more learning from their students.

When administrators have been helped to delineate their own capacities and limitations as human beings and to accept their own feelings in the face of problems and frustrations, they sometimes adopt more realistic attitudes about the role of the schools. Thus, the administrator is able to maintain that the school's chief role is to impart knowledge and techniques for acquiring knowledge. He helps his faculty to see their role as one of teaching and not of being substitute parents. The human emotions of administrators, teachers, and pupils are accepted and allowed ventilation, and more teaching and learning occur.

In one school, following repeated psychiatric consultation, parent-teacher-administrator conferences were held as frequently as possible to discuss each problem child. In each conference an effort was made to delineate the roles of the school and of the parents. Initially, there were many angry protests by the parents. They clamored that the school was failing in its responsibilities to the community. However, later in the year some of these parents in their P.T.A. meetings expressed their appreciation that they were being helped to be more parental with their children. Some parents volunteered that their children were now learning more. Some were beginning to learn for the first time.

I am impressed that the equation from teachers' problems to problem teachers is a reversible one.

Reprinted by permission from "Neuroses of School Teachers, A Colloquy," Joseph C. Solomon, M.D., Mental Hygiene, 44:80-83, 1960.

THE ATOMIC AGE, THE NONLEARNING CHILD, THE PARENT

I. N. Berlin, M.D.

Nonlearner, behavior problem, hostile, violent, restless, apathetic, and indifferent are terms used to describe an increasing number of students in our schools today. Veteran teachers say they have never encountered so many youngsters who have so little desire for, or interest in learning. Many of these teachers emphasize the dramatic shift in their roles in the past decade from teacher to policeman.

As a psychiatric consultant to both small rural and large urban school systems, I have become increasingly concerned with these problems and have attempted to understand them so that I might be of more help to teachers and administrators. In both urban and rural schools the common cry of how do we help such disturbed children to learn, when do we return to teaching instead of policing, has impressed upon me how widespread these problems are. Even in the very wealthy communities teachers are becoming increasingly concerned and vocal about the growing number of nonlearners and behavior problems despite the smaller classes and greater opportunities for individual attention to students.

Everywhere one hears the demand for special classes and special services to meet the pressing and difficult situations that prevail in many schools.

From my vantage point as a mental health consultant I have become increasingly aware that parents, too, are becoming more difficult for schools to deal with. Many parents seem to want the school to take all responsibility for their child. Not only his learning, but also his discipline and moral upbringing are felt by some parents to be the school's job. Administrators and teachers alike have expressed dismay at the mounting angry attacks of parents on the school when their child's problems are broached. In recent years

64

I have been asked with greater frequency to help school people to work more effectively with parents who are often either angry, apathetically indifferent, or impotently helpless when asked to assume their parental responsibilities to help solve the child's behavior and learning problems manifested in school.

In recent years a number of sociologists, psychologists, cultural anthropologists, and students of infant and child development have been studying these and related phenomena of much concern to our nation and our democratic way of life. These workers have been increasingly troubled by the growing number of delinquent and predelinquent youth, the increase in severe psychotic disorders of childhood, and the ever larger numbers of nonlearners in school.

MULTIPLE CAUSES

These behavioral scientists seem to agree on several sociocultural factors that may explain some of this behavior.

They point out that our society since World War II has become a mobile one, roots are not laid down in any community for long, families are fragmented and family ties are fragile. Perhaps because interpersonal ties in family and community are less durable, the major concerns of parents seem to be the acquisition of material evidence of success--as if money and worldly goods will protect them from the fears and anxieties prevalent in a tension-ridden world. Parents tend to give children things and money rather than time and attention, another sign of our accent on material goods as a substitute for relationships. These patterns appear to be related to several important socioeconomic forces. Some students stress the effect of the atomic bomb and its threat of annihilation that makes both adolescents and adults feel they must get their pleasures now and at all costs for tomorrow may be too late. A high level of general anxiety results from not being able to think about or to plan for a future in which the individual has some personal control of his own and his family's destinies.

Another significant stress in our culture is the threat from automation, which makes unskilled and semiskilled workers increasingly less necessary in society and begins to threaten even skilled workers. The threat of unemployment and economic deprivation gives many young people and young parents a sense of having no place in our society and a belief that it is someone else's job to take care of them and their children. With their present level of education and training many parents are unable to provide for their youngsters no matter how hard they try. Discrimination and economic, social, and educational deprivation increase these problems for members of minority groups. Such problems make gratification <u>now</u> an important way of reducing tension.

Many parents of school-age children were themselves raised during the depression and the subsequent war years, when there was great insecurity for their parents, divided homes, and little parent-child contact. Many of them did not have much love or attention and concern from their own parents, and little encouragement or interest in learning. As a result they seem to have little to give to their own children. Their children's behavior and learning problems only aggravate the parents' sense of inadequacy and failure and leave them feeling increasingly helpless and looking to someone else for solutions. They often want desperately to be rid of these problems, hence their anger with school people, who call these problems to the parents' attention.

The children show the results of these parental attitudes and anxieties early, as they, too, seek immediate gratification and satisfaction of every impulse. The only reason for learning to delay impulsive behavior and immediate gratification is the love and concern of parents who reward such goal-directed behavior, so vital to learning, with personal love and approbation. These youngsters early learn to think only of themselves since no one has really been very much concerned with them for very long. Their learning and their welfare are not of primary concern to their distraught parents. These youngsters correctly feel someone owes them something and they are hard put to understand why they should endure the anxiety, tension, and hard work necessary to beginning to learn. It is easier to drift and to let others worry about them or deal with them. If their parents' lives are any example or model, their future as adults holds no rewards for them.

It is small wonder that teachers who have to teach and work with such youngsters find themselves overwhelmed. The restlessness, temper outbursts, short attention span, hostility, apathy, and indifference are difficult to understand as signs of the child's inner turmoil. It is hard to recognize in his violent behavior the student's discontent with himself and his frightened striking-out for some relief from his own feelings of helplessness, of hopelessness.

It is equally hard to see in the youngster's withdrawal into sullen apathy and indifference a defense against the recognition of problems and anxiety. Many youngsters behave as if they had to make sure that no one could reach them behind their protective wall.

Yet there is a desperate hope that someone will penetrate these barriers, that someone will persist past all the obstacles of the youngster's angry, hostile rebuffs to prove they, unlike other adults in the child's past, really care. That desperate hope is repeatedly demonstrated by the intensity of these youngsters' interaction with adults. It is difficult indeed for teachers to live through such painful testing to reach many of these children.

THE THERAPEUTIC ROLE OF EDUCATION

I have become increasingly aware of the important therapeutic role of education for these children. Beginning to do school work does not solve all of their problems, but they do begin to feel themselves to be more competent, effective, hopeful individuals.

The most defended, withdrawn, and alienated children with whom many of us have worked, children with psychoses, have proved the importance of educational measures as part of the treatment program. When these children begin to learn even the tiniest bit academically, this is reflected in reduction of their fears about the outer world.

Similarly, beginning to learn and to master subject matter in school is vital to the nonpsychotic youngsters under discussion. Only through learning can these children begin to feel more secure about themselves in their frightening world. Only through acquisition of marketable skills can they earn a livelihood in our automated society.

For many of these students the relationships with teachers who are concerned about them is vital to their learning. These students begin to believe that someone cares when teachers persist through all their trying protests, hostility, and indifference. The relationships that result from such consistent persistence will be most important to them as models of behavior toward others.

A high school teacher told me with much feeling about one of the toughest and most difficult youngsters whom he taught to read and do simple arithmetic. This hard, belligerent, hostile, burly adolescent tried every trick in the book to discourage his teacher. Every trick but truancy--which meant he was getting something in the relationship with the teacher through the intense struggle.

When this youngster finally understood that his teacher believed he could learn and intended to try to teach him however long it took, he began to try himself and eventually succeeded in learning, with obvious pleasure and delight in his achievement. In his second year with the same teacher for his basic subjects, he took personal responsibility for convincing the new delinquent and predelinquent adolescent nonlearners in the class that learning was important for them and that the teacher was a guy they could trust.

IMPROVING CONDITIONS

To help such students to begin to learn requires small classes and teachers who recognize how important learning is for their pupils. It also requires the utilization of some of the methods developed for retarded, brain damaged, and psychotic children. These methods stress the scaling down of objectives both in scope and time, the extensive use of audiovisual and kinesthetic teaching aids, and rewarding success with expressions of the teacher's satisfaction and pleasure in the student's every small advance. Such expression of pleasure in the child's achievement, these youngsters have not often experienced before with adults important to them. These evidences of the teacher's pleasure in the student's learning are vital to the continuation and success of the work.

Similarly, teachers and administrators who recognize and understand the impasse with which these children's parents are confronted can try to help them be more successful parents rather than emphasize their failures. To do this, administrators and teachers need to be able to verbalize to parents their awareness of how difficult it may be for the parents to encourage and expect their child to do his school work and to persist despite vociferous objections and efforts to avoid the work. When parents feel that school people understand their problems and travail, they may be more open to suggestions about trying to keep their youngsters at their homework. Often when these parents begin to understand how important their help may be to the child and to his desire to learn, they begin to feel better about themselves as potentially more effective parents, who are viewed by the school as being important to their child.

The failure of many teachers colleges to recognize the need for new methods to deal with today's problem children continues to handicap teachers. The problems confronting our teachers today need to be understood and assessed realistically by teacher education institutions. They then can help their students learn new methods of teaching these children and of dealing with their parents. They might also help plan in-service training to help teachers help these disturbed and difficult students to learn.

In addition such reality orientation by teachers colleges would stimulate a realistic appraisal of the class size and supportive services necessary to make it possible for these youngsters to become effective and useful citizens.

SECTION THREE:

COMMUNITY PSYCHIATRY AND THE SCHOOLS

Introduction

Mental health problems in our citizens have become of increasing concern in the last several decades. In schools, too, ever larger numbers of emotionally disturbed children with increasingly difficult learning and behavior problems concern more and more educators. Mental health professionals, including psychiatrists, social workers, psychologists, and public health nurses, are being asked to help educators with these problems. Community mental health work as a specialty is very young. How these professionals can most effectively be of assistance to educators is a vital issue. It is clear that in the foreseeable future there will not be enough treatment time and trained personnel available to help disturbed youngsters and their parents. The collaboration of mental health personnel and educators in developing both preventive and therapeutic educational measures, therefore, becomes vital. The following papers explore some of these new horizons.

WHAT HELP CAN THE EDUCATOR EXPECT
FROM THE MENTAL HEALTH SPECIALIST?

I. N. Berlin, M.D.

Nearly two postwar decades of ever-closer collaboration between
educator and mental health specialist have resulted in increasing
service and help to the school child with mental health problems.
Out of these nearly 20 years of experience has grown a body of
knowledge about the conditions and attitudes of both professions
which makes for fruitful collaboration. We have also learned
something of the problems and obstacles to effective teamwork.
As one of the mental health workers who has participated in these
joint efforts, I have found the collaboration with school people rewarding in terms of the effective working together in the service
of disturbed children. These experiences have been a constant
source of stimulation to my own professional growth. In the light
of these experiences I would like to discuss briefly the realistic
and unrealistic expectations that educators have of mental health
specialists.

AREAS OF DIFFICULTY

Difficult relations between school people and mental health specialists usually come from the unrealistic expectations each profession has of the other. I expect some of my colleagues in education can describe the unrealistic expectations that mental health
specialists have of school people.

I want to describe several such unreal expectations that school
people have of the mental health specialist which get in the way
of their collaboration. Perhaps the most difficult and unrealistic
expectation for the mental health worker to deal with is that he
has some special magic that he could use if he would to solve a
teacher's or administrator's problems. I can vividly recall the
many times that teachers or principals have been angry and acutely disappointed that my interview with a pupil or parent did not
alter the difficult situation, cure the child, or reveal any easy

solution to the school's problem. It was only after many such experiences with the same school personnel that the collaborative value of such interviews became clear. They provided an opportunity for both educator and mental health worker to share observations and findings and then to explore the implications of these data, which may help evolve a plan for working with the disturbed child and usually disturbed parents.

Like most mental health specialists, I have often been asked what I thought about a child being given a grade of F or D, should some children be given a passing grade even though not earned, or in other instances, should a child be retained or passed to the next grade. In these matters the mental health worker is usually not competent to make any recommendations; the educators are the experts in these areas. The literature on such problems is, of course, published in journals of education. Only in rare instances is the emotional state of the child the vital factor in such decisions, and even here the teacher who knows the child and his family is usually a better judge of the best course of action than the "expert." The mental health worker can be of help in suggesting how certain reality situations can best be presented to disturbed children or their parents to secure their cooperation for further work on the school problems.

SIGNIFICANT AREA OF TROUBLE EXPLAINED
One last area of trouble between educator and mental health specialist stems from the understandable fear that the specialist will analyze, pry, or otherwise meddle in the personal problems of the teacher or administrator with whom he works. The mental health worker uses his special knowledge of personality development and maldevelopment to concentrate on collaborating with the educator in resolving the mental health problems of pupils. His understanding of the problems and frailties of all human beings is used to understand his own possible obstacles to his most effective work as a consultant; it is not usefully applied to prying into the lives and motives of his colleagues. Such concerns are both unprofessional and unethical.

THE SPECIALIST'S JOBS ARE OUTLINED
What are the realistic expectations educators can have of the mental health worker? Perhaps most important is that he be prepared and willing to learn about the circumstances, situations, and stresses inherent in the educator's job. Only if he understands

the conditions under which the teachers work and the pressures that come from the community and the superintendent's office can the specialist begin to be realistic in assessing the problems and to be practical in helping to evolve solutions. Such gradually acquired awareness of how a school functions and what the prescribed and extracurricular or grafted-on duties of teacher and administrator are helps the worker to be sympathetic and understanding of the handicaps school people face in their efforts to work with the mental health problems of their pupils.

Let us look for a moment to the special competences of the mental health person and try to see how these competences can be used in a school setting. The specialist is trained in the area of interpersonal relations; he learns about why people behave as they do with each other and especially within the family. Thus his training emphasizes an understanding of the psychological and emotional development of the child, the kinds of relationships in his infancy and childhood that may facilitate or impair his development. He studies the learning process both from the maturational and emotional aspects. He also becomes familiar with the organic, genetic, and emotional factors that may enhance or retard learning. Most workers have also learned about and have had experience in understanding and working psychotherapeutically with both children and adults who have mental health problems. Such work requires an awareness of the genesis of the present difficulties in past experiences. Interviewing techniques and methods are taught so that they can be used to gain the information necessary in order to understand the problems and to help the troubled person reduce his difficulties.

With this sketchy outline of the general competences of the worker we might add the special competence of the psychologist in intelligence and personality testing, the social worker's knowledge of community facilities and referral techniques, and the psychiatrist's knowledge of the physical and neurological aspects of mental health problems.

How can these competences be most effectively used in schools? Perhaps the specialist's greatest contribution to school people is made on the basis of his understanding of the origins and development of mental health problems in children. The teacher and administrator's observations about the troubled child, the data gathered by the school nurse about the home, the impressions of teacher and administrator from parent interviews help the mental health specialist begin to piece together some of the probable relationships and events in the development of the child's troubles. The specialist can use the results of these careful observations of the teacher and others to assess the degree of disturbance, to determine the urgency of the need for professional psychotherapeutic work with the child and family, and to select the community facilities most appropriate for referral of the child and the parents. The worker's assessment of the duration of the disturbance may also help school people to understand that change may occur slowly and take a long time. The teacher may therefore not feel as pressured about what he feels he ought to accomplish with the child.

Sometimes referrals are not acted on by parents, and even where the parents and child are in treatment the results may not be seen for many months. Thus, the mental health worker may be used to help with another important kind of evaluation. What is this child's potential for being helped in school with educative methods? In recent years the study of ego psychology and intensive work with psychotic children has clearly shown that learning and the mastery of academic skills and knowledge are important and potent tools in helping very sick children toward mental health. Therefore, the observations of the teacher about the particular learning problems of the disturbed pupil may provide clues to specific conflict areas and indicate the kind of corrective learning experiences that might be helpful to this child.

DATA FROM TEACHERS IS APPRAISED
From my nearly 12 years of experience as a mental health consultant, I have learned that experienced teachers accumulate a very important body of data about a child. Many of them use these data to formulate their own diagnostic impressions of the child's troubles and often have fairly clear formulations of how they might help the child. In working out a program that will help the child to learn more effectively and that will augment whatever other help the child may receive, such teachers seldom require more than encouragement from the mental health specialist and the confirmatory knowledge that their plans will in no way be detrimental to the mental health of the disturbed child.

In this context I might add that some teachers from their courses in psychology and from experiences with some mental health specialists feel that their reports need to be full of technical psychological terminology and presented like a psychiatrist's or psychologist's case report. In my experience such reports are not as helpful to the specialist as the clear, graphic, simple descriptions of behavior that experienced teachers present so well. The presenting of a psychological type of case report replete with jargon imposes an unnecessary burden on the teacher.

Sometimes teachers and administrators are concerned that a troubled child may adversely affect the other pupils. The mental health specialist's experience is that this is usually not the case when the child is withdrawn and schizoid. In fact, other children in the class frequently gain a sense of tolerance and understanding from the experience of helping such a child to function more effectively. However, the antisocial, hostile, destructive child may disturb other pupils and reduce their opportunities to learn so that special placement for him may be necessary.

SOURCE OF FRICTION IDENTIFIED
One source of friction between school people and mental health workers stems from the fairly frequent request or demand for a detailed prescription of how a teacher should work with a disturbed child. Mental health specialists are naturally reluctant to attempt to offer such prescriptions. In my own experience, the effective teacher would be hampered by such a prescription since he depends on his own intuitive feelings and long experience to determine what he will do in a given situation. The mental health specialist gradually learns to depend on the results of observations, ideas, and recommendations of experienced teachers. The inexperienced teacher may find a detailed prescription reassuring when it is presented. Then he usually finds it impossible to follow the directions since no prescription can anticipate the actual events that the teacher and pupil will live through. The teacher may then feel a sense of failure if the instructions cannot be followed, or if they are followed and havoc and chaos ensue.

Of course, the teacher is concerned that his educative activities and experimental efforts to find ways of working with the child should not increase the pupil's disturbance. The mental health worker can help in this regard. First, he can aid the teacher to understand and to recognize signs of increased stress. He can indicate which of the signs are signals of the child's needs that can be met by the teacher's warmth and firmness. Second, .the specialist can help the educator understand more about the origins and possible meaning of the child's behavior in the class-room. The teacher may then work out with the specialist some tentative approaches to the educative work with the child. The recurrent opportunities to discuss the effectiveness of these ap-proaches permit the working out of instructional methods that fit the particular abilities and experience of the teacher and the particular needs of the child. In this process wise solutions may be formulated for certain problems, and both the teacher and the specialist may experience professional growth.

To recapitulate, I have attempted to present to teachers and ad-ministrators some general principles and ideas that might be helpful in understanding the child's problems and in anticipating his reactions to certain interpersonal situations. Often some discussion of the child's experiences with his parents may reveal problems that indicate the kinds of attitudes and expectations that might be reassuring and encouraging to the disturbed child in his endeavors to progress academically. After such discussions I have encouraged the teacher to use his own inventiveness and to attempt various approaches of sufficient duration so that in our next discussion we (the mental health specialist, teacher, and administrator) could assess these experiences with the child. From these observations we can usually think together about the next possible steps in helping the child in the classroom.

OTHER FUNCTIONS OF MENTAL HEALTH WORKER

It occurs to me that there are several other ways that the mental health worker's competence may be helpful in the school setting. Often he is in a position to help school people assess the impact of social and cultural factors on a child, especially in terms of the individual psychological and emotional problems that may re-sult from particular social and cultural differences between the home and school environment. Of particular help at times is an understanding of how particular parental attitudes in a culture may affect the child. An understanding of the cultural parental attitudes may help clarify the effect certain attitudes of adults in the school environment have on children. The attitudes of school people can be evaluated in terms of how these attitudes may be reacted to by the children. A case in point occurred a-mong the children of migrant Mexican workers. An understanding of the cultural emphasis on almost no discipline for small children, the low status of women, and the derogation of school and learning by poverty-stricken parents who could hardly keep body and soul together made the usual attitudes of these children toward women teachers meaningful. Only by being fair and firm, ignoring provocative speech and attitudes, especially toward women teachers, and by using disciplinary measures only when behavior, not words, made it necessary could these children be reached. These children had to learn that they were not being disparaged and that discipline in the classroom was not a punitive, discriminatory measure but necessary for their learning. These efforts very gradually resulted in increased respect for women teachers, more learning by pupils, and less provocative, hostile, destructive behavior.

Another important function of the mental health specialist may be in helping educators become aware of their unrealistic self-expectations so that they may work with less strain. Educators are subject to ever-increasing pressures from the community to perform more functions as substitute parent, child psychiatrist, and parent counselor. Only when administrators and teachers assess realistically their primary job of educating, analyze the obstacles to good education presented by crowded classrooms and external pressures, and make known the results of this study will they get parents and citizens in the community to help rectify the situation. The mental health person knows from personal experience the importance of realistic assessment of the job on one's mental health. He may therefore provide some help to educators to respond to pressures with realistic assessment of what the school can provide so that the community can begin to understand what the school's needs and limitations are and can help implement the community resources. Otherwise the community and the school district office are never faced with the limitations of their teachers and administrators. These overwhelming demands force many good educators to seek their livelihood where there are fewer pressures and more appreciation of their efforts.

There is also the important preventive aspect of the collaboration between school people and the mental health worker. The early identification of emotional disturbances manifested by hostile, aggressive, antisocial behavior, by isolation and withdrawal from contact with others, or by learning problems permits evaluation of the severity of the problem and consideration of early treatment. This early diagnostic appraisal of the child's troubles may lead to parent conferences. Here the worker may be helpful in suggesting how the educators might best interpret a problem to parents.

SPECIALIST'S ROLE WITH PARENTS

Particular problems in children frequently suggest particular parental troubles that may mean parents will resist attempts to help them understand and accept children's difficulties. For example, the parents of the aggressive-destructive child may feel helpless in handling him at home and anxious and guilty about his behavior elsewhere; but they will, at the same time, resist getting help. They may consider any statement by an educator about the child as forcing them to accept the blame for the behavior. Often such parents tend to be hostile and accuse school personnel of failing in their job with the child. Frequently parents will be more cooperative if the situation is presented at the outset as an effort to understand the problems so that plans may be made for the prevention of future troubles. When school people acknowledge to parents their awareness that the parents too must be concerned about the child and want to find help for the child's troubles, the parents' cooperation is solicited because of the mutual concern of school and parents and not because the parents are blamed. The mental health specialist may be asked to help interview very disturbed parents and to present the data and observations about the child. Such interviews can also be used to help administrators and teachers realize the kinds of parental fears, doubts, self-blame, and guilt that need to be understood and dealt with to gain the parents' cooperation. This often takes several interviews.

The specialist may also be helpful in referral. His knowledge of community facilities may help the school people find the most suitable agency or facility for a particular child and parents. As he shares his awareness of the community resources with administrators and teachers, they may soon find that they are able to make referrals with a greater sense of security about the best resource for particular problem children and their parents. Often the mental health specialist can be helpful by honestly saying he doesn't know. The educator may feel quite disappointed that the person he has turned to for help has failed him, but he may learn from experience that he and the mental health specialist must pool their knowledge to secure the desired results. In doing so they can make an effective team by providing the help children in the school need to enjoy good mental health.

Reprinted by permission from <u>California Journal of Elementary Education</u>, 31:7-15, 1962.

SOME LEARNING EXPERIENCES AS
PSYCHIATRIC CONSULTANT IN THE SCHOOLS

I. N. Berlin, M.D.

Experiences over the past four years as psychiatric consultant in two school systems have slowly clarified my concepts of consultation in such a setting. The relation of these experiences to previously integrated attitudes learned in psychotherapeutic efforts with children and adults has also become clearer to me. It is my hope that by describing the highlights of the events of my own learning as a school psychiatric consultant some ideas might evolve that would both clarify my own thoughts and perhaps be of help to educators and those who work with them as consultants about child-parent-teacher problems.

My first experiences with school problems occurred during my period of training in child psychiatry by means of school-clinic conferences. These meetings concerned children in treatment in our clinic, where I was a member of the therapeutic team. Later, as a staff member and teacher of child psychiatry, I chaired such conferences involving school personnel and clinic staff members working with children and parents. I found that I carried into these conferences some of my previously slowly acquired understanding from work with parents and children, i.e., that often when parents talk about their children they are referring to aspects of their own personalities. They often will unconsciously mask anxieties about certain feelings and attitudes of their own by talking with concern about similar attitudes, feelings, or behavior in the child. Thus, in conferences with school administrators and teachers about problem children, I began to recognize how often the anxieties of school people were not only related to their concern about the disturbed child and how they might best understand him and help him, but also frequently to their anxieties about the kinds of feelings such a child engendered in teacher and principal. They often seemed concerned about how we or others would regard them if they were driven beyond their endurance and had to admit failure by excluding the child from school. I began to observe that when school people had the opportunity to share with us mutual experiences with a difficult child, and usually disturbed parents, they learned that we too were struggling to work with this family and had no easy answers. Then they seemed to relax and were able to express their feelings about the pressures they felt. As the school teachers and administrators began to feel that others understood and empathized with these feelings and were not disturbed or condemnatory at the possible exclusion of the child from school, there seemed to follow some relaxation of tensions and often plans were made to work with the child in the school setting. During these conferences little direct suggestion or advice seemed necessary.

With this background of experience I accepted a position as community agency consultant, which included work with a city and a county school system as well as consultation with the county health and probation departments. In this paper I shall describe my experiences with the two school systems.

The city school system operated a child welfare and attendance division under the long-time direction of a former school teacher with many years' experience in child welfare work. On her staff was a recently hired social worker. The school's psychological services consisted of a school psychologist, a former teacher who was also responsible for the program for the mentally retarded. A psychometrist administered intelligence tests and did occasional projective tests. These four people were eager for psychiatric consultation as an adjunct to their work, and formed a consultation team that worked together for four years.

At our first meetings with the whole group of school administrators and guidance people from the high schools we tried to clarify both what the group felt they wanted and what I felt I had to offer. Since we had no previous experience to help us decide, we finally agreed that a small group of the central office staff would meet to draw up plans. We had no definite ideas of how best to work but had a clear awareness of the need to help school administrators and their teachers with the emotionally disturbed children who were an ever-increasing burden as the population of this area continued to mushroom.

Out of my experiences in the clinic, I had a vague idea that methods that had seemed helpful with one or two teachers and a principal might be equally effective on a much larger scale with all the principals. That is, my previous experiences had shown that reduction of tensions in administrators in connection with specific problems seemed to make it possible for them to better help their teachers. I felt that if we could be of help to the administrators as a group, with their anxieties and tensions around teacher-parent-pupil problems, they could and would be more helpful to their teachers, and their teachers, in turn, to the children.

My efforts to work regularly with a group, much as I had worked with a few individuals, in relation to an acute, disturbing problem did not work out. However, such an idea is not easily laid to rest and I repeatedly returned to it with the usual unsuccessful results until I was finally convinced this was not an effective way for me to work. I must say that the consultation team showed unusual forbearance in permitting me further experimentation in this direction despite their feelings from our previous experiences that we would again not be successful.

Thus, initially we arranged several meetings with the twenty-odd school principals and any assistants they wanted to bring along. At the same time, we arranged to meet in each of the high schools with the administrators, guidance person, and teachers about specific problems presented by disturbed children.

The first meeting with the administrators set the pattern for all subsequent meetings. The principals were somewhat tense and anxious about meeting with a psychiatrist, fearful that what they might say would be analyzed and that they would be exposed and found wanting in the presence of their peers. There was no spontaneity. To increase the comfort of the group, as well as my own, I would start each session with some discussion of children's problems with which I had had experience. This was not enough. The group would have preferred formal lectures on child development, diagnosis of emotional disturbance, and specific or detailed directions about how these could be handled. When these were not forthcoming and the group was encouraged to bring case problems for discussion, they seemed to feel disappointed that nothing new was told them and that they received no real help. Some case problems were presented, but it became clear that each administrator was primarily interested in presenting the case of his current thorn in the side and receiving specific directions in handling the child. Most principals were not interested in listening to other case presentations or in joining in the discussion after each presentation from which some general inferences could be drawn. Staff problems, such as I naively hoped would be discussed, were never mentioned. After several such meetings there was common agreement that they were not very helpful, although some administrators expressed relief at discovering that the psychiatrist was human and even that he appeared to have no magic solution to their problems with difficult children.

The second phase of the first year's work centered around conferences in the three high schools on specific cases. In these conferences the consultant team of psychiatrist, director of welfare and attendance, director of psychological service, the welfare and attendance social worker, and the psychometrist met with the administrators, guidance director, and the several teachers concerned with each child.

Two of the high schools were old, well established schools whose staffs had been together for some time. The third high school had been recently built in an area densely populated by people of racial minorities who depended for their livelihood on seasonal work in agriculture and canneries. The staff of this school was newly organized and had just begun to function, and many of the teachers were new to the school system.

The attitudes in the established schools seemed to be: Here are our problems--you experts solve them for us. They wanted lectures from the consultant to the faculties and were for the most part disappointed that few problems seemed to be alleviated by the consultation and that no prescriptions and ready solutions were forthcoming, and after several conferences in each of these schools they made it clear that the consultation was not of particular value to them.

In the new school there were many problems related to getting the school into operation. The administrative staff was eager to experiment and to find out what worked for them in many areas and accepted psychiatric consultation as a possible help in this period of flux. The superintendent and associate superintendent of schools both wisely believed that in the beginning the consultant service should be used where it was wanted and not forced upon anyone. Case conferences were initiated which included the administrative staff and those teachers working with the child who presented problems. Initially, teachers were reluctant to appear and talk to a psychiatrist. They seemed to fear that their deficiencies as people and teachers would be exposed in front of their administrators. When, despite their reluctance, teachers did come to the conferences and found that the psychiatrist and the consultant team did not analyze them, they expressed disappointment that the psychiatrist listened more than he talked. However, many teachers expressed relief that during these conferences they were able to discuss their feelings about what the administrator expected of them, especially the kinds of pressures they felt. The administrator was very much surprised at these feelings since he had often talked with the teachers about his recognition of the problems they were confronted with and his hope that they would not feel they had to have quiet rooms and be able to handle all their problems to be considered good teachers. The administrator's frank and receptive attitude greatly facilitated such discussions. It became evident that such distortions of administrative policy could best be dealt with in this fashion, with individual teachers discussing specific problems.

I gradually became aware of a repetitive phenomenon in the consultation. It was quite disconcerting at first to find that after the first meetings most teachers seemed disappointed and angry that the psychiatrist had not solved their problems for them. Later they seemed to express relief at having had the opportunity to talk with a receptive group about their difficulties with certain pupils. Thus, while they often loudly proclaimed how little help they got, with few exceptions they were subsequently eager to return and discuss other problem children with the group. Slowly, more and more teachers expressed a desire to present their problems to the group. They seemed relieved that many of their feelings which they had believed were shameful--such as anger or hate, frustration and the desire to quit and run away from a difficult situation-- were often stated for them by the psychiatrist and accepted by the group as comprehensible human feelings. They began to feel that perhaps the presence of such feelings was not so shameful.

Other common feelings brought into the open were feelings that teachers must be fond of all pupils, that their goal was to have their pupils become fond of them, that they as teachers should never feel--and positively never show--anger or discouragement, and that the expression of such feelings would result in irreversible injury to the tender psyches of their pupils.

It was our practice that I not interview or examine the children about whom the staff was concerned. However, in one instance a Negro girl was such a severe behavior problem and so openly hostile and aggressive that her several teachers and the administrators asked me to interview the girl just this once, ostensibly to see if she were psychotic or potentially dangerous to others. I reluctantly agreed and talked with the girl for about forty minutes. I found, as I had expected, an insolently defiant blandness and complacency. After the interview, the consultation group met with the people concerned with this girl. I briefly outlined what I had found and stated that I felt I would have difficulty in working with her and reaching her, that I could certainly understand that such an adolescent might push her teachers to the point of giving up, and that perhaps the only solution might be to exclude her from school. One of the teachers heaved a big sigh and said, "Now you know what we've been up against. I just can't have her in my class." Several others agreed. Then one teacher said that at times the girl had got along in her class and that perhaps if her teachers would try her again and exclude her from class more promptly when she acted up, this might help. One by one each of the teachers related how they thought they might better work with this girl and agreed to try again. We never heard again about this girl. The administrators reported six months later that she was adjusting passably well in all her classes and was no longer the source of such consternation to her teachers.

The administrative staff frequently made inquiries after the meetings and found that most teachers felt relieved, more relaxed and better able to work with their students, that from the conferences they seemed to get the idea that they could be more open and frank about expressing their feelings to their students, and that firmness rather than punitive or retaliatory hostility, which they felt when they were driven beyond their endurance, not only was not harmful but was helpful to their students.

After many months of such meetings, the relationship between the administrative staff and the consultation team became relaxed and easy. Under the leadership of the principal, the administrative staff began to discuss some of their difficulties in dealing with teachers who were hostile and aggressive and wanted to use physical chastisement as a solution to their problems with students, or teachers who were helpless and ineffectual and sent all their problems to the office for solution. They were also concerned with the teacher who was on tenure and was indifferent about her work.

As these problems were discussed, differences within the administrative staff came to the fore. I used some of my learning experiences as an administrator on a children's ward to illustrate the problems and possible solutions that I found worked for me. The friendly relationship between the principal and his staff made it possible for them to express their feeling that he needed to be more firm and to expect more from certain teachers. After much discussion the principal agreed that this might be helpful to the teachers. From these meetings there was evident greater unification of the staff and greater freedom to explore differences.

This congenial high school staff provided excellent and essentially nontraumatic learning opportunities for me. Early I sensed the pressure from the group to have me express "expert" opinion on subjects in which I had no special competence. The temptation was often great to hold forth on grading, on passing or failing students, on curriculum, etc., subjects about which I had only a layman's knowledge and the school staff had expert knowledge. I discovered that as I clarified for myself and the group (and with each subsequent group) the limits of my expertness and dealt only with the emotional problems of children, parents, and teachers, the school people were increasingly more aware of my respect for their competence and were more relaxed in consultation. I eventually learned that even to express an opinion as a layman about certain school matters was not a good idea, for despite any explanations on my part such lay opinions of mine seem to carry unwarranted weight. I finally learned to just tend to my own knitting.

From our work in this school, news began to leak out via the grapevine, at socials, and over the bridge table that psychiatric consultation was helpful to many teachers, and slowly from other schools came some requests for similar services.

At the end of the second year of consultation, it was decided that our time would be best spent with the elementary schools for the next year. The staff of this high school felt that they would like further regular consultation, but with the work of the past two years they could get along without regularly scheduled visits if they could avail themselves of occasional consultation as needed. This plan worked out very nicely and during the next two years only a few meetings were necessary.

The second, third, and fourth years of consultation were spent mostly with the primary schools, at first only with those where the administrators felt a need for consultation. Later an effort was made to spend some time with each elementary school so that the principals and a few teachers might find that the consultation team was composed of friendly and interested human beings with no particular omnipotence and no desire to "analyze" individual administrators or teachers.

As the team worked with more elementary schools, I suggested again that we attempt some meetings of principals with whom we had worked to determine whether they were now able to use group discussion of common problems as one means of helping themselves. The other members of the team, recalling our previous unsatisfactory experiences in such meetings, were not enthusiastic about trying them again, but nevertheless scheduled them. Again we found that the administrators in a group felt pressure to discuss their problems but were reluctant to do so. On one occasion a fortuitous selection of the most verbal, secure, and outspoken principals came close to a free discussion of the administrators' problems. This was a group that least needed such help.

After several such meetings I finally agreed that our efforts should remain on the work with the individual principal and his staff. After another year of such work, we found that a few principals wanted to discuss some of their problems with teachers. We gradually evolved a plan in which the social worker of the team would visit the school one week prior to the meeting and get some idea of the cases to be discussed, help the principal understand the kind of information about the child's family which we found useful, arrange for psychological testing where the I.Q. of the child was in question, where projective testing might help, or where someone else's clinical opinion of the child seemed a good idea. He also began to suggest that the principal might reserve thirty to forty-five minutes of the consultation time to discuss any matters of concern to him about his teachers, if he felt it would be useful. Usually at the first meeting the principal did not avail himself of this opportunity, but sometimes during the second conference he would spend a few minutes discussing some of his concerns about his faculty.

We found that in elementary schools, where teachers had a difficult child all day (in contrast to junior and senior high schools), the teachers' problems often seemed more acute.

The aggressive child and the child who thwarts the teacher's every effort to teach him subject matter by his indifference and apparent refusal to make any attempt to learn were most frequently brought to our consultation meetings. The aggressive child's open defiance, hostility, and restlessness seemed most anxiety-provoking to teachers. The child who was sullen, indifferent to learning, and passively defiant seemed to cause less anxiety but more frequently feelings of frustration and inadequacy in his teachers.

Most elementary teachers appear to feel an overwhelming responsibility for their failure to reach such children and a need to disguise their feelings of anger, hostility, frustration, and helplessness. When their best efforts at being understanding and kind do not alleviate the difficulties, the resulting feelings of disappointment, frustration, hopelessness, and anger are usually repressed as if they dare not feel them, else their colleagues and administrators would believe them to be failures as teachers. Not only do teachers feel they should not feel or express the anxiety, anger, and frustration engendered in them by such difficult children, but they feel that they must also suppress their anger at the administrator to whom they turn for help when he too seems unable to help resolve these problems.

It has become our practice to insist that the teacher, principal, and school nurse gather all possible information on the family history and early life of the child. We try then to sketch in a picture of the child's background and his relationships in the family to help us understand the child's present behavior and to help the teachers see the origins of the child's difficulties in his early relationships which antedate his schooling. Often this alone has given a teacher the sense that she was working with a child who had had long-standing problems which she could expect to modify only slightly and only over a long period of time. We would contrast this to the situational problems where the death of a parent, the father's unemployment, or acute family troubles resulted in emotional upset in a child. In these instances the teacher's sympathy and understanding are very important and frequently immediately helpful to the child.

When we discuss cases of very seriously disturbed children, I have frequently described my own experiences with such children: the difficulties they present in treatment and how long it usually takes to see any appreciable change even if one works not only with the child but with the parents as well. I stress that despite the best efforts of the clinic team we sometimes fail to modify the youngster's feelings about himself and the world around him. Usually the teacher and administrator feel less disturbed at the possibility of their failure to reach and help such a child. After such a discussion of possible failure, teachers are frequently better able to work with the child. It seems to me that this is related to their relief at realizing that they need only be human teachers and administrators and that such failures need not reflect on their professional adequacy.

I have learned that my discussion and depiction of the kinds of feelings such children have aroused in me and other people who work with them is helpful. I cite from my own learning experiences that anger, hate, frustration, disappointment, and hopelessness are both human and universal feelings. I point out that as I could permit myself to experience these feelings with less anxiety and self-deprecation, and could communicate them to others, I felt more at ease with myself and it was less likely that these repressed feelings would erupt into overt or covert hostile retaliatory behavior with the child. I had found that expressing how I felt to the child, while not always necessary or helpful, was much less hurtful to him than the retaliatory withdrawal or punitive behavior that might otherwise break through. I had also learned that when I failed to verbalize such feelings to myself or to others, the resulting internal pressures seriously hampered my attentiveness, alertness, spontaneity, and ability to work without strain. Teachers seemed quite receptive to my discussion of my experiences in learning that to show such "forbidden" feelings with others--and if necessary with the child who arouses them--often eases tension and permits a more rational dealing with the problem.

Thus it has been the frequent experience of the consultation team that after discussion on my part the teachers seemed less involved with what they ought to feel towards their pupils and could accept more easily the feelings in themselves that were actually there. During subsequent conferences some of them reported their increased success with difficult children as they became increasingly firm and refused to permit behavior that could not be tolerated in the classroom. One of the best classroom teachers we had put it very succinctly: "The aggressive child seems to relax and trust me more when I don't put up with behavior that disturbs the class and me. I've learned through the years, to my surprise, that such behavior, when he gets away with it, also seems to disturb the pupil."

This teacher's experiences closely coincide with my own, and I have learned to stress the conviction of many of us who work with such disturbed children that they are often looking for an adult who can understand and tolerate the verbal expression of hostile <u>feelings</u> but who can and will prevent, or at least halt, the impulsive aggressive <u>behavior</u>. Teachers have related many times how distrustful such children seem to be of their efforts to be kind and accepting, and how much easier they become when they experience a fair and unswerving firmness. It often <u>seems</u> that such children are trying in part to force the teacher to react in the retaliatory hostile manner they previously have experienced as a result of their behavior, and in part these children seem to hope unconsciously for a new, and as yet never experienced, interaction with the adult. Hostile retaliatory action on the part of the person working with a child usually means that person has abdicated the adult role and met the difficult child on his own terms, which is rarely helpful either to the child or to the adult. More and more teachers and administrators have reported that as they can rid themselves of their tense and anxious feelings by putting them into words, they have become less afraid that their anger would be expressed in either retaliatory behavior or uncomfortable anxiety about possible loss of control over their behavior. They have then experienced increased ability to handle these difficult children in the classroom.

The team early discovered that our emphasis on firmness and the prompt expression of feelings was taken by some teachers as license to express their feelings through physical chastisement. We have since emphasized repeatedly the difference between expressing one's feelings about what one might feel like doing and the actual carrying out of such feelings in action.

We also found that if we could help administrators to be more at ease about the hostile expressions of teachers toward them (when during a crisis the administrator did not seem to be very helpful), teacher tension was reduced. Those principals who at critical moments could say with equanimity something like "I'll bet you're angry with me because I don't seem to be of much help," found that

often teachers then could unburden their feelings of fury and sometimes despair. Frequently they could then return and work through
the difficult situation with the feeling that their administrator really understood how they felt. Through our meetings some principals began to feel easier about their own fear of failure. During
our four years of work, more and more administrators began to
insist upon the parents' participation in working with the problem
child instead of feeling they should be able to do this all alone.

During the last year of our consultation, the curriculum consultants have been able to participate more and more in our meetings
and have subsequently indicated that they were able to use some of
the attitudes and insights that resulted from such sessions to work
more effectively with teachers.

On our return to an elementary school after a year's absence, the
principal said, "Do you recall our last year's conference on Johnny,
the scourge of our school? Well, the conference helped his teacher
and me to handle his aggressive outbursts firmly and to anticipate
them. You know, on the last day of school he walked up to me with
a clenched fist and said, 'You wouldn't do anything to me today,
would you?'" I cautiously guessed I wouldn't. He then asked me to
press his knuckle, and with some trepidation I did. His hand flew
open and on the palm was written in ink, 'I love you.'" The principal had tears in her eyes as she related this. She mentioned that
Johnny was far from being a model citizen, but he was getting
along and was beginning to do some school work.

At the beginning of the fourth year of school consultation, we met
with a group of new teachers who were having difficulties with their
classes. This experiment was approached with caution by our team
because we had learned our lesson about the difficulties involved in
such group sessions. We thought we would try this because these
teachers all had similar, acute problems and anxieties and it seemed
the only way to reach more than one teacher at a time during a period of need. The teachers were surprised to find that there were
others in the same predicament and as troubled as they. Most of
them, after some initial hesitation, talked freely about their difficulties. They all seemed bewildered that the precepts taught in
education courses and fairly easily carried out in their practice
teaching seemed so ineffectual in their overcrowded classrooms,
with many tense, overactive, disinterested, and rebellious children,
many from minority groups and many in marginal economic circum-

stances. The team's concern with these teachers, and the team's verbalization of the kinds of feelings these new teachers might have seemed to help them talk more freely. During the meeting several teachers began to express the feeling that perhaps they expected too much of themselves--maybe they didn't need to love all their pupils. They all seemed easier as the team related experiences from our work with other teachers. Members of the team gave examples to illustrate that as teachers were able to be more direct and firm and less afraid that setting limits in the classroom would be "traumatic" to their pupils, they felt better, the children felt better, and more learning in a more agreeable classroom atmosphere occurred. After this meeting we heard that several new teachers on the verge of resigning their positions took a new lease on life and most of the group felt more relaxed and better able to handle their classroom situation. In one instance where the situation grew increasingly difficult, we met with the teacher and her principal about a specific child some months later.

This service to new teachers, the opportunity after four to six weeks of teaching to meet with the consultation team and discuss their mutual problems, will become a regular feature of the consultation program.

One of the most gratifying aspects of the consultation work has been the gradual development of the various team members in understanding and the ability to carry on the consultation methods individually. The increasing team-work, cohesiveness, and awareness were reflected in the increased ease and effectiveness of the consultation and the mutual satisfaction evident in each meeting as we strove to increase our effectiveness as a team.

The consultation program in this school system has been expanded from a total of three-quarters of a day a week to two days a week. The staff will be augmented by a psychiatrist trained in the same setting as the author, and by another full-time social worker and psychometrist.

CONSULTATION WITH A COUNTY SCHOOL SYSTEM

Consultation with a county school system was different only in that we did not work directly with the schools since they were mostly small and long distances from each other, and most principals also did some teaching so that conferences were difficult to arrange

Initially we tried to meet with all the staff of county consultants who advised the schools on curriculum matters. In this setting also, and for the previously mentioned reasons, such group meetings did not work out. We thus decided to meet with the guidance group consisting of the consultants in guidance, special education (i.e., program for the mentally retarded, home teachers, etc.), the part-time school psychologist, and the psychometrist, about problems presented to them by the various schools. Occasionally curriculum consultants, principals, and teachers joined the discussions. We also met every two months with the group of special teachers: the home teachers and teachers at the juvenile hall and the hospital.

In these meetings it became important to discriminate between what might be therapeutic (i.e., helpful) and what could be called therapy (i.e., an explicit contract between two people for the specified purpose of working on the personality problems of one of them). These discussions helped to clarify both my relationship to the group and their relationship to teachers, consultants, and administrators with whom they worked. Similar clarification had been helpful in my work with the consultative team in the city school system.

In the county schools, too, the most disturbing child was the impulsive, hostile, aggressive, destructive child. As a result of consultation meetings team members began to work more with parents and to help school personnel include the parents in any efforts to understand and help a disturbed child.

It became clear that rarely were these children "totally rejected" by their parents. The more frequent picture was one of anxious overindulgence and passivity of one parent, the other parent being quite strict, demanding, and often punitive toward the child. Thus it appeared that in most instances the child was caught in conflicts between the parents out of which his behavior pattern resulted. Occasionally it was found that the death of one parent or of both parents resulted in compensatory and undiscriminating overindulgence by the remaining parent or grandparents so that no limits were set for the child.

In our case discussions I had been tying in such impulsive aggressive behavior to early experiences of such children with their parents. These parents seemed to have particular personality problems which were recently described in the literature by Johnson and Szurek (1, 2).

Most investigators would agree that the parents' unanxious acceptance of their own feelings of whatever kind--sensual, sexual, childlike, sad, angry, etc.--would make it possible for them to nurture
the infant, i.e., to easily fulfill all his wants, to gratify the needs
of the growing child and clearly define for him acceptable and unacceptable behavior. Such parents could in each instance help the
child who begins to act in an aggressively hostile or destructive
way to find acceptable alternative activities. Thus the investigation and exploration necessary to growth and development would
not be inhibited. This is especially so if the parents can help the
child achieve a satisfying state of independence by helping him experience the pleasures which come from mastering the details of
self-care as the child is ready to learn them. Such a child would
thus learn from his parents that all his feelings can be both understood and expressed in non-destructive ways consonant with civi-
lized behavior in the family and society.

The inability of parents to set limits on impulsive aggressive behavior often reflects both their anxiety about the eruption of such
feelings of their own and the unconscious vicarious satisfaction
they obtain when the child does something they would like to do but
dare not. The parent who reacts to such impulsive aggressive behavior with harsh retaliatory measures and strictness in all phases
of dealing with the child may see in the child a mocking caricature
of his own attitudes and behavior which may be intolerable and en-
raging to observe. It is probably true that behind both these attitudes of one or both parents is their unconscious longing for gratifications and satisfactions not realized in their own infancy and
childhood which they unconsciously want the other mate to fulfill.
The impossibility of such mutual fulfillment of childhood needs frequently leads to conflicts between parents and also makes it difficult for them to fulfill similar needs and demands of their children.
Thus, often the child feels little incentive to behave in an acceptable way, since he has little gratification in his relationship with his
troubled parents and is confused by their vacillation in setting limits on his behavior.

The meetings with the special teachers over the four-year period
gradually became quite spontaneous. Most of the teachers could
eventually discuss their own need to make up somehow for the failure of parents of sick, retarded, and delinquent children. They
slowly recognized the unreality of their self-imposed burdens as
well as how much energy such impossible expectations drained from

them. This was all the more true since they were usually unsuccessful and felt inadequate as a result. Most members of the group
began to accept the limitations imposed upon them by the child's
pre-existing relationships, his physical and psychological handicaps, and the limited time they had with him. They also began to
see as their primary job the teaching of the child. Paradoxically,
it seemed, as these teachers expected less of the impossible from
themselves, they began to expect more of the possible from their
students. As they slowly felt less overidentified with the child
and overly sympathetic with his handicaps, they seemed to be able
to help the sick, retarded, or delinquent child more, with increased
mutual satisfaction for student and teacher. Repeatedly, as teachers became more spontaneous in the group they talked of their oversolicitude for their students, their frequent exploitation by the students, and their feelings of being caught because as they tried to do
more for their students, the students seemed to do less for themselves.

The problem of the impulsive, aggressive child and the feelings he
aroused were repeatedly ventilated. The differences between authoritative and authoritarian attitudes of school teachers came up
frequently as the teachers were able to reveal some of their own
hostile and retaliatory feelings as they failed to help such children
by sweetness and kindness. In the juvenile hall situations those
teachers who were gradually able to be firm and just with delinquent youngsters, who could be quite honest and direct about the
feelings these children aroused in them, reported their own greater
ease, relief of tension, and decrease of punitive, retaliatory feelings. They simultaneously noted greater responsiveness from
their pupils and less conflict about doing their school work.

The home teachers were concerned with their unique problem of
working with the parents of these sick youngsters. They all resented the parents' overindulgence of the sick child, and often felt
that parents subtly encouraged the child's invalidism and unneces-
sarily prolonged his stay in bed or at home. They felt that many
parents were helpless in the face of the demands of the chronically
ill child so that their job was much more difficult. Often such parents felt the teacher expected too much of their poor, sick child.
These teachers were much concerned at the ease with which these
youngsters avoided responsibility and could get what they wanted
through temper tantrums or threat of becoming ill. Teachers often
felt impelled to tell parents they were not handling the child cor-

rectly and felt anxious at the amount of hostility this aroused in the parents.

As these situations were repeatedly discussed, the teacher's hostility toward the parents was ventilated. Discussions about the dynamics of the relationship between the parents and the chronically sick child occurred frequently. The ambivalent feelings of the parents toward the child, the parents' guilt about their desire to be rid of the burdens imposed by a sick child, the hostile and helpless feelings engendered by the child's demands were brought out and elaborated on by the teachers. Some teachers were able to see and verbalize parallels between the parents' emotions and their own. They could see the sequence of guilt about such "terrible" feelings and the resultant overindulgence and often abandonment of the role of parent or teacher, as if to deny the presence of such feelings of resentment. Some of the home teachers discovered that if they tended to their job of teaching these youngsters and were firm in their expectations of what they knew the child could do, some parents seemed to learn from the teachers' attitudes.

A few of the home teachers also were able to express some understanding of the problems of the parents with the child. Parents would sometimes then turn to them for suggestions and seemed to be able to accept referral to the Family Service Agency or other agencies for help with their problems. Even in those families where the disturbed parent-child relationship continued without change, the teachers seemed to feel less tense and hostile with the parents and were able to work with the child somewhat more easily.

During the fourth year of consultation with the county schools, the psychiatrist previously referred to began to work with the entire consultant staff. Now, some three years after the initial efforts at such meetings had been abandoned, the consultant staff was freer and more receptive to such work and these meetings were more successful and looked forward to by many of the consultants.

CONCLUSION

In my learning experience I came to understand that the consultation process demands the same kind of self-awareness on the part of the consultant as is necessary in the process of psychotherapy. Here too I began to develop some understanding of how long it might take before the team could feel that these efforts might be fruitful.

When I listened attentively to the discouragement of the various team members and occasionally expressed my own doubts that consultation in this form would prove helpful, there would usually be some shift in the tension and all of us would feel somewhat more optimistic. Early it is often disappointing to find that after a precise and, one even dares feel, a brilliant or eloquent discussion, little of what one has said seems to have been helpful and, moreover, it does not appear to have been remembered. Slowly one begins to recognize the impediments within the group to understanding and assimilating what is being said. The anxiety and tensions of the individuals, their own past experiences and present emotional and intellectual readiness, and the state of their relationship to the consultant and to the other people in the meeting are among the many factors that determine how much any one person will derive from any one meeting. One therefore begins to sense the need for continuing prolonged work together and for repeating some of the principles of working with people which is most easily accomplished by case discussions. As the consultant becomes progressively easier and more spontaneous in the group, and expects less of himself, more people seem to understand and utilize more readily what he has to contribute.

When the school staff eagerly turns to the consultant for his words of wisdom on matters of curriculum, grading, retention of pupils, etc., the temptation is often great to be the all-wise, all-knowing person that the staff seems to be looking for in the consultant. Yet, only by clearly defining one's own area of expertness can one be most helpful to the staff.

Although some in a group will be disappointed and disgruntled, an honest "I don't know" is reassuring to the administrators and teachers who both hope and fear that the consultant will pretend a superhuman omniscience. Such all-knowingness may be momentarily comforting to the anxious person, but it tends to make the staff feel even less competent and undermines their belief in their own abilities to handle situations, as they turn to the all-wise one to handle all their problems. Experienced school administrators have many times recounted experiences which bear this out, when early in their work they felt they did or should know all the answers and found their teachers becoming increasingly helpless and dependent on them.

The readiness of the consultant to admit his fallibility, to illustrate from his experiences his awareness of the kinds of feelings teachers and administrators might have in working with difficult children, and his acceptance of the possibility that they might fail and have to exclude a child from school as he has sometimes failed and given up in some therapeutic work seems to reassure the staff and facilitate freer discussion. As illustrated in this paper, often the readiness to accept failure has resulted in the staffs' feeling less self-critical and pressed by the child, and subsequent efforts with the child have been somewhat more successful.

Initially, most of the staff working with the psychiatrist are apprehensive lest they reveal too many of their own problems. They fear being analyzed and having their privacy violated by the consultant. Only continued working together and repeated experiences in seeing that the consultant does not analyze them and their troubles is reassuring. At some point with each staff verbal clarification of the differences between what might be therapeutic (i.e., helpful), and the explicit agreement and permission to work together and explore problems, which is therapy, seems to clear the air of most of the residue of such feelings. This also seems to help the staff in understanding their role with other school personnel and reduces some of the anxiety attendant on such work. It also helps make clear to the staff that they need not feel impelled to somehow solve the teacher's personal problems, which one often senses as an uncomfortable burden among guidance staff and administrators.

It seems to me that the basis for my work as a consultant has been my ever growing confidence in the integrative potential in human beings. Thus I became convinced that if I could be of some help in reducing the anxiety, tensions, and self-doubts of teachers and administrators, they could do their jobs better. I slowly learned that little, if any, direct advice on the handling of a problem was necessary or helpful. I found that I could not advise a teacher about how to teach better. I could only hope to help reduce some of the tensions that served as obstacles to her teaching, learning the techniques of teaching, or learning how to handle emotionally disturbed children in the classroom. In most instances where I felt impelled to give specific advice on the handling of a child, I later learned that the teacher felt burdened by it and could not use the advice in her work. When I spent the time indicating my awareness of the kinds of human feelings the teacher might have without pretending that I, a non-teacher, could understand fully the magnitude or details of the anxieties, this seemed to be more helpful. My illustrations from my own experiences of the difficulties I encountered in individual work with a similar child and what eventually seemed to work with me also seemed to be of some help. I began to sense more quickly the moments when the teacher or administrator was ready to talk and the attentive silence of the consultation group seemed to encourage the expression and discussion of difficult and forbidden feelings with evident decrease in tension in the teachers involved.

I am certain that each consultant must find the ways in which he works most effectively. I hope that this recounting of my own learning experiences will encourage others to participate in the challenging, highly interesting, and enjoyable process that makes up psychiatric consultation in the schools.

Reprinted by permission from <u>Mental Hygiene</u>, 40:215-236, 1956.

MENTAL HEALTH CONSULTATION IN SCHOOLS AS A MEANS OF COMMUNICATING MENTAL HEALTH PRINCIPLES

I. N. Berlin, M.D.

The mental health consultant in a school system often has a unique opportunity to communicate and sometimes to demonstrate mental health principles to teachers.

Perhaps the most important principle he can communicate to school people is that all human feelings can be talked about without shame, blame, or passing judgment on the teacher as a "bad" person. The consultant, by his attitude of concern, attentiveness, and respect for his professional colleague, demonstrates his relationship to the teacher as a colleague whose problems with their attendant mixed feelings are of mutual concern. The consultant's encouragement of verbal expression of all feelings of the teacher about his work is greatly enhanced, in my experience, as the consultant progressively clarifies that he is not there to analyze the teacher, to pry into hidden motivations, or to uncover skeletons about the teacher's personal problems. He demonstrates in many ways that his job as an expert in interpersonal relations is to help the teacher understand himself in terms of the job he is doing, and, in particular, to help him be consciously aware of his feelings about the particular child who is a problem for him. The purpose is always to enable the teacher to do his work more effectively.

Another mental health principle the consultant can demonstrate effectively is that every person has limitations both professionally and personally. Unreal self-expectations and their aftermaths of tension and exhaustion from increasing conflict may seriously interfere with teaching. Thus the understanding, acceptance, and assessment of one's own limitations are important for good mental health.

A third vital principle that can be demonstrated by the consultant centers around authority. Workers in a hierarchical setting need to be able to accept constituted authority and to work under regulations without undue conflict. This may be especially important for mental health when as sometimes occurs the authority is unjust and the regulations are restrictive. Rebellion and its attendant repercussions in the teacher's teaching frequently only increase the tensions between teachers and administrators.

COMMUNICATION OF MENTAL HEALTH PRINCIPLES
TO SCHOOL PEOPLE

Two experiences illustrate the consultant's role in demonstrating the mental health principle that all feelings aroused by a pupil can be talked about. A third-grade teacher and her principal asked to talk with me about a nonlearning Negro youngster whose size and aggression made him a terror in the classroom and out of it. The principal described the boy's behavior in the classroom and schoolyard and the difficulties of the teacher and the administrator in handling the boy. While the principal talked the teacher sat very quietly by and appeared frozen. When asked to add her comments to the principal's, she remarked in a barely audible voice that it had all been said and sat stiffly in her chair. As I began to comment about what a handful this must be for the teacher to contend with all day and that we psychiatrists were pretty lucky because at the worst we had to deal with such a child for only an hour once or twice a week, the teacher grinned tightly. I then talked about a learning experience of my own of which this child had reminded me. This was a severely hostile, aggressive ten-year-old boy who presented a constant dilemma in the early weeks of treatment. If I tried to stop him from attacking me and breaking up the playroom before he got started, he accused me of jumping him before he had done anything, and I felt guilty and uncomfortable about being unfair to such a disturbed child. If I waited until things did get started, it required all my efforts to contain him, and I found myself full of mounting rage and revengeful feelings as I struggled to prevent him from hurting me or destroying equipment. After seven or eight sessions, in one hour I found myself full of murderous fury having been hurt by him and finally finding myself on the floor with a scissor lock around his legs and arm locks holding this ten-year-old down. I was working very hard only to restrain him and not to hurt him.

Beside myself with impotent rage, I told this boy how terribly angry I felt and of my own fear that the anger he provoked in me might cause me to hurt him. If that happened I would feel very guilty and sorry. I told him further that to avoid this possibility I had just decided to restrain him the moment he even looked as if he were about to be violent and that I was quite prepared to be unfair to him at times. I was determined to continue this until he had shown me that he could begin to control himself. After three more hours of testing and protesting as I restrained him at every sign of incipient trouble, he began to settle down and express his feelings through the materials in the playroom.

As I was talking I could see this teacher's face relax; there were little nods as I described my own feelings in the playroom with respect to the child and when I finished she sighed mightily and began to talk rapidly of her own fears, the anger, hatred, and helpless feelings occasioned by this boy's behavior. She accepted my suggestion that she try to anticipate this boy's beginning unrest and stay with him, helping him do schoolwork. Her personal attention at such moments rather than a half hope from a distance that the ominous signs might not bring their inevitable result might slowly begin to help this child. Also she might in time aid this boy to begin to communicate in words his feelings and to find a way out of his tension through beginning successes in schoolwork. On my next trip to this school about six weeks later, the administrator commented that a great change had taken place in the teacher. Since the consultation in which the administrator had participated the teacher seemed more able to talk with the administrator about her problems. The boy, although still a school and classroom problem, was gradually settling down.

On another level, a male high school teacher, after several conversations about other problems, recounted his difficulties with several huge, explosive boys who seemed to dare him to stop them. Although no weakling himself, he found himself indecisive. He feared a fight and riot if he interfered and tried to stop the hostile, provocative behavior and he felt ineffectual and at the boys' mercy if he did not take some action. Involved in this also was his feeling that he could not ask the administrator's help with this recurring problem lest he be thought a poor teacher. As the teacher recounted his experiences the Dean of Boys who sat by became more and more uncomfortable.

My comment that this was a hell of a fix to find oneself in brought a "You ain't kidding" from the teacher and a nod from the Dean. I then recalled a particularly difficult situation in the army with a psychotic soldier who had been a wrestler as well as a much-decorated paratrooper. He terrorized the psychotic ward and was reigning as king when I took over the service. During the first ward rounds he made his stand clear as he towered over me flexing his muscles, saying, "I am running things, see." Since my fear was evident to all in my trembling hands and legs, there seemed no point in denying it. I told this psychotic patient that I was scared of him and what he might be able to do physically to me, but that I could not let him run the ward; I was prepared personally and with all the M.P.s in the hospital if necessary to run it as it must be run. The man glared at me for an interminably long minute. I did my best to meet his gaze. Finally, he shrugged his shoulders and disdainfully said, "Okay, have it your way," and returned to his bedside. I had felt that being painfully honest about my fear as well as clearly demonstrating my determination to carry out my job by whatever means were necessary had been the effective elements of this interchange.

Both teacher and Dean then began to discuss how they could work together to help these youngsters settle down in the classroom. It was clear to me from the Dean's avid following of my account and from his relieved look when our discussion began that he had felt as stymied as the teacher by these boys and therefore unable to be of much help. The humorous aftermath of this consultation came when the Dean, weeks later, commented that this teacher now had a reputation among the tough youngsters for great fearlessness because he could admit being scared.

The following illustrates how the consultant's attitudes toward others and himself may help reduce unreal self-expectations and lead to greater acceptance of realistic limitations.

A typical interchange among teachers, overheard after a group consultation is: "Well, Berlin wasn't really much help today, but it's kind of nice to hear a psychiatrist say he doesn't know something." The honest, "I don't know," or "This is out of my line," in answer to insoluble problems on matters of curriculum and other subjects in which the consultant has no special competence seem to help others not to have to know and be able to cope with everything.

In many instances this begins to help the educator to delineate his job and the kind of work, that is, educating, that he can do. It may also make it possible for the teacher to ask for help from administrators, to call in parents, etc., when necessary, without feeling that such a call for help is an admission of failure. Thus some problems may get worked with earlier rather than at the point of impasse, when both teacher and student are emotionally so disturbed that it becomes difficult to find ways of continued work.

Despite their best efforts, teachers will sometimes fail to help a disturbed child, and they need to be able to accept such failure. The consultant's readiness to illustrate from his own experience that he too has on occasions failed to be helpful demonstrates his understanding of their problem. It seems to me to be helpful to the teacher when the consultant in his comments shows that one can fail with a clear conscience after one has literally done everything one could do within one's own present scope of knowledge and professional development. As many of us have experienced, the readiness to give up and to admit failure often frees both people in a working relationship to try again. I have often witnessed that the consultant's understanding and acceptance of the administrator's and teacher's desire to exclude a child from school because they are at the end of their rope with the child resulted in the teacher's relief. Thus the contemplated action about which the teacher or administrator feel some guilt is accepted as reasonable in the light of the situation which has been discussed. Often later in the same discussion, after close examination of the problems and their possible causes, the teacher has reconsidered the exclusion and has been willing to try to work with the child again.

In my experience, the consultant can often demonstrate that one can accept constituted authority and its regulations even when they are unfair and that one can find ways of working within such a framework. In my own work I have insisted that administrators be present in consultation to decide about the action to be taken after our discussion of the problems involved.

Sometimes teachers are temporarily angered when the consultant does not side with their rebellion against short-sighted regulations or strongly biased administrators. In such instances, it has been possible to help some of these teachers to focus on using their energies more effectively in doing a good job of teaching and working with their pupils. As such energies are withdrawn from their usually fruitless rebellion and transferred to more effective teaching, one begins to recognize how often the problems with authority served other purposes. Most frequently, in my experience, such rebelliousness served as a rationalization for the actual poor job of teaching that was being done. An interesting paradox is often seen. The hostile, angry rebelliousness of many teachers does not become channeled into rational action as citizens or teachers through the organization appropriate for such action until they begin to teach more effectively, with consequent reduction of the irrational aspects of their rebellion.

A number of teachers and administrators have commented that my own acceptance of severe limitations in consultation imposed by frightened, unfriendly administrators has been of help to them. They have watched to see whether I would adhere strictly to the rules that were laid down. It became clear to them that I could and did function under these restrictions until as a result of my behavior the administrator felt less threatened and relaxed the restrictions. One vice-principal who later went on to an important job in another school system said that such a demonstration helped him resolve a problem he had been struggling with for years and made his advancement possible.

DISCUSSION

Mental health consultation is a term made meaningful by Gerald Caplan of the Harvard School of Public Health and used by him to describe particular consultative processes previously written about under many headings. In this process a consultant using specific consultative methods attempts to help a consultee whose internalized conflicts interfere with effective performance of some aspect of his job.

The dynamics of the mental health consultation process are being studied by a number of workers. This paper is concerned with the particular way in which the consultation process lends itself to the communication of certain mental health principles to the teacher and administrator and often through them to other members of the school faculty. In addition, these experiences highlight several aspects of the dynamics of mental health consultation.

The consultant demonstrates in many ways his understanding of the consultees' problems and his assessment of these as work problems. When he relates similar experiences of his own and indicates the mental health principles involved which he, an authority in interpersonal matters, also had to learn, then feelings of turmoil, hate, anger, rebellion, and self-righteousness that were largely covert can become more overt. As some of the defenses against the eruption of such feelings are reduced, the teacher begins to feel that his problems can be resolved and is ready to listen to the methods others have used to deal with similar problems. Frequently a teacher who has been helped will talk frankly and eagerly with colleagues and will emphasize the mental health principles he has learned.

In my own work I have insisted on the presence of administrators at most of the consultations. It reduces opportunities for divisive comments by teachers against administrators when they misquote the consultant to other faculty members. An even more important reason is that in my experience, the consultant is often called in because the administrator has not been able to help his teacher with some particular problems, which may indicate some difficulties on the administrator's part in doing his job effectively. As the administrator listens to the consultative sessions he becomes aware of the consultant's attitudes that seem to help the teacher. He also vicariously identifies with the teacher's work problems. Usually the principal has failed to help his teacher with problems in areas where he is also in conflict. Since he is once removed from the direct consultation, he gains relief and help with his problems without their ever being made explicit. Subsequently he often communicates what he has learned to other teachers and even to fellow administrators. This is especially true of problems concerned with authority and the acceptance of one's own limitations, areas of special concern to administrators.

Experienced consultants have come to recognize how often teacher consultees present the problems they are unable to deal with by behaving toward the consultant as their difficult students have behaved toward them. In my experience, this is especially true in instances of hostile, provocative behavior or when the incessant demands of one or more students for exclusive attention has exhausted the teacher. The teacher finds himself in conflict about what is fair to the demanding student, to the class, and lastly, if at all, to himself. These teachers may come to consultation with a hostile, demanding, provocative, and sometimes belligerent pounding at the consultant for answers to their problems. One senses the teacher consultee's wary, anxious observation of the consultant and the close scrutiny of his methods as he handles this situation. In these instances there is the clearest identification with the consultant and incorporation of his attitudes and methods of handling problems.

In almost all mental health consultation, identification with the consultant and incorporation of his attitudes and methods of working with problems are part of the process of ego integration. From my point of view, mental health consultation is essentially conducted at the ego level. In my own work in mental health consultation during the past twelve years, I have tried to apply the growing insights from ego psychology to refine the consultation process. These insights concern an awareness of the integrative capacities in all human beings, even those who are very sick; efforts to understand the individual's malintegrative behavior in the current situation and to assess that behavior in terms of the current realities; a detailed examination of the problems so that through the attention to the minute details of the current difficulties in functioning one may begin to elucidate methods of resolution usually inherent in the troubles; help in the resolution of conflicts by honest assessment of the reality facing the person and a step-by-step analysis of the ways in which certain obstacles to resolution were noted, understood, and handled by the person. Thus the consultant is task oriented; this helps reduce the regressive helplessness of the consultee and enlists him as a collaborator, not a patient, to work together with the consultant to resolve the particular work problems. The consultant's understanding of the consultee's neurotic conflicts, which make for his work problems, is used to find the dynamically appropriate comments which will help reduce the central anxieties and permit the collaboration to occur.

Inherent in all of this is an underlying thesis in ego psychology: that the conflict between unconscious forces results from malintegrative experiences during infancy and childhood. These conflicts usually become manifest as a struggle between regression and helplessness versus mastery and integrative productive behavior. In the consultative situations involving rebellious feelings and behavior toward authority these aspects are perhaps most clearly seen. The consultee may begin by presenting his own problems of helplessness in handling hostile or rebellious behavior in his students and then go on to talk of his anger and hatred toward the unfair, punitive administrator, etc. In such comments the genesis of the conflicts in early experience often becomes clear. After listening carefully, if one returns to a close examination of the classroom events and especially inquiries about how the teacher handles other classroom problems, one gets a sense of the capacity for effective teaching that is present. A detailed assessment of the actual problems with the rebellious student often gives one clues to the teacher's momentary awareness of choices at critical points of dealing with the youngster -- choices that were not heeded, so that the helpless, regressive feeling overwhelmed the teacher with resulting havoc. At this point some effort to externalize the situation by using experiences of others or one's own may illustrate why such moments of choice are difficult to detect and to use, how one's anger with authority may make such work more difficult. Finally, one can illustrate that other solutions might be possible if these critical moments were recognized and then handled differently.

The above elucidates some dynamics of the mental health consultation process. The development of methods of effective mental health consultation and of understanding its dynamics is one of the most interesting and challenging areas of the application of dynamic psychiatric and psychoanalytic thinking.

Reprinted by permission from the Journal of the American Academy of Child Psychiatry, 1:671-679, 1962.

THE ROLE OF A PSYCHIATRIST IN A SMALL COMMUNITY*

Samuel Susselman, M.D.

The recent war has done much to heighten the public's interest in psychiatry and to stress the need for psychiatric services. Funds have been made available to establish clinics such as the one you contemplate in many communities throughout the country. Medical educators are busily planning programs to turn out more and better trained psychiatrists, while agencies that deal with the psychologically ill are clamoring for help. When a psychiatrist spends a social evening with friends, some of them parents, the conversation sooner or later turns to questions that only thinly veil concern. What does one do with temper tantrums? Is there anything wrong with baby talk? Do children grow out of bedwetting? One feels an almost universal sense of uncertainty. Many are reaching out for reassurance and seem to expect a ready solution to specific problems. Those of us who have become aware of the complexities of the human personality structure, and of the difficulty in effecting ready changes in people's emotional reactions, have no pat answers. We cannot reassure the apprehensive person with a few choice words, nor can we turn off the faucets of enuresis with a phrase.

Psychiatry has its limits. It is the youngest of all the medical specialties, an infant just learning to walk and talk. Its promise of greater things to come presents a definite danger of overselling psychiatry. In the words of Dr. A. W. Freeman (1), "The friends and proponents of mental hygiene have obscured the real importance of the subject by their over-enthusiasm and the putting of propaganda so far in advance of procedure." Psychiatry will go forward on its merits alone. If it has something to offer through an approach that seems reasonable, its influence will spread, perhaps slowly at first, but faster and faster as its contributions are

*Presented at a meeting of Sonoma County Mental Hygiene Society, April 15, 1948.

recognized. The big job ahead makes us humble. We are here to-night to consider what realistically can be done. Towards this end I shall attempt to formulate the contributions a psychiatrist might make in a small community like yours.

The specialty of psychiatry has grown to the point where sub-specialties are in the making. We already have the psychoanalyst. Soon, alongside the child psychiatrist, there may be the psychosomaticist and the specialist in mental deficiency. Some psychiatrists restrict their practice to psychotherapy with neurotic patients, while others prefer to devote most of their time to the treatment of psychotic patients, mostly by means of shock therapy. In a community where there is a scarcity of psychiatrically trained personnel, it becomes necessary to invest many functions in a few persons. Where there is only one psychiatrist, his functions are necessarily broad. He becomes, in a sense, a general practitioner in the specialty of psychiatry, called upon to do many things.

Let us consider why it is that your community has been getting along all these years without the services of a psychiatrist. The immediate and obvious conclusion is that existing agencies and individuals have been meeting many of the psychological needs of the community. I am thinking of the schools who deal with their problem children, of the courts dealing with behavior disturbances, of the Veterans Administration with its psychoneurotic ex-soldiers, of the public health nurses and all the unpredictable situations they encounter, of the physicians burdened with patients suffering from non-organic illnesses, and of the social workers in a variety of agencies. The clergy have always made their contribution in various ways. It is through such agencies that the mental health of your community has been and will continue to be served. There is no substitute for the intimate, friendly, and understanding close relationship that exists between these various services and the people of the community.

However, should agency workers encounter problems for which their training and knowledge have not prepared them, and should help from the psychiatrist be invited, then he has an opportunity to fulfill an important function. He may be useful to the client directly or to the agency worker who is seriously concerned about what is for him both a work problem and an interpersonal problem. The understanding the psychiatrist has gained from psychotherapy with the most difficult clinical cases helps him to understand

workers who encounter similarly difficult work problems. Some
of this understanding represents common knowledge, perhaps
made more explicit; for example, reviewing "function" and
"limits" of agency and worker, redefining and identifying vague
and unclarified policies, sharpening the agreements and contracts
on which working relationships are based, pointing out the importance of careful inquiry into a problem, etc. In addition, a psychiatrist can place special emphasis on the interaction of individuals and their possible meanings, the vagaries in the use of authority, the meaning of varieties of conflict in behavior and when and
how to intervene to reduce conflict. Experience with children and
their parents in psychotherapy has yielded him insights that are
useful in solving problems in community situations (i.e., schools,
probation, etc.) and in understanding agency problems when they
are similar to family problems. These are just a few areas in
which collaboration with a psychiatrist can reduce workers' concerns about work problems. I can conceive of no more important
service the psychiatrist can render to the mental health of a community than that of helping to resolve those crises which through
their wear and tear on workers impede the efforts of individuals
in existing agencies. Perhaps I can illustrate this by relating
briefly the story of Robert.

He was a ten-year-old boy, an orphan, regarded as incorrigible.
He had a history of sexual play with younger boys and girls, had
set fire to a house and had threatened to poison the younger child
in a foster home in which he had been placed. He was finally
placed in an unlicensed private home. The probation agency took
exception to this placement, but it had to serve pending a more
suitable arrangement. At the time Robert was first seen at the
clinic he had been in this new foster home for four months. There
had been certain minor behavior infractions, but he had learned to
respect and like his foster mother, who did not consider him a
particular problem. Yet the agency, still concerned about Robert
as they had known him, felt he should be in an institution. They
felt no home was adequate, particularly this one--at least until
Robert had undergone a period of preparation in a hospital. However, when the facts were discussed and when the members of the
agency were able to express their feelings of uncertainty and anxiety about Robert and about the possibility that the placement would
fail and they would be saddled with him again, a new objectivity
emerged. They saw that despite their concept of what a foster
home should be, Robert was getting something from an adult that

he had never received before, and that for the first time he was making an adjustment far beyond the agency's expectations. As a consequence, they agreed to leave him in this home, where he has now been living for seven months. He no longer presents a major problem, and the agency, now satisfyingly freed of Robert and his problems, has been able to turn to other problems.

Perhaps the most important resource that any community possesses is the parent. Someone has said that the three impossible professions are politics, psychiatry, and parenthood. Parents are the agents through whom society transmits its mores and values. They are the ones who must teach their young to live productively within the expectations prescribed by established institutions. They are held responsible. They must do their jobs or suffer serious consequences. It is a difficult task that they are expected to perform. The rearing of children is a major problem for all parents, even when they are not harassed by the struggle to provide a measure of financial security for their family. Every parent is acquainted with the many situations that evoke emotional responses, and when these emotional responses begin to grow out of hand, when common global anxieties are generated, psychiatric or other professional help may aid the parent. Perhaps around the well-known figure of speech, "As the twig is bent, so the tree shall grow," we can work out a basis for proceeding. The important thing in the bending of the twig concerns how the twig is bent and by whom. A twig can be bent so violently that it breaks at the base, or it may be injured in such a way that its future growth is stunted. On the other hand, it may be treated so ineffectually that no change in direction occurs. The gardener who feels secure in his own knowledge of what should be done will treat each twig individually. He will apply firmness where firmness is needed, and gentleness where gentleness is indicated. His manner will be steady, unequivocal, unworried, unambivalent, and relaxed. The same considerations hold true when dealing with children. The mature parent is free enough of his own anxieties that he fosters security in his children. The relatively anxious and worried parent rears relatively anxious and worried children who often do exactly what the parent tells them not to do.

To deal with education for mental health and prevention of emotional disorder, a child development center and guidance clinic is important--a place where children can be studied, where incipient developmental disturbances can be detected, and where parents can receive information and help both prenatally and postnatally. But what is most important, if our thesis about the role of the parent is correct, the anxieties, the unspoken concerns of the parents can be brought out into the open to help the parents gain new perspective in dealing with their children. Perhaps parent development centers and parent guidance clinics are the most appropriate terms for such services. As with agency personnel, the parent is the medium through whom the mental health of the community is improved. It is quite possible that such a frank approach may appear to lay the responsibility for psychiatric problems in children in the laps of the parents--and it does just that. This does not mean that the parent is being blamed. The parent, too, is a result of his or her familial and environmental influences. I am only trying to point out the link in the chain of circumstances where efforts limited by time, at least, will be most effective.

Perhaps you will feel that instead of the public's being educated to seek psychiatric help it will be driven away. An honest and realistic approach that is concerned with parents as people carries with it no such danger, and I think the approach described is both realistic and honest. If there is any deterrent to carrying out such a program of help for parents, it lies in an over emphasis of the magic potentialities of psychiatric help.

It must be difficult for modern parents to maintain their perspective when advice pours in on them from many sources. For example, how free can they feel to express anger when angry? Should they suppress this emotion even though Jimmy seems to be practically begging for a licking? One authority would say, "Never spank a child in anger," and another equally competent authority will say, "Never spank a child unless angry." Which is it? Or, when parents are moved to display tenderness towards their child, should they restrain themselves for fear of spoiling him? How much simpler it must have been for our grandparents who knew no fancy theories about bringing up children, who had no idea how much a baby should weigh at six months, who knew nothing about psychological tests, and who had no scruples about taking Johnny behind the woodshed and impressing their expectations upon him if that seemed indicated.

I do not mean to convey the idea that a return to the old buggy whip days is being recommended. I am only trying to express my recognition of the position in which a parent may find himself, usually through no fault of his own, and to emphasize that the parent usually knows what is best for himself and his children. However, when uncertainties and anxieties arise and when parents ask for help, a psychiatrist may help them to clarify their emotional dilemmas, not by giving advice, but by offering psychotherapeutic attention to the emotional conflict that usually underlies such handicapping dilemmas.

Perhaps the following sketch of a case history will illustrate something of what I am trying to say.

Mary was a ten-year-old girl who lived with her mother in the grandparents' apartment house where the mother was reared. The other tenants were the maternal grandparents and the maternal uncle and his family. Mary's brother John, a veteran, was fifteen years older than Mary and attended college in a nearby town. Her father was described as a pleasant, friendly person who gambled. He had been in jail three or four times for forging checks to pay his gambling debts.

Mary was said to be a very bright, willful child who insisted on getting her own way. She had been "spoiled" by her father, her grandparents, her brother, and her aunts and uncles, probably because she was the only girl child in the family.

When Mary was first seen, her father had just started a year's prison term because of another forgery. Her mother, a vacillating and indecisive person, found Mary unmanageable. She would not mind, and any attempts to make her do such things as wash or comb her hair would cause her to yell and scream. However, Mary had no difficulty at school. She was an outstanding student and revealed none of the behavior that she showed at home. It was quite evident that the main area of disturbance lay in the relationship between Mary and her mother.

Attempts to start a treatment program failed. Over a period of ten months Mary was seen at other clinics and finally was made a ward of the juvenile court because of her early morning screaming, about which the neighbors had complained to the police. Plans were being made by her probation officer to send her to a state institution, since "all the agencies in town are washing their hands of Mary and her mother, and the neighbors are clamoring." In the meantime, the mother had divorced the father. Finally, at the insistance of the probation department, the mother reapplied to our clinic. However, because Mary refused to come to the clinic, it was decided to work with the mother alone. In the first three months there were two calls from the probation officer in response to complaints by neighbors, but none after that. Mary's mother began to understand something about her own rivalry with her daughter for attention and affection from the rest of the family. She also became aware that she had been so overjoyed at the return of her son from foreign service that she had neglected Mary, something that Mary resented bitterly. Mary always created a major scene when her brother returned home from school, so that he was forced to stay away. The mother used to visit him surreptitiously at college in a nearby town without informing Mary. She couldn't even mention his name at home without inciting fresh outbursts from Mary.

When the father was released from jail he attempted a reconciliation with his wife. In the meantime he was being allowed to see Mary, who was devoted to him. On one occasion he discussed his son John with his wife in the presence of Mary. She immediately started a characteristic, violent tantrum. The father took one look at Mary and said in a firm, unequivocal tone, meaning every word, "If you don't stop that yelling, I'm not going to like you." To the mother's amazement, Mary stopped at once. The father seemed to mean business. Twice more, the mother reported, John was discussed, and each time the father and daughter looked meaningfully at each other for a moment and that was all there was to it. The mother found such simple and direct displays of her feelings difficult. She was so insecure and anxious in relation to Mary that she would have been confused by mere advice. She progressed sufficiently, however, so that Mary was no special problem and continued to do well at school. The necessity for institutionalization at that time seemed remote. The contrast between the mother's and the father's ability to deal with Mary during a temper tantrum is a classical example of what I am trying to describe about the importance of parental attitudes.

Now that we have discussed present services in your community, the role of the parent, and the possible manner in which a psychiatrist might participate in the mental health activities of the community, we should note that the addition of a psychiatric service adds another agency, which in a particular and special way can supplement the work already being done. A mental hygiene clinic has as its aim therapeutic as well as educative and preventive aspects of mental hygiene. Both these words, educative and preventive, are inextricably bound together, and it would be difficult to discuss them separately.

The goal of education is to help people learn from the experience of others, and to experience a process which is designed to promote full emotional and intellectual growth. How can psychiatry contribute to the further development of the individual? Textbooks, monographs, and articles written by eminent authorities might be useful. If these could be read and integrated they might do much to advance growth, comfort, and a sense of well-being. But you do not need a book to raise a child. If anything goes wrong, a textbook will be of little help. Education that is not pertinent and timely yields poor returns. Of the numerous talks we hear and of the books we read, how many exert a profound effect on our lives? We are receptive only when we feel a need within ourselves--when we are ready to learn, or are anxious to change customary or characteristic ways of solving problems. We progress best when aid is propitious and relevant to immediate needs.

Many people who are keenly aware of their anxieties will seek psychiatric aid if it is available. It is enough to inform them that a clinic is ready to serve them. Others may be reluctant to seek help, may be fearful about visiting a psychiatrist for many of the same reasons that stigmatize any social illness. It is important that such individuals be educated to seek help. The community needs to learn that there is no stigma attached to the emotionally ill and that those who discourage others from seeking help are often fearful because they, too, are troubled and in conflict.

Much can be done to help parents, teachers, nurses, and members of other professional groups to recognize the early symptoms of emotional illness and to institute corrective measures. However, with regard to a "preventive mental hygiene program," I can do no better than to quote the words of Dr. Kent A. Zimmerman (2), who said, "It may be a surprise to you, but actually we cannot today honestly say that we know how to prevent mental illness per se." Unless we understand this and unless we clearly establish our limitations, there will be areas of misunderstanding that will impede any concerted effort to improve the mental health of the community. We can work constructively to help prevent emotional illness by dealing with the concerns and anxieties of parents and with the problems of children, especially in their early years.

In conclusion, the role of the psychiatrist in a community where there has been none before is quite broad, embracing many activities. These include work with children, parents, and a variety of significant workers in the community to reduce and prevent emotional conflict directly through clinic services and indirectly through consultation with agency personnel. Fundamental to this effort are the lessons learned by the psychiatrist from psychotherapeutic work, especially empathy with others gained while working out his own reactions to problems of his patients. Above all, it must be stressed that he can function only where he is needed and wanted, and within the limits of what can be realistically expected from psychiatry.

REFERENCES

1. FREEMAN, A. W. Mental hygiene and the health department. American Journal of Public Health, 28:241-244, 1938.

2. ZIMMERMAN, Kent A. Mental health services in the health department program. California's Health, 4:187, 1947.

ANTISOCIAL BEHAVIOR AS FAILURE AND DISTORTION IN LEARNING

Introduction

Aggressive antisocial behavior is perhaps one of the clearest examples of early distortion of the learning process. The vicissitudes of society, poverty, slums, and delinquent community environment influence the infant and small child first through the medium of his parents. Since apparently the same social and family environment produces both criminals and productive, creative citizens, the variables of hereditary factors and specific parental interaction with a specific child need to be studied. At present the hereditary factors appear relatively unalterable. One needs, then, to consider not only how to change the potent influence of the community environment, but also, how it may be possible to alter the relationship of the parents to their children and of parent substitutes to the youth of the community.

Some possible causes of delinquency and antisocial behavior as well as some methods of working with such youngsters, their parents, and the courts, are presented in the papers that follow.

THE GENESIS OF ANTISOCIAL ACTING
OUT IN CHILDREN AND ADULTS

Adelaide M. Johnson, M.D., and S. A. Szurek, M.D.

Previous publications by the authors on antisocial acting out are
to be found mainly in the literature of child psychiatry. The present article, synthesizing concepts developed by the authors for
over a decade, is addressed to a wider psychoanalytic audience.

THE PROBLEM

The character problems under consideration are those of young
children and adolescents in conflict with parents or some other
external authority because of an acting out of forbidden, antisocial
impulses. There is no generalized weakness of the superego, but
rather a superego defect in circumscribed areas of behavior,
which may be termed "superego lacunae." For instance, a child
may be entirely dependable in virtually every sphere of activity,
regular in school attendance and honest in his work; but he engages
in petty stealing, or perhaps in serious sexual acting out. Mild-
to-severe neurotic conflicts usually accompany such superego lacunae. We are not immediately concerned with the sociologically
determined delinquency seen in slum areas, in which individual
superego defects are not involved. Nor shall we discuss delinquent children reared in institutions, deprived of a sustained object relationship, although some understanding of such children
may be derived from our discussion.

The thesis which emerges is "that the parents may find vicarious
gratification of their own poorly integrated forbidden impulses in
the acting out of the child, through their unconscious permissiveness or inconsistency toward the child in these spheres of behavior.
The child's superego lacunae correspond to similar (unconscious)
defects of the parents' superegos which in turn were derived from
the conscious or unconscious permissiveness of their own parents" (1). These conclusions are the results of the collaborative
study and treatment of the child and the significant parent or par-

ents, as reported briefly by Szurek (2) in 1942 and by Johnson (3) in a paper given at the Chicago Psychoanalytic Society in 1947. These authors have elaborated the concepts involved in their chapters in <u>Searchlights on Delinquency</u> (1, 4), from which chapters the authors have borrowed extensively in the present paper, with the generous consent of International Universities Press, Inc.

CONCEPTS OF DELINQUENCY

The literature reveals a variety of descriptions and discussions of the etiology of such circumscribed superego defects. Reich (5) coined the term "impulsive character." Alexander (6) conceived of the need for self-punishment as a motive for acting out, i.e., delinquent behavior. It is granted that these patients frequently suffer from neurotic guilt. Yet, the question remains of why the resolution of guilt was sought specifically in acting out.

Schmideberg (7) believed that people who act out their conflicts have a greater constitutional inability to tolerate frustration than the more inhibited persons. Greenacre (8) reported in some detail a number of cases of psychopathic personality, but without concomitant study of the parents. She found that the fathers of such patients were usually ambitious and prominent, and the mothers usually frivolous and superficial, giving little attention to the home. She discussed the interrelationships of such parents with the child in respect to its superego development, but did not report defects in the parents' superegos.

Aichhorn (9) very early lent great impetus to investigations in this area. He, as well as Healy and Bronner (10), stated that some antisocial children have identified themselves with the gross ethical distortions of their parents. These observers noted such gross pathological correlations as forgery in the parent and stealing in the child. They did not note the subtle unconscious correlations described here. Healy and Bronner attributed the child's inability to develop a normal superego to the coldness and rejection of the parents, so that one child in a family may steal and another will not, depending upon the one being unloved and the other loved. Other authors stress the patient's receiving insufficient love and warmth, so that a strong positive identification with loving parents is impossible. This lack of love is considered by them to be the basic cause of superego defects. Even granting that unloved children may not develop a normal superego, it does not follow that coldness of parents alone can lead to the superego lacunae under discussion. Some very cold parents can create such great guilt or need to make restitution to a needed object that a very punitive superego is developed in the child. It is equally true that there are also relatively warm parents whose child may act out antisocially.

PARENTAL ATTITUDES

What constitutes "love" and "warmth" needs definition. If these include rationalization by a parent of guilt about his own sadomasochistic, i.e., hostile and submissive, impulses, and appear as "gentleness" or "indulgence," the child experiences them as condoning, as acceptance of his impulse. Firmness with respect to the form of expression of the child's egocentric or revengeful impulse is to be distinguished from sadistic suppression. Firmness bespeaks a parent who has learned how to gratify all his essential egocentric impulses nondestructively to himself and to others; such firmness may be devoid of masochistic or sadistic coloring and distortion. The stable parent has learned how his own interests may either eventually be gratified in some measure, or how to choose which interest is pre-eminent, while clearly recognizing and accepting the consequences of his choice. He may even have learned how all of his major goals may be reached in some creative course of action. He may have the capacity to experiment before committing all his energies to any goal, and continue flexibly to search out the way to satisfaction of his major needs and wishes.

Such parental attitudes provide a child with various experiences encouraging the child in turn to anticipate, first, that his basic impulses are gratifiable, at least eventually; second, that his disappointment, rage or revengefulness at delays to his satisfactions are understood and accepted as natural reactions, but that their form of expression may invite retaliation from others; and third, that the parent will patiently respect such reactive feelings, prolonged though they may be. In short, there are, most generally, ways of obtaining sensual and other satisfactions at appropriate times and places, with appropriate people. Pertinent and amplified discussions of the concepts of "love," "guilt" and "restitution" have been presented elsewhere by one of us (Johnson, 11).

STUDIES OF PARENT AND CHILD

In 1939, the present authors and colleagues (12, 13) at the Institute for Juvenile Research of the University of Illinois observed, in their collaborative therapy studies of neurotic children and their parents, that the parental neurosis often provided the unconscious impetus to the child's neurosis. It seemed logical, therefore, in the cases of the delinquents, to seek some possible links between the superego of parents and the child, even when the parents themselves were not known to act out. As a result of this work, Szurek (2) described the psychopathic personality briefly as a defect in personality organization, a defect in the individual conscience. He also defined its genesis. He clearly distinguished between, first, the psychopathic personality, and second, the delinquency in slum areas which is on a sociologic basis and does not involve individual superego defects. He stated:

Clinical experience with children showing predominant behavior which is a problem to others and concurrent therapeutic effort with the parent leaves the impression that the genesis of some of the human characteristics included in the definition of psychopathic personality is no greater mystery than other syndromes in psychopathology. Almost literally, in no instance in which adequate psychiatric therapeutic study of both parent and child has been possible has it been difficult to obtain sufficient evidence to reconstruct the chief dynamics of the situation. Regularly the more important parent--usually the mother, although the father is always in some way involved--has been seen unconsciously to encourage the amoral or antisocial behavior of the child. The neurotic needs of the parent whether of excessively dominating, dependent or erotic character are vicariously gratified by the behavior of the child, or in relation to the child. Such neurotic needs of the parent exist either because of some current inability to satisfy them in the world of adults, or because of the stunting experiences in the parent's own childhood--or more commonly, because of a combination of both of these factors. Because these parental needs are unintegrated, unconscious and unacceptable to the parent himself, the child in every instance is sooner or later frustrated and thus experiences no durable satisfactions.

Interestingly enough, Ferenczi (14), in an address on Confusion of Tongues Between the Adult and the Child (read in 1932 but not published until 1949) arrived at a similar point of view. His sound concepts of the etiology of character and superego disturbances in children were based upon deductions from his experiences with the transference and countertransference of patient and analyst, rather than upon clinical evidence derived from the study of child and parent. Emch (15) explored similar concepts, independently and productively.

The unwitting employment of the child to act out for the parent his own poorly integrated and forbidden impulses was observed by us at all economic and educational levels, with the frequency, regularity and predictability of a well-defined psychological mechanism determining human behavior.

SELECTION OF THE SCAPEGOAT

The subtle manner in which one child was unconsciously selected from several children as the scapegoat to act out for the parent was striking. Analytic study of the significant parent showed unmistakably the unique significance of this child to the parent, and the tragic pattern of parent and child moving inexorably in a fatal march of events, usually unconsciously. A profound sympathy was evoked for these consciously well-intentioned parents, whose unconscious needs were unwittingly inviting disaster upon the family.

A striking illustration of "scapegoat selection" occurred in several families whose children included an adopted child. The common pattern was a parental acting out through the adopted child, which conveniently provided the rationalization of inheritance to account for the delinquency.

In other instances, parental guilt, born of unconscious hostility toward one child, made firmness and fair-dealing difficult. Parental vacillations appeared to be critical factors in the genesis of specific superego lacunae.

The sources of such hostility of the parent are varied. The child may have become unconsciously a rival for the indulgence of the other parent. The child may represent a parent's sibling with whom the parent has unresolved sibling rivalry. The child may be born or reared at times of high tension between parents. Numerous other factors and combinations of factors operate.

Frequently a dual purpose is served: not only is the parent's forbidden impulse acted out vicariously by the unfortunate child, but this very acting out, in a manner distinctly foreign to the conscious wishes of the parent, provides a channel for the hostile, destructive impulses of the parent toward the child. Often, parents may reveal blatantly the child's acting out to schools, family friends and neighbors, in a way most destructive of the child's reputation. This becomes a source of the greatest rage in the child. An adolescent girl recently hanged herself because her mother, missing ten dollars, telephoned the school authorities to search the girl's purse.

Thus, the parents' unconscious condoning of the acting out of asocial impulses by the child may serve the two-fold purpose of allowing the parent vicarious gratification of forbidden impulses, as well as expression of hostile, destructive impulses toward the child. This hostility in the parent is doubly directed: inwardly, toward the parent's own ego and outwardly, toward the child.

Similarly, the child, usually unwittingly, exposes the parents to all degrees of suffering through his acting out. One mother, revealing that her six-year-old daughter's constant masturbation at home and at school was a repetition of her own childhood experience, was frightened lest her husband learn of the latter. To observe her child flagrantly masturbating was thus doubly agonizing. The acting out may often be an exaggerated portrayal of the unconscious impulses of the parent. Again, the child's hostility is doubly directed: toward his own ego as well as toward the egos of his parents.

EARLY SUPEREGO RIGIDITY

We must first understand the behavior of a well-integrated parent, and the subtle conscious and unconscious ways in which this behavior directs the child's superego development, in order to be able to recognize the evidences of destructive sanctions in less integrated parents. To be sure, the dissolution of the oedipus conflict puts the definitive seal on the superego, but it is well to be aware of all the preoedipal and oedipal subtleties in the family involved in this development. To the child in the early and middle latency period, there may be alternative modes of reacting on an ego level, but when the superego is involved the child normally is reared as if there could be no alternative reaction in regard to the suppression of the impulses to theft, murder, truancy, and so on. The well-integrated, mature mother who tells a child to do something does not immediately check to see if it has been done, or suggest beforehand that if it is not done there will be serious consequences.

Such constant checking or such warning means to the child that there is an alternative to the mother's order and an alternate image of <u>him</u> in the mother's mind. Identification with the parent does not consist merely of identification with the manifest behavior of the parent. It necessarily includes a sharing by the child of the parent's conscious and unconscious concept of the child as one who is loved and honest, or sometimes unloved or dishonest. It is essential to appreciate this fact if we are to understand the etiology of superego defects and plan a rational therapy. Angry orders, suspiciousness, or commands colored by feelings of guilt, convey to the child the doubtful alternative image of him in the parent's mind. The mature mother expects the thing to be done, and later if she finds the child has sidestepped her wishes, she insists without guilt on her part that it be done. The mother must have this undoubting, firm, unconscious assurance that her child will soon make her intention his own in accordance with her own image of him. This, however, produces a rather rigid and inflexible attitude in the young child. According to Fenichel (16), "After the dissolution of the oedipus complex...the superego is at first rigid and strict...and...later in normal persons it becomes more amenable to the ego, more plastic and <u>more sensible</u>."

In adolescence the superego is normally still fairly rigid and the child is greatly disturbed when adults express doubts about its probity. Nothing angers adolescents more than to be warned about or accused of indiscretions of which they were not guilty. Such lack of faith in them threatens their repressive defenses, lowers their self-esteem and weakens their assurance that they will do what is right. It suggests an alternative code of behavior which at that age frightens them.

Let us examine the evidence for the hypotheses developed as revealed in some relatively uncomplicated cases of superego lacunae, although still recognizing that a child may evolve and employ character defenses constructed of multiple determinants.

TRUANCY

How does truancy originate? Parental coldness and rejection are insufficient causes, contrary to some authors; these are nonspecific stimuli. The child of six, sensing coldness and rejection, may say angrily: "You don't love me--nobody loves me--I hate you all!" Then, and not infrequently, the specific stimulus may be applied by the parent: "Very well! Why don't you just pack your bag and go live some place else if you think we're so awful?" We have observed that some parents even go so far as to pack the child's suitcase--a terrifying experience for the child. The suggestion to "run away" comes more frequently from inside the home than outside, for rarely do small children tell their friends that their parents are "mean," or get suggestions from other children to leave home.

How an adult can initiate "running away" is found in the illuminating account of Aichhorn (9), who deliberately resorted to such provocation as a technique of treatment. In managing the transference he purposely used a simple suggestive device to provoke a boy to run away from the institution. His aim was to establish a positive contact with the adolescent, in which he had been unsuccessful. This very narcissistic boy, with no positive feeling for Aichhorn, constantly complained about the institution. Aichhorn made subtle suggestions about the attractiveness of the outside world and an hour later the boy ran away, as Aichhorn had anticipated. In keeping with the therapist's predictions, some days later the boy returned, having found the outside world uninviting. He entered at once into a positive relationship with Aichhorn.

Six-year-old Stevie is a good example of the parent's need for vicarious gratification. The child had been running away since he was four. His father knew an inordinate amount of detail concerning the boy's episodes of exploration. This struck us as very significant. This father reported that during these same two years he himself had been forced to discontinue his work as driver of a transcontinental truck, a job in which he had revelled. His present job confined him to the city. It was striking to observe this father asking Stevie to tell of his most recent escapade, and, when the child guiltily hesitated, supplying an intriguing reminder. The account obviously fascinated the father, who eagerly prompted the child from time to time. Then suddenly the father angrily cut off the child with, "That's enough, Stevie; now do you see what I mean, Doctor?" Stevie could not fail to sense his father's keen interest and pleasure in his tale upon each return home, despite the inevitable whipping. The father was a kind, well-intentioned man who rightly feared for his little son's safety; but he was quite unconscious of the fact that the stimulus of his own thwarted need to travel was easily conveyed to the small, bright boy of whom the father said: "Stevie's really a good kid--he would follow me around the top of a wall fifty feet high." A smile of tacit but unwitting approval often belies a parent's complaints of impulsive and daring behavior of the child brought for treatment.

Helpless resignation in one area of the child's behavior and firm conviction in another area are common among the parents under consideration. On the one hand, effective action regarding a child's temper tantrums may seem hopeless; on the other hand, there may be unquestioned prohibition of the child's violence to a sibling or the destruction of objects in the house.

Summarizing, we found that careful examination of parents and children in cases of the child's running away revealed that it was the parents who unconsciously provided the specific stimulus for the defections, impelled by such motives as a need for vicarious gratification, or hostility, or both.

STEALING

Similar mechanisms operate in petty stealing by children. A woman patient, in analysis for nine months, became very angry at her nine-year-old daughter who was detected stealing money from the teacher's desk. The patient stated that she knew Margaret had occasionally taken nickels from her purse since she was six or seven but had said nothing, believing that Margaret would "outgrow it"; besides, "it was never serious, so the less said the better." The mature mother, we have observed, does not anticipate trouble or constantly check up on her child. But neither does she dismiss a significant transgression as unimportant; instead, she resolves the problem promptly without anxiety or guilt. She is neither the nagging, checking detective, nor the permissive, lax condoner.

During the same analytic hour, the patient recounted a recent dream, in which she stole a beautiful object from an elegant store. The therapist remarked upon the patient's failure to project the theft upon some other culprit. "Perhaps you are generally permissive of minor thefts?" For the first time the patient told of her own frequent stealing in childhood and adolescence; her mother had always protected her.

Three generations revealed themselves: our patient, after acquiring considerable insight, clearly recognized her own mother's countless little deceptions and covert permissiveness with the two grandchildren. Hitherto unnoticed, her mother's deviousness now carried meaning in the light of her own new understanding. The grandmother's visits were curtailed until the grandchildren were older. As the analysis progressed, the patient was able to take a definite stand with her daughter, without anxiety or vacillation, without the permissiveness born of the need for vicarious gratification. The child stopped stealing. Formerly unhappy and unpopular, she became a favorite and outstanding pupil at school.

This mother's behavior reveals an attitude commonly observed in parents of children who steal. The parent whose own superego is defective will say, "My child will outgrow this fault." Often, it is the parent who is not involved in the acting out who finally insists upon treatment for the child. "He will outgrow it" is the permissive protective attitude that keeps the problem active. Many such parents, whose own poorly integrated prohibitions permit them to overlook slight offenses, suddenly react with guilt and alarm at the first suggestion of criticism from outside the home, with righteous accusations and punishment of their child. The child is confused and angry at the parental betrayal. If he is not too ashamed or frightened, he may give voice to his recollections of similar parental deceptions, initiating a vicious cycle of hostile blackmail and mutual corruption.

Another illustration was seen in the adopted adolescent son of the head cashier in a large manufacturing concern. The son was brought for treatment because of stealing. The thefts were revealed when the mother surreptitiously secured, actually stole, the key to the boy's diary and discovered a well-ordered bookkeeping system of amounts extracted from guests' purses balanced against his own expenditures. The mother's duplicity was exceeded by the father's who, scrupulously honest in business, had for two summers confiscated checks the boy received in payment for employment by the father's firm. To the boy, such behavior was not only an outrage, but an obvious sanction for his own predatory behavior.

Many have observed that children and adults with severe compulsive neurotic symptoms, such as intensive handwashing, may also steal repeatedly. Such stealing, or the kleptomania of adults, again denotes the existence of one defect in the superego through which the patient may act out tension. Detailed study of such stealing in our adult patients with a compulsive neurosis shows clearly whence this permission stemmed.

There are many variations on the main theme that deception encourages deception, such as the admonition of the mother who says to the child: "Here is a dollar, but don't tell your father." To evaluate integrity as a virtue is difficult for a child who has experienced repeatedly broken promises, made lightly and disregarded without explanation or apology. The "more sensible" superego of the parent forgets the rigidity of the superego of the six-to-nine-year old to whom such behavior is not "sensible" but dishonest.

Perhaps the concepts in this section may best be epitomized by the words of a nine-year-old girl who asked the therapist "When is my mother going to do her own stealing?"

SEXUAL ABERRATIONS

Sexual aberrations also have become more understandable to us when viewed in the light of the concepts described. In several cases of long-standing overt homosexuality, search has revealed an unwitting fostering of some aberration by one of the parents. If this be true of patients in conflict and seeking treatment, one can but conjecture how great is the superego defect in cases in which the overt homosexuality arouses little or no conflict and no desire for treatment.

Little boys and girls in the oedipal or earlier stages may insist on being of the opposite sex and wearing the clothes of the opposite sex. Detailed collaborative therapy reveals a fostering influence by one parent, such as that of the mother who gave her six-year-old boy all her cast-off clothes. Interestingly, the boy's desire to be a girl dated from the birth of a favored little sister three years earlier.

A young man of great professional talents had been an overt homosexual for several years, since the age of eighteen, when his mother told him that his father was not her husband. The mother's hostile motivation was clear. The youth's unconscious rage was the immediate potent determinant of his homosexual turning to men as a protection against murdering a woman. The precipitating event occurred in a confused family setting, characterized by distorted adjustments and undue maternal permissiveness since our patient had been a child. His rage at rejection by his real father was rapidly erotized.

We have recently treated two men whose mothers were grossly

maladjusted maritally and extravagantly seductive with their sons
The mother of one, twenty years old, said to him when his father
was dying, "Jim, I'm madly in love with you; you are so hand-
some." This was but the culmination of years of varying degrees
of seduction. The major factor in the patient's passive homosexuality had been the protection afforded by his father against the
patient's murdering his mother, even transcending in importance
the factor of fear of the father, tremendous as it was. This young
man refrained from overt homosexuality only with a great struggle, and came to analysis very disturbed.

A colleague (17) treated a homosexual young man whose mother
had the adolescent son escort her clandestine lovers home, "to
make things look better." The boy, aware of everything, erotized
his rage toward these men, spiting his mother as well.

The unconscious sanctions of parents and their seductions of sons
and daughters into homosexuality are revealed by their guilty,
anxious, angry interrogations into the children's early conscious
or unconscious homosexual play and explorations. Thereby may
be stubbornly fixed what otherwise might have been a transient
stage of normal growth. The heterosexual or homosexual acting
out of a child is thus parentally guided.

A depressed, forty-two-year-old woman came to consultation complaining primarily of the sadistic promiscuity of her twenty-year-
old son. Since his adolescence, the mother had intently absorbed
the minutest details of his accounts of intimacies with girls. The
patient's husband was a beaten and submissive man. The sources
of her ambivalent seductiveness with her son were easily adduced.
Her own father was a Don Juan. From her early adolescence he
came to her bedroom nightly to fondle her and even made attempts
to enter her bed. At the first such instance, the patient sought
protection from her mother. But the mother did not dare reproach
the father, "lest he kill her." From the father, to the patient, to
her son, sanctions of the forbidden are evident in three generations.
The son, refusing treatment, will provide still another generation
toward the biblical ten.

Among adolescents, whose parents we have also been able to study,
we have seen no exhibitionism or voyeurism that has not revealed
indubitably from which parent the necessary sanction stemmed.
Admittedly, the opportunity to study such parents is limited; they

refuse or soon discontinue treatment. Undoubtedly, multiply determined neurotic conflicts contribute to exhibitionism and voyeurism. We have been concerned here only with the immediate mechanism which precipitates acting out.

SANCTIONS FOR ACTING OUT

The fantasies, hopes and fears expressed by parents regarding
some behavior of a child is a common and powerful influence toward healthy or maladapted living. Horrified parental anxiety
over some behavior is expressed to the child: "You are beyond
me; I can't handle you any more; if this doesn't stop, you will end
in the reform school." Or, "You are just like your uncle; he came
to a bad end." Parental fantasy guides the child's course of action.

Mothers who have seriously erred premaritally frequently betray
acute anxiety regarding their daughters' behavior on dates. Accusations, detailed questioning and dire warnings, rather than
preventing undesirable behavior, constitute unwitting permissions.
The overly anxious mother with poorly integrated promiscuous
impulses or reaction-formations against sex may function similarly, even though she may never have acted out. The father also
may contribute. Exasperating rigidity about dating, with a casual
provocative suggestion, often upsets the balance. Only close collaboration between the two therapists of the parent and the child
can reveal the unmistakable mutual provocation.

One mother, early in analysis, glossed over an account of sexual
acting out as a girl, in which there had been no conscious fear of
pregnancy. A year later in her analysis, anxiety developed lest
her young daughter "...may go with a fast crowd, drink and get
into trouble. All adolescent girls do too much sexual playing.
One eggs on the other. I will worry about her getting pregnant.
A girl cheapens herself. It's degrading. I don't know how to warn
her but I must." The mother's poorly integrated masochistic impulses, partially repressed, were projected to the child. Not consciously fearful of pregnancy herself, she nevertheless feared her
child's being cheapened and becoming pregnant. Her fantasies implied both destructiveness to the child and vicarious gratification
for her own repressed impulses. Eventually, it was revealed that
the patient's stepmother, as glamorous as she was unstable, frequently discussed sex, and suggested, "You will probably be more
highly sexed than your stepsister--and have more trouble!" The
stepmother was subsequently entranced with lurid accounts of the

patient's dates. The patient's analysis fortunately progressed, so that the heritage from the stepmother was not transmitted to the daughter, whose dates no longer aroused undue anxiety.

In the parental voicing of fears for the imagined acts of a child-- even of violence--the transmitted image of the act leaves a bolder imprint than the fear of it. An infant on the lap of a social-worker colleague put his hands about her neck. With genuine fright, the mother said, "I hope my son won't be a killer!" By the age of fifteen, he was. Another mother, reading a news account of a brutal murder, said to her son, "I'm glad it wasn't you who did it." His crimes soon eclipsed those of the news story.

Analysts themselves must take care lest they inadvertently provide sanctions for acting out by their patients, be they children or adults. Patients displaying sexual perversions or even more serious antisocial tendencies are sometimes warned that they may act out. Such a warning to a patient with a defective superego can be tragically destructive, ruining the developing structure of the patient's belief in the therapist's ethical concept of him. Warning or questioning without factual justification may be interpreted both as a humiliation and a permission.

We believe such warnings against acting out are to be distinguished clearly from Freud's concept of warning the patient against future acting out in the transference. To warn a patient regarding acting out of the transference is entirely different from the warning against antisocial impulses outside the analytic hour. In fact, Freud warned analysts against too rapid mobilization and interpretation of impulses that might be dangerously expressed outside the analytic hour, particularly sadism. A loose and unclear concept of what is meant by "acting out" has led a number of analysts to carry over Freud's suggestions about "acting out" in the transference to the "acting out" in a serious antisocial way.

COLLABORATIVE THERAPY

Except by simultaneous study of parent and child, the concepts presented in this paper could not have been developed, nor can they otherwise be subjected to further scrutiny. Such studies can be carried out by two collaborating therapists, if they are unambivalent, uncompetitive and entirely cooperative, or by a single skilled therapist experienced in collaborative therapy dealing with both parent and child.

Prior to our appreciation of this principle we failed repeatedly to understand relatively simple cases of acting out, despite frequent treatment periods (four to five hours per week) extended for months or years. Our consistent warmth and affection failed to stay the continued stealing, truancy and sexual acting out.

It is now apparent that any guilt the child may have mustered toward us was readily dissolved by unconscious permissions at home. The child became increasingly confused and fearful of us, and resolved his immediate conflict by discontinuing treatment. Instances of acting out were managed successfully only if we could either treat the significant parent or separate the child from parents during treatment.

Treatment of the parent requires great care. If his role is unconscious, the uncovering of his own problems is a miserable ordeal for him. If the parent has provided conscious sanctions, treatment is usually impossible.

In serious acting out, treatment of the child is futile unless the significant parent is also adequately treated or the child is separated from the home. Treatment otherwise may be not only useless, but dangerous. The untreated parent can and does act out through the child, foisting responsibility upon the therapist, much as parents incriminate heredity in adopted children.

THE ROLE OF GUILT

Guilt, and a need for punishment, have been advanced by Alexander (18) and others as a major etiological determinant of antisocial acting out, citing as evidence the frequency with which such acts are rigged to facilitate detection. While examples are numerous, our experience has not borne out this concept of etiology. It is our impression that the desire to be caught is a groping for protection against committing even worse offenses which might bring down extreme retaliation, even destruction. The sequence does not appear to be guilt causing acting out so as to be caught, which assuages guilt. Rather, it is unwitting parental prompting which caused acting out, with a fostering of detection aimed at checking more serious future acting out with major dreaded penalties.
The fear displayed by an apprehended delinquent child only simulates the genuine anxiety of an internalized conscience--neurotic guilt. On the contrary, we have found that such fear frequently stems from anticipated punishment, with no guilt coloring.

Failure to appreciate the distinction by the analyst impressed with the apparent guilt of the offender may even foster further offenses by an immediate search for sources of unconscious guilt. There is unconscious guilt in abundance in the cases under discussion, as in all neurotic personalities. A tide of welling hostility against a young sibling may be effectively dammed by defenses. A rent in those defenses, created by unconscious parental permissiveness for a specific form of acting out, may provide an outlet for the emotional energy. Thus forbidden impulses derived from a variety of neurotic conflicts may find expression in stealing, arson, truancy or worse, depending upon the nature of the sanctions. Very commonly, great guilt about sex is acted out in stealing, given appropriate parental permission.

These concepts indicate the error of probing for hidden guilt as the first approach to delinquents. With the rent in the defenses unsealed, the immediate result may be an increased impetus to act out with even greater seriousness through the permitted, though antisocial, channel. The first therapeutic efforts should be directed toward repairing the superego lacuna. In an adolescent who has great guilt about hostility toward siblings, and who unconsciously feels permitted to steal, unless the superego defect of stealing has been adequately managed, it is dangerous to mobilize the neurotic conflict with siblings, for the acting out may then increase. Only later is it safe to proceed with thorough analysis.

THERAPY

We cannot here detail the therapeutic procedures employed. The broad outlines may be indicated and have been drawn in part in the preceding discussion.*

Effective therapy necessitates the development of a positive and usually dependent attitude toward the therapist, with whom the patient may identify as an ego ideal.

The patient first must be made guilty and neurotic in the area of his acting out. The superego lacuna must be filled. In the process of arousing guilt with neuroticism about the previously unrestrained impulse, therapy continues. It culminates in analysis of the patient's conflicts.

---

* For further discussion of therapy, see Searchlights on Delinquency (1,4).

Ideally, the final result should include an independence of the therapist and be characterized by a consciously discriminating, reality-oriented ego function supplanting the superego lacuna, and a freedom from the former self-destructive, rebellious impulsiveness.

THE "CAUSE" OF ACTING OUT

Science can seldom ascribe any phenomenon to a single cause. Our goal has been to emphasize a major cause of antisocial behavior while still recognizing that the antisocial child reared in a family is the product of a multiplicity of variables of mixed quality and quantity.

Scientific proof of causation is not satisfied by demonstrating the invariable presence of the suspected cause (unwitting parental permissiveness) whenever the effect (antisocial behavior of children) is observed. It must also be demonstrated that the suspected cause does not occur unless the effect is also seen. This, too, has been our experience. Parental permissions have never been revealed without ultimate antisocial behavior in at least one "scapegoat" child. The superego lacuna of the child has always been traceable to a specific parental permission. Our thesis is not post hoc ergo propter hoc. The enmeshing interplay of parent and child in the affected area bespeaks more than a fortuitous time sequence.

SUMMARY AND CONCLUSIONS

In this paper the authors have assimilated material from their experience and publications since 1942, dealing with the etiology of acting out antisocially. The observations apply equally to the young "delinquent" or the "psychopathic personality" of later years, who is etiologically a delinquent grown older. By means of collaborative therapy of children and parents the authors have observed that the parents may unwittingly seduce the child into acting out the parents' own poorly integrated forbidden impulses, thereby achieving vicarious gratification. A specific superego defect in the child is seen as a duplication of a similar distortion in the organization of a parent's own personality. The outcome is doubly destructive toward the child's and the parent's ego organization, unless adequate therapy of both is provided.

REFERENCES

1. JOHNSON, Adelaide M. Sanctions for superego lacunae of adolescents. In Searchlights on Delinquency. New York: International Universities Press, Inc., 1949, pp. 225-245.

2. SZUREK, S. A. Notes on the genesis of psychopathic personality trends. Psychiatry, 5:1-6, 1942.

3. JOHNSON, Adelaide M. Sanctions for superego lacunae. Read before the Chicago Psychoanalytic Society, March 25, 1947.

4. SZUREK, S. A. Some impressions from clinical experience with delinquents. In Searchlights on Delinquency. New York: International Universities Press, Inc., 1949, pp. 115-127.

5. REICH, Wilhelm. Der triebhafte Charakter. Vienna: Int. Psa. Verlag, 1925.

6. ALEXANDER, Franz. The neurotic character. International Journal of Psychoanalysis, 11:292-311, 1930.

7. SCHMIDEBERG, Melitta. The mode of operation of psychoanalytic therapy. International Journal of Psychoanalysis, 19: 310-320, 1938.

8. GREENACRE, Phyllis. Conscience in the psychopath. Amer. J. Orthopsychiat., 15:495-509, 1945.

9. AICHHORN, August. Wayward Youth. New York: Viking Press, 1935.

10. HEALY, William, and BRONNER, Augusta. New Light on Delinquency and Its Treatment. Inst. of Human Relations Publication. New Haven: Yale University Press, 1936.

11. JOHNSON, Adelaide M. Some etiologic aspects of repression, guilt and hostility. Psychoanalytic Quarterly, 20:511-527, 1951.

12. SZUREK, S. A.; JOHNSON, Adelaide; and FALSTEIN, Eugene. Collaborative psychiatric treatment of parent-child problems. Amer. J. Orthopsychiat., 12:511-516, 1942.

13. JOHNSON, Adelaide; FALSTEIN, E. I.; SZUREK, S. A.; and SVENDSEN, Margaret. School phobia. Amer. J. Orthopsychiat., 11:702-711, 1941.

14. FERENCZI, Sandor. Confusion of tongues between the adult and the child. International Journal of Psychoanalysis, 30:225-230, 1949.

15. EMCH, Minna. On 'the need to know' as related to identification and acting out. International Journal of Psychoanalysis, 25: 13-19, 1944.

16. FENICHEL, Otto. The Psychoanalytic Theory of Neurosis. New York: W. W. Norton & Co., Inc., 1945, pp. 468-469.

17. KOLB, L. C. Personal communication to the authors.

18. ALEXANDER, Franz; FRENCH, Thomas M.; and others. Psychoanalytic Therapy: Principles and Application. New York: The Ronald Press Co., 1946.

Reprinted by permission from Psychoanalytic Quarterly, 21:323-343, 1952.

CONCERNING THE SEXUAL DISORDERS
OF PARENTS AND THEIR CHILDREN

S. A. Szurek, M.D.

Anyone who has had clinical contact with psychiatric facilities to
which children are brought knows the broad variety of impulsive
behavior they present in both sexual and apparently nonsexual acts.
Anyone who makes it a regular practice to interview an impulsive
child's parents may and does become aware of some connections
between such a child's behavior and the attitudes and behavior of
his parents. Those who for practical and theoretical reasons in
any therapeutic efforts with such clinical problems of children
regularly include concomitant therapeutic work with both parents,
are becoming more and more convinced of an ever-present, intimately etiological connection (2,5,8,9-14,17). One day a fuller
chapter will be written from such therapeutic studies of families
about the details of these connections in the whole range of the
psychopathological spectrum: from impulsive disorders through
the neurotic illnesses to the psychoses (4,15,18,20,21). Some of
us, like Dr. Adelaide Johnson and her co-workers (3), have already much clinical experience, only some of it recorded in the
literature. Not much of what is recorded is in the psychoanalytic
journals. More of it is being "recorded" in the training experience of many young psychiatrists who are learning to work with
parents as well as with the child. This is perhaps more generally true in psychiatric clinics for children, but also in other centers where analysts-teachers bring to their teaching such background from working with parents of child patients.

There are good reasons for this paucity of literature. To work
therapeutically with three people rather than with one requires

time, often collaborators, as well as clarification of technical, therapeutic principles and procedures deduced from these principles. Collaborators of equal training and sufficient sympathy to the idea not to allow ambivalences to cloud one's vision of the import of clinical data so obtained are difficult to find and to keep together working in the same therapeutic community. Often, then, one needs to train a team, which takes many years (19). Results of the work of such a team may not be, and in some respects cannot be regarded as wholly and strictly comparable to clinical data obtained by the classical psychoanalytic method. Some of these teams work in clinics where frequency of sessions with patients is low and where elementary psychotherapeutic procedures have to be learned and taught to a constant stream of psychiatric trainees.

Yet it would be an error wholly to disregard clinical data and results obtained under these circumstances. Although frequency of therapeutic sessions may be low, the total duration of therapy may be long enough and some of the therapeutic skill found among the more experienced members of such teams may partially compensate for whatever deficiency there may be in such work as compared to psychoanalysis by formally well-trained and more experienced analysts. Careful compilation of the life history of the child correlated with the more readily recollectable events of the total family history, together with the ante-marital history of each parent, makes available the facts of the child's actual experience, especially in the first two or three years of his life, as a more reliable source of data than reconstructions based on data in analysis. The contrast between the unconscious intrapsychic elaboration and/ or distortion by the child of these events and of the thus better known actual attitudes of his parents is then more apparent and better grounded in empirical observation. The therapeutic work of each member of the family with one or several therapists reviewed frequently and collated with the effects of such work, not only upon his own behavior but also upon that of other members of the family, offers an operational check of hypotheses that is in some measure comparable with that of the classical psychoanalytic method (1,22).

In brief, when the transferences of each parent and the child begin even to be loosened in such therapeutic work, the release of even small amounts of energy from internalized conflicts in any one member of the family at times results in potentiating effects within the family, which may offer dramatic validation of postulated relations of symptom-formations or exacerbations in all three: child, mother, and father. This does not mean that therapeutic work in especially the more severe disorders can be shortened for thorough resolution of conflicts. It often does mean that such concomitant work with all three tends to reduce the more durably destructive effects of intercurrent crises upon the personality development especially of the child. Now and then it permits not only the reduction of ongoing neurotic fixations, but also reversal of the neurotic processes when methods of approach with one member of the family have failed or have proved insufficient to do so (3,22).

For all these reasons and others which cannot be discussed because of limitations of space, I think consideration of some impressions and of some clinical data derived from what is usually known as "psychotherapy" as distinct from "psychoanalysis" may be of interest to both psychoanalysts of adults and child psychoanalysts.

A CASE OF PHOBIAS AND SEXUAL ACTING OUT

As an example of one kind of sexual problem seen in such clinics, I would like to sketch very briefly the clinical data of the staff's contact for about nine months with a 15-year-old girl and both of her parents.* Within five or six days after severe phobias about going to school, of death, and of leaving her mother developed in the daughter, a very anxious mother brought this second of her five children to the clinic. Therapeutic work with all three, each being seen once a week by the same therapist, began about a month later after several exploratory interviews. In the context of decreasing family income, father's rather premature ejaculations, mother's lack of orgasm, and much quarreling between them, the daughter, who felt herself uglier, less intelligent than, and envious of her 17-year-old sister, had begun secretly to have sexual relations with a boy four years her senior who was "a big wheel" in school. She experienced no orgasm with him but a great sense of pride and power, and at the same time she felt extremely guilty about her sexual activity and her provocativeness and fearful that only her compliance with the boy's sexual demands would keep him interested in her. She hated her father, who had once told her that her

---

*I am indebted to Robert Dalton, Ph.D., for the summary of his work with the family upon which this sketch is based.

mother had been sexually promiscuous and "no good" before marriage. Although the initial phobias centered around staying near her mother and preventing the mother's leaving home without her, later her phobic symptoms spread and involved the whole family. She herself refused to go to movies and prevented on occasion the rest of the family from going by brandishing a knife, which made father very anxiously decide not to leave her home alone. Father felt afraid the girl might hurt someone or herself in her rage, which was what he himself feared he would do when he became destructive in his own rages. She was also unable to sleep at night without a light during this period. Father found his daughter one night turning on the gas in the kitchen.

The mother, who frankly discussed her sexual dissatisfaction with the father in her sessions, eventually talked of a guilty extramarital affair which was sexually very satisfying. This affair occurred sixteen years before this period, just before she became pregnant with this daughter. The mother felt extremely anxious and guilty about what part she might have contributed to her daughter's illness. She was also very guilty about phantasies concerning sexual affairs with other men, in which she indulged even during coitus with her husband. She was afraid the therapist would tell of these phantasies to her husband. She deprecated her husband, calling him a rabbit, saying his short stature made it impossible for her to become sexually excited by him. His size, she said, made her feel as if she were in bed with her little brother. She had promised herself, when single, that she would never marry a small man, and yet here she was tied to just such a man. She compared her husband unfavorably to the therapist, who, she felt, was better looking and more considerate of her feelings. Incidentally, the daughter's phobias erupted in severe form during the weekend of a visit from the mother's brother who arrived to show them his new car, although the girl's sexual activity had been going on for the previous four months, and although she had generally been moderately anxious.

Father, a little man, lonely and rather isolated and self-deprecatory all his life, had lost both parents by death when he was 5. He had felt exploited by an older half-brother and his wife while he worked hard on their ranch, getting up at five o'clock in the morning, until he ran away when he was 11 years of age. After several years of "knocking around," he got a job at a grocery store, where he worked for fifteen years. He then was similarly steady in his post office job after this store closed. He spoke of himself as being always "very independent, maybe too much so." He was fearful of any close or tender feelings, recalling how a man he considered his friend once stole all his belongings in the middle of the night. He was easily hurt and angered as well as helplessly baffled by the daughter's symptoms and mother's neurotic involvement with her. When angry with his wife he frequently did not come home from work for meals, or slept in the afternoons at home, and, according to mother, he was generally uninterested in the four older children, who were all girls, or in doing things about the house. He seemed interested only in his youngest child, a boy.

The school phobia of the girl abated about six weeks after initiation of therapy shortly after her therapist discussed with her his understanding of her feelings, but pointed out the futility of continuing therapeutic work as long as she continued to be helpless about both her phobias and her sexual activity. During the week following this interview, after mother had gone to church despite the daughter's protest, the girl became more disturbed and confessed her affair to her mother. The mother, smiling and occasionally laughing while telling the therapist of the incident, said, "I didn't say anything for two or three minutes, just walked up and down the floor trying to decide what my reaction should be." Nevertheless, she told father when he came home. When their daughter told them she had confided her affair to a cousin, they both became very angry and slapped the girl because she had not kept her sexual behavior a secret within the family.

Following this, the girl stopped having coitus although not all of her sexual play with the boy, and very gradually during the next five months most of the phobias were reduced as all three continued to work with the therapist until his departure from the staff.

Both mother and daughter manifested strongly positive transference attitudes, competitive at times with each other, with mother frankly speaking of her sexual feelings for the male therapist. Father, although suspicious that mother, who looked better, gained weight, and lost many of her anxieties, was in love with some man, continued his work with the therapist with a generally positive attitude towards him and gradually gained more confidence in himself. There were repeated quarrels between the parents during this phase of therapy. These quarrels, however, tended to clarify the situation between them, unlike those prior to therapy, which ended in prolonged self-deprecation and sulky, hurt emotional isolation on the part of each of them from the other. Father told the mother several times in these later quarrels that she was free to seek a divorce; that she was as crazy as the daughter and that she babied her too much. He became at the same time more aware of the effect on himself and on the family of his previous prolonged periods of emotional estrangement from them, and although he stayed away from the holiday meals because of mother's refusal to visit his relatives, he provided the money for the family's holiday. Mother, accusing herself of being crazy for staying with her husband, became angry not only with her husband but with her daughter as well, and she would leave home for several hours in the car. She became annoyed and irritated with her daughter's refusal to go with her boyfriend, but "took out" her irritability on her husband. She gradually became aware of this and eventually recognized that in spite of his faults and her sexual dissatisfaction with him, she needed to stay with him because of the children, and that he was a good man who did the best he could as did she herself. Mother then decided to go back to work the following year as she had done during the war and looked forward to this prospect both as a pleasure for herself to be with other people and to help with the financial problem of the family. Both parents decided to let the daughter decide whether she wished to go on in school or not, rather than-- as mother had first thought of doing--demanding that she stay home and care for the youngest children while mother worked.

A CASE OF TEENAGE PROMISCUITY AND THE FAMILY
Another clinical example is provided by the following biographical sketch, summarized from the statements of both parents, who had never been formally married, of an adolescent girl who came to our clinical attention at the age of 14 years. The father, 42, a professional man, was seen only once at the clinic, when he gave information chiefly about the daughter and his life with her and the girl's mother. The few other facts about him were obtained from studies of the case by other clinicians prior to the referral to the clinic. He was said to be the only child of European-born parents. He had his pre-professional education in Europe, and he was said "not to believe in marriage." He was also described by the mother as artistic, Bohemian in tastes, irresponsible, but charming. At 19 he was having affairs with many women while living openly with one, by whom he had two children. He left this woman to live with our patient's mother, also in a common-law relation.

The mother, 38, and attractive, separated from her third husband at the time of referral to the clinic, was the only child of a sea-captain and a woman to whom she remained closely attached most of her life. She feared her daughter had inherited something from herself and her father "which should not be perpetuated," and she had determined never to have another child which brought such frightening responsibilities. She saw the same difficulties in the other children of the father by other women. Although very much in conflict about the daughter, the mother was not much interested in any help for herself and, expressing much hostility, came for interviews, she said, only because of the requirement of the Juvenile Court.

The parents had lived together until the daughter was about 1 1/2 years old. Thereafter, "because of temperamental differences," they were separated more often than living together until the child was 6, when separation was final and father thereafter provided no financial support. The girl, at 5, frequently "snuggled up and burrowed into adults" in a way that father thought was more than childish affectionateness. After separating from the father, mother took the daughter to her own mother's home town for the next two and one-half years, sending her to a boarding school during the week. When she was 8, male neighbors complained to the mother that the girl was too provocative with them in their homes, and they asked mother not to permit her these visits. When confronted with these complaints by the mother, the girl accused these neighbors of sexually approaching her. She also hugged and kissed several of her mother's boyfriends so effusively that some of them did not return for further visits. At the same time, the girl gave the impression of being very jealous of the relation between her mother and grandmother.

When she was 8 1/2, the mother lived and worked in the same city as the father, and sent the daughter to live with him and his third common-law wife and their three children. The third wife was said to be an alcoholic who on a spree was arrested for neglect of the children. Our patient was so unruly that the father returned her after one month to the mother, who had further difficulty with her because of her continued sexual interests and talk of sex with various people in the neighborhood, and the landlady's son. Mother returned to the grandmother's city, placing the daughter in two more boarding schools, each of which after a period refused to re-admit her because of her tantrums, sexual interests, her "dirty jokes" and bad influence upon other pupils. When she was 11 years of age, she again lived with her father for four months, during which time she paraded nude before her 73-year-old grandfather whose young wife then left him. She was so sexually provocative with a married Japanese male house servant that he left, and she was having violent temper tantrums with her father, who made futile efforts to keep her at home during the evenings. She accused her father of being sexually promiscuous, and she herself became obese and unclean.

The mother then married an orchestra leader and took the girl back but placed her in boarding schools again. Here, and also on weekends at home, her behavior became even more difficult. She sneaked out of windows at night to meet boys, or invited them into the house when her parents were away, using her allowance to buy them liquor, and boasted later of having had her first coitus at 12 with a man twelve years her senior. When taken to a therapist, who gave a poor prognosis, she told him that her mother and grandmother performed cunnilingus upon her. She was placed in the Home of the Good Shepherd for several months, again telling what were considered fantastic lies and being the center of troublesome groups. Mother removed her against advice after her third husband left the country, and again placed her in another boarding school, where the girl told other girls of being pregnant and of needing an abortion.

When the school refused to readmit her for the next term, the mother in desperation returned her to her father, who was reluctant to have her again because of a recent coronary attack he had had, and because he was separated from his third common-law wife. The girl was out most evenings, talked of being pregnant, saying the father of the child could be any one of thirty or forty men, and might be either black or white. Upon examination she was found not to be pregnant. Three or four months after coming to live with her father, she ran away from home, phoned him repeatedly for money, telling him she was in Mexico and other places intending to marry a gangster. After his repeated requests that she return home, she did so, saying that the gangster had given himself up. In a week or two she left home again. This time father reported her disappearance to the police, who picked her up at an apartment where she boasted that she had "taken on six or more teenage boys in a gang-bang on a dare."

While confined at the Juvenile Court detention home, she accused her father of having one of his women friends perform cunnilingus upon her, then of having a man friend have coitus with her, and finally of the father himself having intercourse with her. She spoke also of having been raped by an abortionist after she had had the benefit of his services. She looked forward eagerly to the front-page publicity she would have as a result of her father's trial. Incidentally, the girl's mother testified in the father's defense and sympathized with him. The girl rather boastfully repeated the stories of incest, cunnilingus, etc., to the Court and to any clinician involved later in the study of her problems. She did not "know how she felt about George," as she called her father. She said that he was quick-tempered, generally irascible, and that her mother had had her only to hold her father, but she (the mother) should have know better since he had left another woman to live with her. She "knew" her mother hated her, and she herself needed love since she had never experienced it. The various examiners commented on her apparent lack of guilt or of any anxiety.

Upon the Juvenile Court's insistence, mother and daughter came for weekly interviews at the clinic and were seen by rather young and inexperienced therapists for about three months while the girl was kept in a closed home for girls. The father was not included in this work because he lived in a distant city and was planning a trip to Europe after he had been exonerated at his trial of this daughter's accusations.

Mother continued throughout this period to be deprecatory of herself, of the Juvenile Court authorities, and of the therapist. On the one hand, she was reluctant and anxious about again assuming parental responsibility for this girl which she felt would almost entirely preclude earning her own living or having a life of her own. On the other hand, she guiltily wished to find someone else, medical or Juvenile Court authorities, to relieve her of any further care for her daughter. This reflected her own deep doubts of her own worth, lovability, and competence to take care of herself. At times she experienced a desperate need for a father surrogate for herself whom she feared she would again exploit and devour or be exploited or devoured by him.

The daughter, intelligent, somewhat obese, talked in her interviews of having no faith in anything but wishing she did, of her confused feelings, of a need for love, of her greater ease with older people than with persons nearer her own age. Her sophisticated manner, her expressed interest in art and dramatics, and her ambitions to know prominent people covered a more insatiable infantile yearning for passive gratifications at which she thus indirectly hinted. Strong negative reactions in the therapeutic situation following her therapist's declining to convert the interviews into social discussions were frequent.

Both mother and daughter declined to continue with the successors of their first therapists as the girl's behavior had become calmer, and as the probation officer's anxiety and concern were relieved. Consequently the Court's requirement of "forced psychotherapy" was removed as the girl and mother agreed to live together again. A few months later it was learned that mother was relieved of her care by the daughter's marriage to a man in his twenties who was reportedly very fond of her. The mother was free to seek a fourth marriage partner.

A CASE OF ADOLESCENT SEXUAL ASSAULT

A similarly life-long story of general impulsiveness culminating in repeated attacks upon women in the streets by an adolescent boy, the son of a rather egocentric couple who were divorced, with the boy thereafter shunted between them over many years, could be detailed. The father was an impulsive person, repeatedly changing his work, residence, and women friends of whom he made no secret to the boy, and even advised, or tried to provide the boy with sexual satisfaction at houses of prostitution as his attempts to cure his son of the penchant for knocking women down in the streets and being arrested for this by the police.

The mother, an extremely neurotic woman with recurrent hysterical symptoms, sought and obtained the boy's release from the reformatory. She did this partly to get state financial assistance for his care when she felt unable to continue her sales-clerk work after a physician advised colpoplasty for an injury sustained during her son's birth. Her helplessness during a sudden hysterical attack of paralysis one evening led her, after lying on the floor all night, to ask her son in the morning to lift her back into bed. Although extremely guilty and anxious about it while telling her therapist about this later, she continued to have the boy carry her back and forth from bed to the bathroom for several days thereafter. Not too long after this incident the boy again was suspected by the police of several attacks upon women in the streets, which were not confirmed.

Therapeutic work with all three was rather irregular and interrupted repeatedly, especially at first by father, who was very reluctant to assume any financial obligation for the boy, and later by failures of the boy to keep his appointments regularly. It ended after thirty months when the boy was caught by the husband of a provocative young woman whom he was coming to visit for the second time. He had followed her from a movie on the previous evening and had been admitted by her somewhat reluctantly to the house through a window while her husband was away from home. He was eventually committed to the state hospital for the criminally insane for institutional study of his sexual aberration.

SADISTIC SEXUAL BEHAVIOR IN A TEENAGE GIRL

A fourth clinical experience, illustrative of yet another variety of impulsive sexual behavior, might exemplify--if space permitted a more detailed presentation--the factors in the past of the family history and in the current present events in the family life that one finds in any case of symptomatic behavior of a child which is well studied.

A mother, a former nurse, brought her 14 1/2-year-old daughter to the clinic complaining that for over three years the daughter had been extremely preoccupied with sex. She grabbed at mother's breasts and struck them whenever mother walked by her. When angry, which was frequent, she pulled at the penis of her brother and father and once kicked the latter in the groin. When this behavior first appeared, she had exposed her genitals to her brother, of whom she had always been jealous, later saying she wished to impress him with her pubic hair. Although she and a girlfriend had once done a strip act in front of a window at home, most of this behavior was confined to the home and towards the members of her family. She was usually rather shy and withdrawn and had few friends at school or in the neighborhood. Mother also said she had been frightened of possible homosexual tendencies because her daughter had frequently rubbed up against mother's breasts "in a very sexy way."

Upon investigation, it was learned that mother herself had had repeated attacks of neurotic illness since her marriage, with which she was continually dissatisfied both sexually and because of her husband's poor income. She had sought and received pediatric care for the daughter from the age of 4 and almost continuous psychiatric service since the girl was 6. In the girl's early childhood the mother was anxious about her daughter's masturbation, which began at 2 1/2 years of age, and asked pediatricians for repeated vaginal and urinary examinations of the girl, which were always negative for infection or other disease. Later mother complained on various occasions of her daughter's negativism, temper tantrums, which mother felt helpless to deal with, of her daydreaming, attacks of choreiform movements, sleeping poorly, doing poorly in school and being teased and abused by other children.

Every psychiatric clinic in the city and several pediatricians knew of her, as the mother went from one clinic to another whenever discontented, or to family service agencies; and five months before her application, the daughter had been in the psychopathic ward of the county hospital for ten days, where for a time she was considered as possibly schizophrenic. Mother, too, was thought variously "a simple schizophrenic," "paranoid," and "untreatable" by various clinicians. On one occasion the father had become very disturbed, threw things, and had severe headaches, and his wife feared he would kill the family. He was seen only once at a psychiatric clinic.

Each of these past episodes of the mother's increased complaints about her daughter during the previous eleven years was on closer scrutiny related to various events in the mother's, or in the family's, life disturbing to the mother. Some of these events were the murder of her brother, who was stabbed by the wife he had left; the father's loss of a job during the depression and the family's going on relief; the maternal grandmother's coming to live with the family and interfering with the parents' management of the children and with the mother's ability to experience orgasm in coitus while her mother was sleeping near their bedroom; the grandmother's subsequent sudden death from a skull fracture due to a fall down a flight of stairs while visiting her sister; the father's night work at one period; the mother's difficulty in learning welding during the war and her suspicion that her fellow pupils made unfavorable remarks about her; the father's reported periodically lessened sexual desire while mother's libido increased; and subsequently, repeated changes in staff of a psychiatric clinic she attended periodically and the staff's decreasing hopefulness about the outcome of their work with the mother.

Both mother and daughter were seen in regular interviews for over four years each by a series of therapists, each of whom remained working with each of them at least a year or two. During this period many of the original symptoms of the girl decreased markedly and she did better in school, eventually graduating from high school as the mother became progressively less anxious and began to work again as a nurse during the last year of their visits to the clinic. It is not possible to do more than mention that as mother's neurotic anxieties and inhibitions about her own sexual impulses, about her rage, and about work were gradually reduced, and similar problems of the daughter were also somewhat relieved in therapy, the close neurotic nexus between them was also loosened. Each then began to be able to have more satisfying relations with others both within and outside of the family. These changes included both a lessening of mother's sadomasochistic libidinous drive and a more consistent satisfaction in coitus.

SEX MURDERS BY ADOLESCENTS

If space permitted, one could give similar vignettes of clinical experience with adolescent and preadolescent boys who have murdered girls. In those boys of whom we have any detailed knowledge, there appeared to be present an almost complete inhibition or denial of sexual impulses and interests. Generally we could also discern some unconscious provocativeness, or at least opportunities for sexual stimulation, of the boys by the mothers. Some of these mothers manifested severe repression of their own sexual and hostile impulses and a marked immature, anxious helplessness about injuries which either they themselves or their sons suffered. The sons recalled these latter episodes of injury, and their mother's paralysis about taking care of them, with bitter, cold hostility and contempt. The father was either absent by death or was unassertive in the home in relation to the mother and sometimes sexually unfaithful to her.

SEXUAL ACTING OUT IN PSYCHOTIC CHILDREN

Although in a way unrelated to the present subject of sexual impulsiveness in children, I cannot resist mentioning that we have also seen sadomasochistic sexual impulsiveness, or at least symptoms related to the genitalia, in several schizophrenic children. In one boy, whose psychotic episode of about three years' duration began when he was 4 1/2 years old, after the birth of his only sister, we saw among other symptoms during his hospitalization prolonged efforts at tearing off his penis and a desire to be a girl, which was most often expressed to his mother, who was thereby extremely disturbed. Corresponding anxiety and loss of sexual desire for long periods and extreme feelings of general incompetence were apparent in both of his parents, who had married young and were not only extremely infantilized by their own parents late into their adolescence, but who were still much ambivalently dependent upon their own mothers during the greater part of our four years of therapeutic work with this family. For a long time these parents could not sleep together when the boy was home because mother felt it necessary to sleep with him in order to calm him by keeping her hand on his head, as he demanded, until he feel asleep.

Another boy, who was entirely mute, once cut his penis, and frequently held his genitals in his hand when approaching nurses. He was the issue of his mother's one extramarital affair in which she indulged because her husband's severe hypospadias and an unsuccessful surgical repair precluded satisfactory intromission and coitus. Another 11-year-old, mute, schizophrenic boy, perhaps the most extremely and most persistently isolated child in our experience, was not only still sleeping with his divorced mother at home on weekends, but mother also took showers with him. We have also had the opportunity to learn during therapeutic work with mothers of other schizophrenic and neurotic children, especially girls, that the mothers were extremely guilty about their own sexual responsiveness during bodily contact with the child. In each of these instances the symptoms of the child included severe nocturnal terrors while sleeping with mother, or in the case of the psychotic children much open genital and anal masturbation, exposure of breasts, invitations addressed to nurses to perform cunnilingus upon them, and such acts as grabbing of the nurses' breasts and legs or lifting of their skirts. In some of the neurotic girls one of their chief symptoms was obesity. In an instance of an early adolescent girl's episode of severe anorexia alternating with marked obesity, the child told her therapist, towards the end of a two and one-half year period of treatment, that her obese mother did not want her at home because her periodically alcoholic father tried to fondle his daughter's breasts.

DISCUSSION

Such clinical data as I have here barely outlined and merely suggested in these vignettes and impressionistic statements do not, of course, form a sufficient, detailed basis for any well-grounded theoretical formulations. They do, however, suggest the necessity of taking very much into account--in any effort to understand the genesis and maintenance of the child's disorder--the psycho-sexual actuality of both of his parents. It is important for me to know the experience with this actuality of any child who presents any clinical, preoedipal or oedipal problem--whether this problem is overtly an impulsive character disorder, neurosis or psychosis. In particular clinical instances such facts of the parental, interparental, and parent-child experiences concerning libidinous impulses may not always require any important modification of therapeutic methods with the child himself. This is perhaps particularly true of the transference psychoneurotic disorders of childhood where thorough, classical psychoanalysis of the child may be sufficiently efficacious.

My impression from over fifteen years of experience in psychiatric clinics for children is, however, that in many of the severe impulsive and psychotic disorders of childhood a concomitant psychotherapeutic approach with the parent, particularly with both parents, may not only provide a more hopeful and sometimes a more effective therapy; it may also provide the detailed clinical data upon which our theories of personality development, and of etiology of the whole psychopathological spectrum, may be made more precise and specific. Formulations based on such clinical data concerning the earliest, pregenital vicissitudes of the child's libido, especially of its sadomasochistic transformations in the climate of parental regressions, may permit a clearer and mayhap simpler delineation of the factors, inherited and experienced, determining both the degree of ego-superego-id schisis or malformation and the degree of genitality, i.e., of intrapsychic integration achieved by any human being. In particular, the role and nature of the incorporations, introjections of, and identification with both parents as actually experienced, and their phantastically revengeful, caricaturing intrapsychic distortions may be more obvious from the facts of a child's experience in his life situation. In sum, in our efforts to understand the most impulsive or the most bizarrely psychotic symptoms, we may then need less recourse to hypotheses, hitherto relatively unprovable in the individual case, of genetic constitutional factors.

THE CHILD'S INTRAFAMILIAL EXPERIENCES AND SEXUAL DISORDERS

If the child's endowment transmitted to him through the genes is excluded from consideration for the moment, a tentative list of at least some of these more or less independently variable, experiential factors and their possible relations would read as follows:

1. The particular <u>intensity</u> and <u>form</u> of the <u>neurosis which one or both parents</u> bring in their personality organization from previous life experiences to the marriage or to the time of the child's birth.

2. The particular <u>events in their marital history</u> which constitute a stress or frustration to one or both of them and which specifically and quantitatively in combination intensify the pre-existing, and more or less latent, parental neurosis. Among these I would include both those stresses determined wholly or in part by their neurotic tendencies and those which occur independently of such tendencies, but which significantly affect them. Examples of the latter are wars, general economic factors, somatic illnesses--their own or those of close relatives upon whom they are ambivalently dependent--and so forth. I think the birth, or the time of the birth, of the child himself or his sex, his intelligence, his health and attractiveness, may be included here.

3. The <u>developmental phase</u> or <u>phases</u> of the child during which he experiences these neurotic attitudes of his parents in response to those of his needs which are characteristic of his state of biological immaturity and helplessness. Because of the child's unsatisfactory experience during these phases, this factor determines the particular zonal fixations and the future libidinous regressions upon later stress, the specificity of which is also here determined. The earlier the developmental phase, the deeper is the later regression, other factors being equal.

4. The <u>duration</u> of operation of these factors which determine the <u>intensity</u> of the zonal libidinous fixations and the readiness of his later regressions. To put it in other terms: the longer the neurotogenic factors operate, the greater the fixation, and the slighter the later stress or frustration which precipitates the regression.

5. The <u>child's reaction</u> to these factors is, of course, not only one of libidinous fixation, but also consists of the incorporations and introjections of, and identifications with, both parents' conscious and unconscious attitudes towards their own libidinous, bodily tendencies which are reflected in their behavior--neurotic and integrated--towards each other and towards the child. These two factors, the libidinous fixations and the internalization of the

parents' attitudes, determine which impulses of the child become ego-syntonic and which are repressed. To the extent that these factors interfere with the child's satisfactory experience in any developmental phase, the internalized attitudes are revengefully (i.e., sadistically) caricatured and the libidinous impulses are masochistically distorted, i.e., the libidinous energy of both the id and the superego is fused with the rage and anxiety consequent to the repeated thwarting. It is here that Dr. Adelaide Johnson's phrase "superego lacunae" belongs. If the parental attitudes are not solidly integrated in their own personality organization, i.e., if they are seriously ambivalent in their libidinous tendencies, or manifest reaction-formations in regard to them, the child's identifications may combine the lack of firmness and a similar corruptibility of both parents in his own superego. The child's resulting disorder may then overtly appear more severe than that of either parent.

Necessarily the other results of all these processes are (a) <u>ego malformation</u>, of a degree directly proportional to these malintegrative processes, and (b) learning disability which may be specific, or more generalized as in mute, very isolated schizophrenic children--or in the impulsive character disorders. As we know in both of these disorders, later experience even with persons other than the parents is integrated only slightly, if at all. The well-known poor prognosis in response to the usual form of analytic therapy, I think, is another expression of all this.

6. It is perhaps hardly necessary to add that this neurotic development of the child's personality has a further potentiating, neurotogenic effect upon the neurosis of the parents. It is the presence of these vicious circles thus established between the parents and between them and their child which, to me, often constitutes the indication for therapeutic work with all three.

Finally, it seems to me that the time in the family history of the occurrence of these factors, and their particular combination, determines not only which child develops thus--if only one of several in a family is primarily affected--but also what the form of his disorder will be.

REFERENCES

1. BERLIN, I. N.; BOATMAN, M. J.; SHEIMO, S. L.; and SZUREK, S. A. Adolescent alternation of anorexia and obesity. Amer. J. Orthopsychiat., 21:387-419, 1951.

2. FABIAN, Abraham A., and HOLDEN, Marjorie A. Treatment of childhood schizophrenia in a child guidance clinic. Amer. J. Orthopsychiat., 21:571-581, 1951.

3. GIFFIN, Mary E.; JOHNSON, Adelaide M.; and LITIN, Edward M. Parental seduction as related to acting out in young and adolescent children. (Paper read at meeting of the American Psychoanalytic Association, December, 1953, in New York.)

4. JOHNSON, Adelaide M.; FALSTEIN, Eugene I.; SZUREK, S. A.; and SVENDSEN, Margaret. School phobia. Amer. J. Orthopsychiat., 11:702-711, 1941.

5. JOHNSON, Adelaide. Sanctions for superego lacunae of adolescents. In Searchlights on Delinquency. New York: International Universities Press, Inc., 1949, pp. 225-245.

6. JOHNSON, Adelaide, and SZUREK, S. A. The genesis of antisocial acting out in children and adults. Psychoanalytic Quarterly, 21:323-343, 1952.

7. PUTNAM, M., et al. Case study of an atypical two-and-a-half-year-old. Amer. J. Orthopsychiat., 18:1-30, 1948.

8. RANK, B. Adaption of the psychoanalytic technique for the treatment of young children with atypical development. Amer. J. Orthopsychiat., 19:130-139, 1949.

9. SPERLING, Melitta. Analysis of a case of recurrent ulcer of the leg. In The Psychoanalytic Study of the Child. New York: International Universities Press, 1949, 3/4:301-408.

10. SPERLING, Melitta. Problems in analysis of children with psychosomatic disorders. Quart. J. Child Behavior, 1:12-17, 1949.

11. SPERLING, Melitta. Neurotic sleep disturbances in children. The Nervous Child, 8:28-46, 1949.

12. SPERLING, Melitta. The role of the mother in psychosomatic disorders in children. Psychosom. Med., 11:377-385, 1949.

13. SPERLING, Melitta. Mucous colitis associated with phobias. Psychoanalytic Quarterly, 19:318-326, 1950.

14. SPERLING, Melitta. The neurotic child and its mother: a psychoanalytic study. Amer. J. Orthopsychiat., 21:351-364, 1951.

15. SZUREK, S. A.; JOHNSON, Adelaide; and FALSTEIN, Eugene. Collaborative psychiatric therapy of parent-child problems. Amer. J. Orthopsychiat., 12:511-516, 1942.

16. SZUREK, S. A. Notes on the genesis of psychopathic personality trends. Psychiatry, 5:1-6, 1942.

17. SZUREK, S. A. An attitude towards (child) psychiatry. Quart. J. Child Behavior, 1:22-54,178-213,375-399,401-423, 1949.

18. SZUREK, S. A. Some impressions from clinical experience with delinquents. In Searchlights on Delinquency. New York: International Universities Press, Inc., 1949, pp. 115-127.

19. SZUREK, S. A. Remarks on training for psychotherapy. Amer. J. Orthopsychiat., 19:36-51, 1949.

20. SZUREK, S. A. The family and the staff in hospital psychiatric therapy of children. Amer. J. Orthopsychiat., 21:597-611, 1951.

21. SZUREK, S. A. "Critique" in chapter on Langley Porter Clinic Children's In-Patient Service. In Residential Treatment of Emotionally Disturbed Children, by Joseph H. Reid and Helen R. Hagen, pp. 216-221. Pub. by Child Welfare League of America, 24 W. 40 St., New York 18, N. Y., 1952.

22. SZUREK, S. A. Some lessons from efforts at psychotherapy with parents. Amer. J. Psychiat., 109:296-302, 1952.

MENTAL HEALTH CONSULTATION WITH A
JUVENILE PROBATION DEPARTMENT

I. N. Berlin, M.D.

My services as mental health consultant with a juvenile probation
department in central California began as a result of a community
interagency agreement to hire a psychiatrist as consultant to several child-serving agencies. The intent was to help the school,
probation, health, and welfare departments increase their effectiveness in dealing with their clients, so that when a community
mental health clinic was opened it would not be overwhelmed by
referrals. Only those persons with the most severe and urgent
problems would be referred to the clinic.

Although I was hired as part of a package deal, the contracting
agencies were not very clear as to what real help I could offer
and what methods I would use in my work. The chief probation
officer was caught in a dilemma which he described later as follows: He had to endorse a community-sponsored service, and
yet had no conviction about his agency's need for it and no understanding of how it could be helpful. Even after some time his
feelings about having a psychiatrist in his agency were ambivalent. For the first several months, therefore, my monthly consultation meetings were taken up with lectures to the staff about
child development and parent-child relationships and with discussions of the diagnostic categories of mental illness in children
and adults. In the lectures I presented several case histories
and experiences from my work with adolescent delinquents and
their parents, highlighting the difficulties I had encountered. I
attempted also to speculate about the factors involved in several
failures. I hoped these examples would give the officers a feeling that I might be able to understand their problems.

THE WORKERS' PROBLEMS UNFOLD
After each lecture period, I was given an office in which to consult with any of the probation officers who had special problems.

The chief probation officer did not draw up a schedule of appointments or specifically encourage his supervisors to ask their workers to bring special matters to me for consultation. For many
weeks I sat alone in the office, receiving an occasional visit from
a curious probation officer who would talk about some problem
that was not very acute or difficult. Nevertheless, I listened
carefully and tried to be helpful. After a while, I began to get
a feeling that the officers were overburdened and that some of
them feared that ventilating their concerns about their most difficult cases would cause the dam of problems to break open, leaving them overwhelmed and unable to carry on. This may have
been one reason why each of the officers who came to see me discussed cases which were not difficult or pressing. Gradually I
sensed that perhaps the problems they presented were similar to,
but milder than, the problems in those cases that were extremely
disturbing to them.

The officers in the boys' division reported their difficulties with
hostile and violent delinquents. They gradually began to describe
their fear of these youngsters, fear they felt they had to hide.
They believed it necessary to behave with these youngsters as if
the fear did not exist. They also began to describe some of their
retaliatory and punitive feelings.

For the most part, the young officers, who were recently out of
college and bore their psychology courses freshly in mind, tried
to win over the adolescents by their sympathetic, good Joe, and
big brother attitudes, hoping by these methods to reduce and a-
void the boys' hostility and aggressiveness. They overlooked
and excused missed appointments. They ignored or were ignor-
ant of the lies, deceptions, and half truths communicated by the
probationers and their parents. Often they sensed the truth but
felt uneasy about facing the parents and the youth with this knowledge. Some seemed blind to the evidences of petty thievery,
truancy, and other delinquency. In a few instances, they ignored
all of the signs of impending major delinquencies as the youngsters became more insolent in their attitudes toward the officer
and more indifferent about keeping appointments. They failed
to make inquiries which would have revealed flagrant violation
of the terms of probation, especially those requiring regular attendance at school, obedience to the curfew, and no socializing
with former gang members. Then, after the major delinquency
or crime was committed, they would express righteous anger for

being deceived after having trusted the youth. Frequently, an officer in that situation would then recommend a harsh punishment unconsciously designed to get the youngster out of his hair.

In consultation, it became clear that some officers resented the fact that the probationers were not punished by the courts for their misdeeds. Several said that their fathers would have beaten them for such behavior and they recommended beating as the only way to "cure" the delinquent. Nevertheless, when relating the particular delinquencies and crimes of their probationers, the same persons often made comments like, "Man, it took guts to do that," or "Boy, what a sharp operator that guy is!" In these instances, one could sense the vicarious identification with the delinquent which made work with him difficult. The officers' contacts with their probationers' parents, some of whom were indifferent, apathetic, or delinquent themselves, occasioned comments like, "It's that kid's old man and old lady that need the beating," or "This kid's folks don't even know he's alive." A few stated that the attitude of their probationers' parents sometimes reminded them of experiences with their own parents.

As the consultation became helpful to a few officers, more of them wanted to present their cases to me. Later, the supervisors began to attend and finally they began to plan the conferences so they could be present when their staff discussed cases.

HUMAN FEARS

In consultation, as I began to pick up the unspoken fear that a few officers had of their probationers, I described the kinds of feelings I knew these adolescents produced in people. Sometimes I related an experience of mine where I had been forced to recognize and admit my own fear. For example, one day when I was in the military service a psychotic paratrooper stormed into my office on the ward and demanded the morphine he'd had at other hospitals. My corpsmen stood around terrified and I could not hide my own fear in the face of this huge, menacing soldier. I knew he'd been riding roughshod over the nurses and corpsmen, all of whom were afraid of him. Despite my fear I knew I had to take a stand. I told him that I was "scared as hell" of him and that I knew he could "tear me apart" but that, no matter what he did, as a physician I could not give him a drug I felt was dangerous to him when I knew he needed other medication. He glared at me malevolently for what seemed many minutes and I tried to keep my shaking head steady to meet his gaze. Slowly he lowered his eyes and asked, "Well, what do you think would help me?" I prescribed a sedative, which he took, and that was the turning point on the ward. Subsequently, he became fairly cooperative, took medication, and seemed more relaxed.

My purpose in telling this and other anecdotes was to help the officers feel that, by admitting and expressing their fears of their probationers, they might be less burdened by them and eventually might find a way of dealing with them through close attention to the tasks confronting the officer when dealing with such delinquent youth.

The unconscious factors which led to such fears and desires to appease their probationers were not discussed. Instead, we began to talk about what kinds of experiences these youngsters must have had to bring them to delinquency. I especially pointed out how parents who were unconcerned or who behaved erratically sometimes ignored or even encouraged their child's predelinquent acts if these acts could relieve them of the responsibility of giving personal attention to the child. I used the experiences recounted by the officers to show how the tendency to ignore signs or hunches about violation of probation, along with lack of vigilance and firmness in playing these hunches, could make it appear that they did not value the delinquent (just as fear and indifference had produced the same effect in the parent-child relationship) and could encourage repetition or continuation of the child's delinquent behavior pattern.

Some children use delinquent behavior as a means of compelling adults to behave in an authoritative and concerned way toward them. In my own experience, an adult who fails to understand or recognize signs of impending destructive or antisocial behavior is himself "delinquent." The adult's failure to act promptly and firmly once he is aware of such signs -- because he vainly hopes that nothing more will occur -- usually results in the execution of the dreaded acts. One time in my own home, for example, I made the mistake of not putting down a book in which I was absorbed, getting up from my chair, and putting a stop immediately to some potentially destructive behavior by my youngsters. A few minutes later they broke a lamp. When I reacted with vehement anger, one of them remarked: "You knew this would happen, didn't you? Why didn't you stop us before it was too late?" He was correct. Although I sensed that inevitably something would be broken, I still hoped that nothing would happen. Most officers were able to relate similar experiences from their own work.

I gave many other examples of being conned or taken in, and of trusting a youngster's insincere promises against one's better judgment, with the inevitable recurrence of trouble. To illustrate how vigilance and prompt action may help a delinquent, I told of my early experience as a child psychiatrist with a delinquent eleven-year-old who was in the hospital. This youngster was so sly and clever that he could maneuver other children into stealing or violence without putting himself in a position to be caught. Whenever he was accused, his wide-eyed innocence would enrage the staff. One day we decided with the nursing staff that we'd hold him responsible for every antisocial act on the ward; no matter who the culprit was, we'd isolate this eleven-year-old or take away his privileges. We frankly admitted that this policy might be unfair to him, but because we were convinced this would be helpful to him we were prepared to take the risks. After a few days of using this technique for every disturbance on the ward, this smooth-talking, hard, self-assured youngster became jumpy and anxious; he pleaded with others to maintain order, and for the first time participated eagerly in all the ward chores instead of bossing the other youngsters. As his usual methods of dealing with people and of evading the consequences of his actions no longer served him, he also became more amenable to psychotherapy and began to improve.

When delinquent youngsters and their parents meet (perhaps for the first time) an adult whose firmness in dealing with irregularities and falsehoods is consistent and continuous, they are usually compelled to behave somewhat differently.

Thus, the officers and I discussed how the dynamic principles of authoritative, but nonauthoritarian and nonretaliatory, behavior will alter delinquent character structure. These discussions seemed to help them see their tasks in a somewhat different and clearer light and do their jobs more effectively with less stress.

UNDERSTANDING SEXUAL MISBEHAVIOR

Women officers whose charges were usually sexually promiscuous as well as antisocial also were helped. A few of them were, overtly, coldly disapproving of the girls' sexual behavior; unconsciously, they envied them. The envy was evidenced by angry, hostile comments about the girls' sexual freedom and the lack of responsibility for the children resulting from their promiscuous relationships. Eventually it became clear that the officers' covert hostility was alienating the girls, who had used sex as a means of feeling emotionally close to and wanted by someone. Thus, the officers were unable to establish the type of relationship that could sustain the girls in school and jobs. In several instances, officers who were overtly solicitous with these girls were not particularly helpful to them. It became evident in the course of discussion of these cases that the solicitude -- i.e., the "you poor dear" attitude -- was also hostile and deprecating and indicated that the officer felt superior to the girl. The solicitude also seemed to be another way of denying the fact that such sexual impulses and behavior were human and part of the officer's emotional experience. The probationers spotted the "phoniness" and gave these particular officers an especially bad time.

The officers found it helpful to discuss possible reasons for the girls' sexual acting out and for their brittle "I couldn't care less" attitudes. Using various illustrations, we repeatedly discussed how difficult it was to feel friendly, interested, and helpful in the face of these girls' challenges, defiance, and indifference. While we never talked about the officers' unconscious envy of the girls' acting out of sexual impulses, we did talk about the experiences of persons in other fields who have to deal with disturbing sexual behavior. Our culture, our upbringing, and our resulting sexual attitudes make it difficult for us to feel easy about impulsive and overt sexual behavior. The fact that sexual activity is often used to express other feelings, desires, and needs is therefore difficult for us to understand. When underlying feelings are misunderstood, the offensive behavior is not dealt with clearly. After a while, several of the officers began to talk about their probationers with more understanding and their relationship with the girls changed markedly. One of the supervisors seemed to find these discussions especially useful and was subsequently able to help her own workers with many of their problems.

ATTITUDES TOWARD PARENTS

Some of the officers in the protective and adoptive services division were especially handicapped by their anger toward and resentment of the neglectful, indifferent, helpless parents, who -- as it became clear from their comments -- represented parental

figures out of their own past. After consultation, several were
able to find strengths in some of the parents. They were also
able to understand the difficulties and dilemmas of foster and adoptive parents of difficult youngsters. When we began to explore
what made parents behave as they did, how deprivations during
the parents' own childhood affected their capacities, this group of
officers seemed to feel less anger toward the parents they worked
with. I described the experience that other child psychiatrists
and I have had of overidentifying with the child until we were able
to learn, from direct work with the troubled parents, that they
were not the monsters we judged them to be from our work with
the child alone. As we gathered data on some of the serious deprivations suffered by the parents -- deprivations which made it
difficult and sometimes impossible for them to give very much to
a child -- the officers seemed to understand the parents' problems
more clearly.

RESULTS OF CONSULTATION

Consultation once or twice a month for several years helped a number of probation officers with some of the most difficult problems
imposed by their job. Their increased firmness, vigilance, and
promptness of action seemed to make the total job easier. Several
workers reported that, through the insights gained in consultation,
they were able to use the probationers' reactions to their attentive
vigilance as a means of assessing and then selecting those who
might benefit most from more intensive work. Increased efforts
with these youngsters began to pay off.

Supervisors who participated in consultation sessions became
aware of those attitudes and methods used by the consultant which
seemed most helpful to the staff. They began to apply these methods, with gratifying results.

As a consequence of the workers' and supervisors' experiences,
the chief probation officer began to realize the possible value of
consultation and started telling me of various administrative concerns, his problems with several supervisors in the agency, and
his relations with the juvenile court judge. He then went on to review carefully the job of the supervisors and subsequently decided
that requiring them to carry a heavy caseload of probationers in
addition to supervising staff was unrealistic. The judge, who had
made increasingly favorable comments about the work of the department, began to listen more carefully to the chief probation

officer's requests for additional staff to do a better and more thorough job and gave more active support to the requested budgetary increases. Subsequently, the Board of Supervisors granted an increase which made possible the hiring of more probation officers.

In analyzing with the chief probation officer the part that consultation played in bringing about this long desired and frequently requested budgetary increase, we clarified several important developments.

First, as the probation officers were helped to work more thoroughly and efficiently they could begin to assess how much of their time was required to do an effective job. They and their supervisors could then estimate the caseload size which permitted such thorough work -- not in terms of ideals set up by the probation authorities but in terms of actual experience. Once the probation officers could keep up with their load, they could present the true dimensions of the problem to the judge and the County Board of Supervisors.

Second, just as teachers are burdened with certain unrealistic expectations -- that they must love all children, that as surrogate parents they must make up for the lack of love or character attributes not provided by the actual parents -- so are workers in juvenile probation departments. In our culture, parents and their substitutes decry, abhor, and deal harshly with violence, antisocial behavior, defiance of authority, sexual misbehavior, etc. Yet, we are educated, by magazines, movies, and television, to admire, envy, and applaud such acts. The father who preaches obedience to law and respect for authority may be sadistically cruel in punishing his child. The mother who teaches virtue, chastity, and purity may avidly and continually be gossiping about the sexual behavior of her neighbors. This division of feeling, both conscious and unconscious, complicates the job of the probation officer and may lead him to be excessively harsh in order to defend himself against such envy of or identification with the probationer's behavior or to be excessively placating and ineffectual because of the fears and anxiety presented by these ambivalent feelings.

It is in reducing the general strains and burdens imposed by these conflicts that the mental health consultant in a probation department finds his reward and satisfaction.

SUMMARY

Juvenile probation officers are faced with rather specific problems which stem from the authoritative nature of their work. They find that in working with angry, defiant delinquents, sexually misbehaving young people, and their often indifferent and disturbed parents, the fears, anxieties, and hostilities common to all human beings are highlighted and aggravated. They find, too, that the problems these young people present impinge upon the specific experiences of the workers' own past.

Mental health consultation may be helpful in reducing the tensions of the officers by helping them function more effectively as they begin to understand how to deal differently with the job's specific problems and anxieties. They then can more accurately assess the effectiveness of their work, their goals, and how they might begin to achieve these goals.

Reprinted by permission from <u>Crime and Delinquency</u>, 10:67-73, 1964.

SECTION FIVE:

LEARNING: THE THERAPEUTIC TOOL IN A SCHOOL ANTI-DELINQUENCY PROJECT

Introduction

In the last several decades the increase in antisocial, delinquent behavior in students with both deprived and well-to-do backgrounds has concerned educators everywhere. Schools have dealt with their delinquent students in a variety of ways over the years.

San Francisco developed a pilot project to explore the effectiveness of educative methods in helping the most seriously delinquent youngsters. The hope was that such efforts, coupled with special help to youngster and parents by mental health professionals, would reduce delinquent behavior in the schools.

The following papers include work of some persons not on the staff of the Langley Porter Children's Service. However, we feel that insights from the Children's Service and its theoretical framework have contributed in a major way to the thinking and functioning of the psychiatric consultant who was a member of the project staff. Each paper describes the efforts of a staff member to accomplish his particular task as a member of the special team assigned to this project.

The effectiveness of this project and others that followed it is reflected in recent legislation in California to help schools finance programs for educationally deprived and handicapped children.

Shorter versions of the papers in this section appeared in the California Journal of Secondary Education, 35:175-202, 1960. Permission has been obtained from the California Association of Secondary School Administrators to include these articles in this volume.

THE HISTORY OF
SAN FRANCISCO SPECIAL REMEDIAL CLASSES

Alice C. Henry, M.A.

In all parts of the country today public education is being studied,
its methods are being questioned, and its product evaluated. One
of the knottiest problems that educators face is what to do with the
non-conformers in the classroom, those who break the rules or
are delinquent. It is not that this is a new problem; teachers have
always been concerned about discipline and the educational use of
authority. What gives this topic a certain urgency today is that
just at a time when new learning in the fields of psychiatry and
psychology is beginning to suggest ways in which such boys and
girls can be handled constructively in the classroom, educators
are being pushed to eliminate these misfits from school. The following papers describe the attempt of one school department to use
the combined efforts of educators and child guidance specialists to
work with anti-social, delinquent adolescents in school.

Like many other school systems, San Francisco has had a long
history of efforts to provide for this type of child. For a quarter
of a century it operated a 24-hour school for delinquent boys, the
Jesse W. Lillienthal School, which closed in 1929, and a similar
day school, the Ethan Allen School, which closed in 1932. In 1941
it established the Child Guidance Services, which provided a small
number of school social workers and psychologists to work with
the classroom teachers and with problem pupils and their families.

The program we will describe began in October, 1953, when one
of the commissioners of the Board of Education proposed that special disciplinary classes for high school boys be established in
order to relieve the regular teachers from the disruptions caused
by their misbehavior. A year's discussion of this proposal resulted in a counter-suggestion; namely, that a pilot program be established, with classes for boys and girls in an elementary, a junior,

and a senior high school, and that the classes be provided with specially selected teachers and the services of a social worker, a psychologist, and a consultant psychiatrist from the department's Child Guidance Services.

Administrative regulations were set up to govern admission to the classes. Only boys and girls who showed severe disciplinary problems were to be considered for placement; prior acceptance of the program by pupil and parents was to be secured; class size was limited to fifteen at any given time. In the elementary school youngsters were to attend the special class for the full day; in the secondary schools they were assigned for academic subjects for from one to four periods out of a six-period day; during the remainder of the day they were to attend regular classes. The teachers were recruited from the school department staff at large, on the basis of expressed interest in working with this type of boy and girl and demonstrated competence in teaching; the Child Guidance Services staff members were detached on leave of absence from their regular jobs and assigned to work with the three classes.

The three classes went into operation in February 1955 and continued, essentially as planned, until June 1958, when the special project was ended. The major consideration that led to the discontinuance of the classes was the cost of the program, particularly if it were to be expanded into other schools whose student bodies also included large numbers of boys and girls with similar problems. All programs such as this are confronted with the task of justifying to the public the wisdom of spending large sums of money on today's misfits when no startling "cures" can be demonstrated immediately and when few people are willing to look ahead and consider what society has been saved by helping these youngsters to become more responsible adults. The years of childhood sometimes seem very long to youth itself, to its parents and its teachers; but boys and girls do grow up and become the adults of tomorrow. Projects such as this one must be sold to communities as good investments in view of the dividends that come when these young people are helped to become better citizens.

Today, with increasing attention being given to the social and economic problems faced by young people who are dropped from school before graduation, state and federal agencies have expressed interest in similar programs and are beginning to provide financial aid to local districts.

In all three classes the general approach was similar; the papers that follow will describe the operation of the senior high school class. Perhaps the most important factor in whatever success the project had was the close collaboration between the school staff and the workers from the Child Guidance Services staff. A few words about the background of each may serve as an introduction to their own stories.

Mrs. Lena O'Neill had been dean of girls at this high school for many years; she was highly respected by students and faculty alike. She was acutely aware of the problems faced by boys and girls in her community and welcomed the establishment of this class as an opportunity to provide more service to these students and a chance for her to work more closely with Child Guidance Services staff.

Like Mrs. O'Neill, Mrs. Clara Royston, the public health nurse assigned full-time to the school, was an old-timer in the school. She had a long-established working relationship with the dean of girls and was sensitive to the problems faced by both boys and girls. She had used previously the services of the Child Guidance Services and had also worked with psychologists and psychiatrists from the San Francisco Department of Public Health.

The teacher, John Ott, came to the project class from the city's Continuation High School. He had served previously overseas with the U. S. Navy and had worked as a carpenter. His interest in teaching such a class as this arose in part from his experience in teaching some of the under-privileged youngsters at Continuation High School. This project offered him his first experience in working with social worker, psychologist, and psychiatrist.

The Child Guidance Services staff members had the advantage of working together for many years. Mrs. Florence Hagee, a senior social worker on the staff, had worked in schools at every level, had supervised beginning staff members, and volunteered with enthusiasm for this job. When for administrative reasons she had to leave the project after a year and a half, she continued to serve as a liaison person with the central office staff and her experience continued to be an integrative factor in the project.

Miss Marjorie Kuhl, the social worker who replaced Mrs. Hagee, also brought with her years of experience, and the change of workers fortunately caused little disruption. Her enthusiasm for the opportunity to work closely with students in one school led her to decide to stay on at this high school after the class was discontinued.

Mr. Vard Kazanjian had been a psychologist on the staff for two and a half years before the class began. In his work at the Child Guidance Services he had consulted with staff at the elementary, junior, and senior high school level and was competent in administering psychological tests for diagnostic purposes. His forthright attitudes contributed to his working well with the social workers and psychiatrists on the staff.

The psychiatric consultant for this class was Dr. Irving Berlin, who had been one of the Child Guidance Services consultants since 1951. Dr. Berlin is also Associate Clinical Professor of Psychiatry at the University of California School of Medicine and Training Coordinator for the Children's Service of the Langley Porter Neuropsychiatric Institute of the California State Department of Mental Hygiene. His conviction about the values of close collaboration between significant adults who are engaged in the effort of helping youngsters to learn was a source of great support to the members of the team as the project developed.

The papers have been planned so that each person describes some part of the program from his point of view. It is our hope that the reader will be able to gain some of the flavor of the class and in addition appreciate some of the values--and the problems--of the team approach.

THE DEAN'S REPORT ON THE SPECIAL CLASS
IN SENIOR HIGH SCHOOL

Lena O'Neill, M.A.

During my years as a dean of girls, questions that remained un-
answered were: What does one do with students who fail to adjust
to general school environment? How does one find time, as a dean
or counselor, to give these emotionally disturbed students status,
security, and understanding within the school program? In 1954,
when our school was chosen for the organization on an experimental basis of the special remedial class, I felt that the needs of
emotionally disturbed boys and girls might, at long last, be met
within the framework of the school society. In such a school setting their behavior might be more competently observed, understood, and worked with.

The news of the selection of this high school for the new class
stimulated questions from the faculty such as, "Why do we have to
be the school to deal with these delinquents?" "Won't this give us
an even worse name among the other high schools in the city?"
"Why can't we take care of our own discipline problems?" "Won't
we be required to give endless reports on these selected students?"
"Don't we have enough clerical work to do?" "Why must there be
a special team for the project?" "If these students can't adjust or
won't adjust wouldn't it be a service to the school to just expel
them?"

There was an air of hostility and derision towards the class before
it was organized. Faculty members who were excellent teachers
and usually were receptive to new ideas were manifestly angry
about the project. Students also asked questions, "Do you have to
be crazy or delinquent to get into that class?" "Will it be a Blackboard Jungle?" Such attitudes delayed cooperation and understanding and much time had to be spent in explanation and clarification
for each student and each teacher he or she had. Some of the ad-

ministrators also did not believe in the philosophy underlying the objectives of the project, and their unexpressed misgivings were communicated to the faculty. Had there been more preparation of administrators and faculty perhaps some of the troubles might have been avoided or at least the purposes underlying the class could have been clarified.

Newspaper publicity and teachers' questionnaires also had aroused considerable comment, rumors, debates, and some frank criticism about this kind of help for this select group of students. Some administrators and teachers seemed apprehensive about their own educational qualifications for participation directly or indirectly in this type of school service and were anxious not to be drafted for the project. Administrators were wary about having a "school within a school." They deplored the lack of precedents and guidelines that could be called upon in organizing this unique project. There was concern about the time and teacher personnel required to fit the project into the over-all school program.

The first few weeks after the class started I found myself asking questions quite different from those I asked when I was literally pleading for help for those "poor disturbed students." I thought, "Why am I being so overworked, with endless conferences, meetings, and debates when I am already swamped with the problems of 900 other girls. Why do I feel so guilty, so tense and baffled, even frustrated, by suggestions for this special kind of education and therapy--in marked contrast to my response to the more direct and, of necessity, on-the-spot decisions demanded by most cases coming before me?" When I squarely faced the issues involved in the treatment of these students, my own attitudes and reactions were clarified and I could accept these facts: that the special class would give no immediate evidence of its worth; that it would take weeks, even months, before changes might become noticeable in the lives of these students; that the other administrators and the faculty had to be, shall we say, oriented to live with these phases of the program.

The first few weeks after the special class was organized, problems appeared that called for administrative support and understanding. Mr. Ott, the teacher, became the target of ill-timed criticism, since he was under great pressure in starting the program. When he was the target of what appeared to be good-humored jokes about "his delinquents," the veiled barbs made his life more difficult. The administration, too, complicated things for the teacher by their lack of united support. In fact, as time went on, only one administrative person was closely tied to all phases of the experiment during its entire operation. Another of the administrators could participate only occasionally in the project, since he was assigned to other school activities. However, in spite of some early reservations he loyally supported the experiment. The third administrator was not wholeheartedly in accord with the plans or set-up of the class. His rather negative attitude acted as a deterrent to a fuller development of resources that would have strengthened the work of Mr. Ott in the classroom. Mr. Ott's position was unusual in relation to the regular school program because he was teaching students of varying abilities on different grade levels, all in the same classroom from two to four periods per day. Since the unorthodox and difficult behavior of these students had been the basis for their selection for the class, his role as teacher demanded some unorthodox teaching techniques, originality, and infinite patience. He needed from the administration encouragement, constructive criticism, and a feeling of support and freedom to experiment in this unusual classroom situation. Unfortunately, most of the time, as far as administration was concerned, he had to "go it alone" and often it was rough going. Problems continued until Mr. Ott, with the help of the Child Guidance Services staff and Dr. Berlin, was able to evolve his own workable classroom techniques and to come to terms with his role as teacher, and not as parent, psychiatrist, or social worker.

During those first weeks the students in the class were even greater problems to the deans and to their own teachers. They were aggressive in the classroom and in the halls; their impudent and defiant behavior was expressed in their attitudes, sometimes put into words, "we are different." As the weeks went by Mr. Ott slowly evolved his role of teacher and he gained, step by step, a grudging respect and admiration from many members of the faculty. The project, after its rocky launching, finally settled down and was accepted in the school. As each member of the project learned and evolved his role as part of a team and in turn was accepted by each member of the team, then and only then was there the concerted action, and mutual respect necessary to carry on such a program. This phase of team work and mutual understanding seemed to usher in improved behavior of the students, who hitherto had often felt trapped and hostile to even the minimum standards set for them.

As we recall some of the members of the special class we tend to be selective, using our best examples for the record. However, there were some who did not graduate, but who we feel were helped by the program. Among these was Rose, a fifteen-year-old who was blatantly rebellious, foul-mouthed, a member of a gang who defiantly rode a motorcycle around the school grounds. She was unhappy at home, but played the mother there, loving, guiding, and admonishing the younger children. Her behavior was so disturbing in school that she was about to be excluded. The class was her last chance. Her improved behavior kept in step with her increased ability to learn and was evident to all. After a year she left to be married. She often returns to visit us.

Carmen, a member of a delinquent gang, was nervous, apathetic, sickly, indifferent, and defiant in class. She was a failure in most school subjects, and was unable to talk with anyone about her problems. In the special class she had her first success in passing to another grade. She also found out that some adults could be trusted and were concerned with her. She was spurred on to find her first summer job, then came an offer of a full-time job by the same employer, which we advised her to accept.

There were some students who failed to adjust as members of the class and who voluntarily left school, or were requested to do so.

However, to illustrate the potential for adjustment of some of these disturbed students the example of Tina might be cited. When Tina's record was sent from junior high school we were alerted by the notation that she was a fighter and well-versed in foul language and belligerent behavior. I met Tina during a visit to my office about an absence. She was the last one on the list for that period and her friendly, courteous, and frank manner intrigued me and was in contrast to the description of her behavior in her former school. It seemed a good time to get acquainted. A few questions led this pretty oriental girl to chat with me about her family. Just before she left, her conversation took this turn. She said, "If I don't like a teacher or dean I won't do anything for them and I won't ever like them, and I won't do any work." But, she added, "I like you." I laughingly replied, "How do you know you do? You have just met me." She gave some of her reasons, calculated to win friends and influence people. We talked a while longer and the bell rang for lunch period. Tina went over to the window, looked out toward the street, turned around, faced me and said, "There

is something I want to tell you that you should know about me."
"What?" I said. She replied, "I fight anyone I don't like, kids who
hurt me or my friends, especially if my friends are smaller."
And so the gauntlet was laid down. I saw her occasionally during
the next two or three weeks.

Then Tina was really in trouble in school and outside of school.
She was mixed up with a neighborhood gang who were always fighting, and truant. A series of incidents brought her into the Juvenile Court; and the Probation Officer asked us to put her in the
special class for several periods a day, which we were about to do
anyway since she had been annoying teachers and disrupting their
classes by using every disturbing attention-getting device known to
teenagers.

As a result of staff conferences and suggestions from the psychiatrist, definite limits were set and communicated to Tina as to what
she could and could not do in school. I saw her frequently, often
on a voluntary basis, and often because she was sent to me by patient, but exasperated teachers. It was difficult to set limits for
Tina, and at the same time to give her a feeling of friendship and
understanding. This was a period of learning for me too. Sometimes she literally blew up when she was crossed, rending the air
with vituperation against all authority. To complicate matters,
her mother worked against us. She aided Tina by writing flimsy
excuses for absences from school and shielding and protecting her
in the face of clear misbehavior.

Following discussion with Dr. Berlin we finally helped the mother
to understand the importance of her cooperation in supporting the
limits that the school had set for Tina. Thus we began to be notified about dental appointments, etc. Each such appointment was
made for a stated time and checked upon by the mother and me.
I was on the telephone constantly with Tina's mother, learning the
exact and truthful reasons for each absence. This procedure paid
off handsomely, as Tina's mother began to assume some of her
parental responsibilities. Tina's attendance improved, but it was
slow going, involving patience and "playing it by ear."

Then Tina tried a new trick, feigning illness in order to get out of
class or to go home. She had a new ache or pain daily. When
these efforts were handled firmly and sympathetically by the school
nurse, Tina oddly enough became less truculent. She began to

listen, to ask me for opinions and advice, mainly on clothes, but opinions nevertheless. She confided in me one day how much she liked Mr. Ott, that he was "just wonderful." Fine, I thought, we are really making progress. She appeared in my office, that same afternoon, in a rage. No actress could have been more dramatic, telling me how she hated Mr. Ott. He, too, had held to the advice of setting definite limits for Tina in the classroom. Tina took this as a personal affront and felt outraged that Mr. Ott, who she thought was her friend, had let her down. She said to me, "I don't trust anyone--no one." When her anger subsided she said quietly, "Yes, I do, you"--a pause, then in a whisper, "and Mr. Ott."

Another intelligence test was given, since Tina's grades were so poor. The results showed her to be well above average in intelligence and she was pleased when we discussed the results of the test with her. All during these interviews I became aware of the great conflict in Tina, a conflict between the oriental culture pattern in her home and the western culture pattern at school and on the city streets.

The next time she was in trouble her rebellion broke out in these words, "I wish I had never taken those tests. I don't want anyone to put trust in me. I don't want it, I don't want it"--and she cried, the first tears we had seen. Despite the changes, her constant demands made me wonder if I could take Tina much longer. Her quick changing moods, vacillations, her demands for attention, along with usual comment from the faculty, "Is she a mental case?" were all a strain. However, we noted continued slow progress. She was more courteous, less belligerent and the crowning touch was when she brought a friend to the social worker so that she, too, could be helped.

Then one day Tina was almost involved in a very serious fight in the girls' gym. She was accused of taking another girl's skirt. She vehemently denied this, and both girls were ready for battle, both equally matched and members of a minority group. Suddenly Tina said to the accuser, "I'm not going to get kicked out of school or go to Juvenile Court; let's go to the office and settle this." To the office they came, the girl accusing and Tina stoutly maintaining her innocence. First, I heard the accuser's story, then Tina's, and I must say that she had a good alibi and a rapid-fire rebuttal.

In spite of her protested innocence I felt sure that she was guilty.

A couple of discrepancies, her mannerisms, tended to confirm my suspicion and since I couldn't immediately prove it, I could only hold fast to my convictions that I must try to get to Tina so that she would not win one more victory as she usually did by conning an adult. It was difficult but fascinating to stand by and watch Tina wrestling with her problem in this battle of wits--of maintaining face or physically fighting her way out of her dilemma, and impudently riding over her accuser, who, in turn, doggedly kept at her. Then I interviewed each girl separately. Tina was given a bill of particulars as to what would happen if the skirt was not returned, and what would happen if she fought her accuser in or out of school.

In the estimation of some, perhaps, Tina did lose face that morning, but she did get the stolen skirt back to the owner, maintaining thereby her own quixotic notions of loyalty and guilt as they may relate both to herself and to her friends. Tina's progress may not continue under the stress of her struggle for a new self. The special class may not be effective or provide sufficient support to warrant our belief in it as a suitable instrument to help Tina. However, it is more than apparent to me, as dean of girls, that in the absence of the special class Tina would in all probability have long since become just another casualty of the failure of the secondary school system to provide for these disturbed students.

Some students, as we have said, did not adjust and were transferred to Continuation School or were excluded from school. The following semester some of this group pleaded to be allowed to return and rejoin the special class. Those who were permitted to return made good and were graduated.

Progress was manifested by less disturbed and disturbing behavior and in generally better citizenship of these students. Their school work in the regular classes and in the special class improved. One cannot measure objectively the help and assistance given these boys and girls toward the solving of their personal problems and changes of attitude. However, the noted changes might serve as criteria for the judgment of improvement. The dean's and the counselor's work had been lightened considerably as far as the serious problem cases were concerned. There was a reduction of time-consuming cases that often necessitated long telephone conversations with parents, social service agencies, and the Juvenile Court. These contacts and meetings were now taken care of by other staff members of the project. At the staff meetings, student problems were given the benefit of concerted group thinking and action. Thus, the dean was able to meet a larger number of not so difficult students and to participate in other school activities rather than spending most of her time with the most disturbed students. The assistance given by Dr. Berlin and the other staff members on special class problems could be used to advantage in the not so serious behavior problems that reached the desk of the dean. The attendance of faculty members at some of the staff conferences also was a time-saver for the dean, as well as proving advantageous in helping the teachers to a better understanding of some of the methods used with the most difficult students.

Our objective in organizing the class was to try to find ways of helping disturbed students to begin to learn and to take advantage of the school environment. It was hoped that, in this special class, teaching techniques and appropriate subject area materials such as textbooks and visual aids might be developed that would be appropriate for teaching disturbed students with little academic achievement. Mr. Ott presented some interesting data on the educational needs of these students. He described the methods that had proved effective for him and those sometimes cherished methods that he had to discard as ineffective. As dean I was increasingly concerned with the number of drop-outs not only in our high school but in the schools across the nation. As they came to my office to be checked out I was aware of the sameness of the answers to my question, "Why are you leaving high school?" The answers may be summarized, "I am failing again this semester and I am already way behind most of my friends." It seemed important to me as an educator that these students should be given a selective and special type of assistance to succeed within the limits of their abilities in school subjects and to receive competent help with problems that often prevented them from learning. This class was perhaps a step in the right direction, but much more needs to be done if the public senior high school is to meet the varied needs of all of its students and assume its part in the development of useful citizens.

The faculty also was assisted by the removal of these students from classrooms where their presence had been disturbing and disruptive to the learning process of others. The faculty finally not only accepted the class but often suggested candidates.

The class proved also that disturbed students need more of this specialized help than can be given in a school program for average students. When they were removed from the regular classes (where they had been non-conformists) to a special class, a gradual change was noted. This was because in the minds of these students there was a step-by-step breaking down of prejudice toward school, teachers, a fixed routine, parents, and other objects of hostility.

As an administrator I found this project extremely helpful in an area where little or no research or experimentation had been done. This pilot study showed that students who were severe behavior problems could be assisted within the general framework of the school program. Also, the student who was a potential "drop-out" might be motivated to complete high school requirements. That the State of California and other communities in other states have enacted legislation to meet this problem is indeed encouraging.

In conclusion, I should like to leave this thought in the form of a question. In large high schools in most cities there are special classes for the mentally retarded, the slow learners, the non-readers, the physically handicapped. Why, then, should not our educational philosophy include a similar organizational apparatus for the emotionally disturbed students?

THE SOCIAL WORKER: CONSULTANT ON THE FIRING LINE

Florence Hagee, M.S.W.

The psychologist and the social worker were assigned from the
Child Guidance Services to the project staff two weeks before the
class was to start, to help in its organization. Though we could
not foresee just how we were to function we had one objective
clearly in mind, to encourage collaborative thinking and planning
of operations so that the efforts of all members of the staff would
be coordinated. No one had been made head of this project. The
Superintendent, who had outlined the project, had made it directly
responsible to him, but he never met with the staff. With time
pressing, we had to evolve ways of working together and plan program and procedures to get the class started.

From the beginning I, as social worker, took major responsibility
for calling staff meetings, planning agenda, and setting up consultation schedules. Though high school administrators are busy
people and meetings were hard to arrange, we met frequently during the first two weeks and throughout the first term. Much time
in early meetings was spent in guessing and varied second guessing as to what the Superintendent wanted. Eventually we came to
interpretations and decisions on which we could all agree. Selection of students was the first task. There were diverse opinions
about the criteria for selection. Understandably, the deans wanted
to get help for and relief from the most troublesome of their students. The teacher concurred with their choices, for he wanted
to save these disturbing young delinquents from being lost in Continuation School or as drop-outs. The psychologist and I considered prognosis and wanted to choose those who showed some promise of being able to profit from the help available to them. On this
basis we opposed, unsuccessfully, inclusion of anti-social chronic
truants.

When the spring term started, two weeks after we had first met as
a staff, we had selected eighteen students for the class. Choice

was based on all the information gathered from cumulative folders, attendance records, health, grade, and test records and knowledge of the students from their counselors, teachers, the public health nurse, and the deans. Selection was made in meetings of the total project staff, with the final responsibility resting with the deans.

The composition of the group selected reflects the initial resolution of our concerns and differences about criteria. Though far more boys than girls had been proposed, nine of the eighteen chosen were girls. All of the races and nationality groups in the school were represented. All eighteen were chronic discipline and/or attendance problems. Twelve of the eighteen were past or present wards of the court. All were academically retarded, most of them grossly so. Disrupted home backgrounds were the rule. Only two lived with both natural parents. Eight lived with their mothers but with no man in the home. Seven had stepfathers, one a stepmother. As a group, the eighteen could be described as untrusting, angry, rebellious with adults, uncertain, and unsatisfied in their peer relationships.

During the three and a half years of the project, criteria for selecting replacements for the class changed as the result of experience. The proportion of chronic truants dropped markedly and so did the number of grossly delinquent boys, those apt to spend months at the Youth Guidance Center. A few less disruptive students were scheduled to balance the class, youngsters whose symptoms were more self-destructive than socially disruptive.

PREPARATORY WORK WITH STUDENTS AND PARENTS
As soon as selection of students was completed and the deans had secured the consent of students and parents for placement in the project program, the psychologist and I began interviewing students and parents. A requirement for admission set up by the Superintendent was that students and their parents agree to work with the social worker and psychologist toward resolving whatever social or emotional problems were interfering with the students' learning. It took us all the first term to do the initial interviewing in the three schools. Unrealistically, we had anticipated that by the end of the term we would have completed a thorough evaluation of each student, including psychological evaluations and a series of parent interviews. By term's end we were suffering from deflated expectations.

UNREALISTIC EXPECTATIONS

We were not the only ones disappointed by results of that first term of work. The Superintendent and the administrators had thought that for some students a few weeks of remedial help might enable them to straighten out their behavior and learning disturbances enough so that they could be scheduled back into regular classes. There were no miracle cures. The deans had hoped the class would relieve them of work with this group of persistent trouble-makers. Instead, they had been called on more often to set or enforce limits and to talk with students or parents. In addition, they had had to give time for countless scheduled or impromptu staff meetings to discuss problems or policies. The teacher, despite his unstinting efforts, had not been able to hold all of the students in school. A number had been lost to the Juvenile Court or to the Youth Authority, or had been transferred to Continuation School. Finally, in this first term there had been no marked improvement in the group's academic achievement.

As a team we were deeply involved in our mutual challenging task, but felt frustrated because of the lack of demonstrable accomplishment, and at times critical of ourselves or others. The psychologist and I, for instance, felt pressure from ourselves and from the rest of the staff to give more direct service to these adolescents. The teacher and administrators had expected that all of the students would be "in psychiatric treatment," and now felt that change for the better hinged upon our offering treatment.

The second term, in response to this wish for a quick change in the attitudes and behavior of the class members, the psychologist and I began therapy groups, he with the boys and I with the girls. We did not expect to, nor did we, work the hoped-for miracles.

GROUP THERAPY

There were, however, a number of constructive outgrowths of the group therapy. One of these was improved relationships among the staff. Through shared understanding of first-hand experience with these youngsters, the whole staff came to understand them in broader dimensions. The collaborative work with the rest of the staff entailed by these groups resulted in our teamwork becoming more effective. As a result of closer teamwork these untrusting adolescents had repeated opportunities to learn that the entire staff was concerned with them and was working together to help them.

One of the jobs of the social worker and the psychologist was to consult with the class teacher regularly, and with other members of the staff. I had this responsibility in the high school. To this aspect of my work, especially consultation with the key person, the teacher, I have given special consideration.

FRONT LINE CONSULTATION

I was available to the staff every day for on-the-spot consultations in addition to scheduled weekly sessions. Dr. Berlin, our consulting psychiatrist, came to us for one hour a week bringing the perspective of his uninvolvement and his trenchant understanding which we so badly needed.

I was on the front line, as it were, offering support or help in times of crisis or exhaustion, facilitating explorations of thinking and feeling in connection with difficulties, helping to bring into focus problems that were interfering with effective functioning, and culling out for discussion with Dr. Berlin those that were most pressing, or that were recurrent and unresolved.

Our staff room was a refuge for the teacher, John Ott. He came not only for weekly scheduled conferences, but daily, to share frustration, or success, or a funny story, to talk over a problem or an idea. From the first his warm interest in his students was apparent and also the fact that the incessant demands and needs exhausted him. He felt keenly with these youngsters their confusion, angers, fears, and insecurity. Soon it became apparent to me that they drained him because he felt it was up to him alone to heal their hurts, to meet their needs.

A goal became clear, to help John as I could and as he was ready for it to know that his wish was unrealizable. He had to learn that he could best serve these troubled young people by teaching them to the best of his ability. John knew that their learning difficulties resulted from life's scarring, but he was not fully aware that through the hard task of helping them learn he could aid them build the self-confidence and self-respect they so sorely needed.

FROM STUDENTS' PROBLEMS TO
PROBLEMS OF TEACHING AND LEARNING

For most of the first year John focused not on problems of teaching but on the problems of his students, their difficult life situations, distorted values, and inner stress. Over a period of many months

he shared with me his deep distress about two very troubled youngsters, the first a delinquent boy and the second an appealing, runaway girl. Finally, and it seemed to him the awareness came in a
flash, he realized his over-involvement and saw that his abortive
attempts to meet all the needs of his students had been unrealistic.

Actually, this insight had grown slowly and was an outcome both of
his frustration and of the many opportunities he had taken to talk
over with me his concern and discouragement. I had been able to
help, a little at a time, now by underscoring reality, now by bringing alternative approaches into perspective. Perhaps of most help
had been my confidence that he could find his way through the mo-
rass of over-involvement and unrealistic self-expectations.

As soon as John recognized that he had been confused in his role,
he wanted to understand his confusion and resolve it. We used our
next hour with Dr. Berlin to discuss this problem and its implications. The hour was a constructive one. Dr. Berlin moved the
discussion from role confusion to role focus. He pointed out that
teaching these disorganized youngsters can provide them with the
integrative ego-building experience of learning. By now John was
ready to hear him. Several weeks later he asked for a session
with Dr. Berlin to discuss his difficulties in teaching one particularly discouraging boy. This was his first request for help in
understanding the dynamics involved in teaching these chronic nonlearners. It was the beginning of his acceptance of his functional
responsibility and the development of a deeper respect for both its
demands of him and its value to his students.

John Ott faced a demanding and often a discouraging task, for even
at best progress was far from spectacular. During the first term
whenever he felt most frustrated, he pressed the psychologist and
me to take the members of his class into treatment. They were
mixed-up kids and needed somebody to straighten out their thinking. Therapy could change them! Or could it? He did not understand the mysterious process, which we were unable to explain
adequately. He vacillated between not wanting and wanting us to
offer therapy, between distrusting our approach and hoping we
could perform the relieving miracles. As counterpoint to these demands on us one could chart his self-distrust and his hope to be the
miracle worker.

John was caught in a dilemma. He was not as yet fully aware of his over-involvement with these teenagers, not as yet free to learn how he could be of basic help to them through patient, persistent teaching. If therapy for them were the answer, which he could neither offer nor understand, what need, then, did they have of him?

Though I offered treatment the first term to only one girl, I did talk with all the members of the class. When I began interviewing students their anxiety about this new experience triggered John's skepticism. He had been wary of me and my social work orientation from the beginning. We had not worked long together, had not as yet experienced any shared successes.

One day John dropped in to see me, obviously upset. "Florence, these kids really give me a hard time when you send for them! I know they pick on little things; they don't like the way you always take off your glasses and put them on again. But some of what they complain about has to make sense--this business of just sitting, staring at them with a smile on your face! They can't take it! I couldn't myself! You know, you really put these kids on the spot."

I listened with mixed feelings, anger that my co-worker was attacking me, a shaky feeling that perhaps I could not reach these youngsters with whom he had established rapport, and relief that his distrust, in full force, was out in the open. John was not through.

"When you send for somebody the whole class starts putting up a gripe! I honestly don't put my heart into getting them here. I tell them, 'Look, you've got to go, but you don't have to talk!'"

It was not too difficult to corral my defensive feeling and center on the job to be done.

"Look John! Much of that griping is a front. Those kids would lose face if they didn't gripe about coming to see the social worker. When they get here most of them find it helpful to talk about themselves and be listened to, even if they do come in sort of frightened or angry. Never mind the griping. As Mrs. O'Neill says: 'Just get the bodies here!' I can put up with their mistrust and anger when they get here and try to understand them. That's my job."

John seemed relieved and said in half-apology: "I wish I could feel cool and matter-of-fact about it."

I said: "Just get them here. You don't have to convince them it's a good thing. That wouldn't be easy when you're not sure it is!"

John laughed. Then I asked something of him. "How about getting Rose down here once a week the second period? Mrs. O'Neill said today she's afraid she can't keep her in school. Rose is constantly exploding, in other classes as well as yours. I've talked with her several times and I'd like to try seeing her regularly."

With no enthusiasm he agreed. "Okay. Try it if you want to. I'll get her here. Things that girl does don't make any sense to me. She's so illogical! Maybe your way will help. I don't know."

With this depressed admission that Rose stumped him I had a vivid sense of his present discouragement with these adolescents for whom he cared so much. With earnest appreciation of his effectiveness with another difficult girl, as well as of his contribution to her resistance to me, I talked about Milly.

"I've been thinking, John. I won't ask Milly to come in again. You managed to get her here today but she took you literally, didn't say a word. I can't reach her, you can. You have! That's the beauty of working together. On a difficult job like ours, what one of us can't accomplish perhaps another can; we can each do a part. I can't help Milly. You've gained her confidence. As far as we know she's never trusted anyone before, but she trusts you. And the results are showing; she's beginning to work. Her last report card showed it!"

John's depression lifted. The old enthusiasm returned. "You know, she's been turning in some darn good work in my class. She's got a good head. The kids have a lot of respect for her and they don't respect anybody much. They listen when she says something."

The following week I began to see Rose regularly.

The following term I started a therapy group with all the girls in the class. Though John had urged that we offer more treatment he was lukewarm.

"Go ahead and try it. But how do you do anything without something like a lesson plan? It's more of that sitting and staring at each other. In class we have some really productive bull sessions. The kids talk a lot about their problems, but the conversation branches off from class work. I have a topic, a starting point and I tell them what I think. I underline the moral and the religious issues in their own language. There's a plan to it and we get somewhere. You people start cold and as far as I can tell, you just sit. I don't get it. But go ahead, it's your funeral."

The therapeutic process seemed as illogical to John as Rose's impulsive behavior. His training as a teacher had stressed structure, logical progression, clearly defined goals, and he could not understand how we could be effective without them. He was intrigued, though, even occasionally said he would like to try therapy himself just to find out what it's like.

However, though John talked in terms of logic he functioned in relation to people not on an intellectualized basis but as a total person, his emotional reactions, intuition, and imagination all vigorous and alive. These were the aspects of his personality that enabled him to understand his students and earn their trust and loyalty. In his consultation with me and with Dr. Berlin he demonstrated remarkable ability to explore emotional logic, so often running counter to rational logic, to examine and sort out his own feelings when he found them interfering with a work problem. This ability and his sense of humor made it a delight to work with him, most of the time. On occasion it was rough going.

One afternoon some months after Rose had started regular sessions with me, John came in to the staff room looking tired and angry. I greeted him saying I knew Rose had been on a rampage. John turned on me accusingly: "You know, we're spoiling Rose! Every time something doesn't go well she can come running to you! What about the business of helping these kids face reality? We're spoiling her. We're not helping her grow up!"

"Spoiling her?"

"Darn right! She blew her top downstairs somewhere and came banging into my room demanding a pass to see you. And when she demands, she demands! She wouldn't tell me a word about it. I let her go but I didn't like it!...What was the trouble? She sure stayed up here long enough."

John was angry, but he was also troubled about Rose. As I sketched the interview which had been revealing and moving to me, he listened and grew thoughtful.

ESTABLISHMENT OF COLLABORATION IN CONSULTATION

In our next consultation session he talked again about not really understanding or trusting the way the psychologist and I worked, and about his discomfort in attempting to be firm about getting students to leave his class to come to us for individual or group sessions when they protested. "It may be," he suggested, "that they sense the way I feel." I agreed that they could. He looked depressed. I asked if he'd like to use our next hour with Dr. Berlin to talk about it. "I'd like it!" he said at once. "That man's phenomenal! He's always a tremendous help! He can get right to the heart of a problem and help me understand things that maybe have been troubling me for months!"

After a few minutes of talking about the help he had gotten with another nagging problem he left, looking refreshed. "You should know, John," I thought, as he left, "that at times I resent how extremely helpful you find Dr. Berlin. I understand your explosion about Rose." It might have been helpful had I said it aloud, then or months before. At least I had said it to myself and had utilized my understanding.

Despite my twinge of jealousy, the thought of John's opening up this recurring problem with Dr. Berlin refreshed me, too. I was weary from his pounding at me with it and from corraling my impulses to defend myself. I, too, needed Dr. Berlin's perspective and help.

It usually happened that when any staff member brought a problem to Dr. Berlin it was more clearly stated and better understood than when it had been opened up with me. So it was this time.

INTEGRATION OF ONGOING AND CRISIS CONSULTATION

In the consultation hour John described his dilemma vividly. Dr. Berlin, who never rushes in with interpretations, waited, respectfully. Then John said, with distress, that he abhorred the idea but that maybe, without being aware of it, he had been feeling competitive with the social worker and psychologist, jealous of our working with his kids. Dr. Berlin listened comfortably, as to a familiar story. He said he thought it quite understandable that at times

John would feel overwhelmed by problems the class presented and want others to help, or even to take over, yet at other times would be so engrossed with the satisfactions of his work that he would. want to succeed alone, without having to share credit for the results. This, he said, was a common phenomenon with anyone tackling such a difficult job.

As Dr. Berlin talked, the concept of competitiveness and jealousy as abhorrent faded. No one spoke of how disruptive these can be in collaborative work when they are not recognized and controlled. There was no need to do so; John had presented the problem because it was disruptive.

John was not the only one who profited from this consultation hour. I was able to evaluate, as I listened through the hour and remembered the preludes to it, the process of collaborative consultation in which Dr. Berlin and I were engaged with the teacher and the staff. I knew that I felt competitive with Dr. Berlin at times and that such feelings need not and had not been disruptive. I welcomed and gained perspective from his skillful and helpful crystallization of the problem that John had presented to him. And I found satisfaction in knowing that I had helped John, bit by bit, lay the groundwork for this productive hour. Because divisive feelings had not interfered with the work of the two consultants, the consultee had been able to utilize the help of both, each in its own place and time, for growth in understanding. Our joint efforts had proved helpful to an extent that perhaps neither of us could have achieved alone.

After this consultation hour John's competitive feelings, recognized and accepted, ceased to get in the way of our collaborative work. The class members found they could no longer play one member of the staff against another and their trust in us grew. John was able to accept the psychologist's and my contributions as therapists to his students and to turn his attention more intensively to his difficult job of helping them learn. With the strain gone in relation to me, he was free to make more purposeful and effective use of his consultation time with me. The resolution of his problems in collaborating, culminating in the consultation hour with Dr. Berlin, accelerated the professional growth for which he had great potential.

The intent of the special project had been that a group of specialists should work.together to further the personal and educational growth of the disturbing and academically failing adolescents selected for the special class. These young people had had little experience with adults working persistently together in their behalf. It is a tribute to the caliber of collaboration achieved by the project staff, in part as the result of consultation, that the class members, almost without exception, came to look on their special class as a niche of security in what had seemed a completely untrustworthy adult world.

MANDATORY PSYCHOTHERAPY IN A SCHOOL SETTING

Vard Kazanjian, M.A.

Before volunteering for the project I was a staff psychologist operating from the Child Guidance Services central office. In retrospect I realize it was a protected environment. In that setting, I consulted with schools. I made psychological evaluations, did individual psychotherapy with children and parents, and liaison work with community agencies. In the project schools, I did essentially the same things but both the social worker and I were housed at the school site, and we worked more frequently and intensively in consultation with school personnel. In addition, after the first six months we both did mandatory therapy with groups of youngsters but had a minimum of therapeutic contact, if any, with their parents. I also saw youngsters in individual treatment under the same conditions.

At the beginning, we found that in our work in the project schools some parents of the special class children were characteristically "hard to reach." They frequently cancelled or broke our scheduled appointments. When they could be reached, they seldom followed through on referral to a social agency or psychiatric clinic. If they took referral, they frequently broke off after several interviews. In some cases they could not be reached at all. As a staff in the schools' Child Guidance Services we had a long history of similar results with these "hard core" parents and their children. Because of these experiences we decided to experiment with seeing children regularly, with their parents' consent but usually without parental participation.

The social worker and I introduced voluntary therapy to a selected number of students of the special class. We naively felt that being in a school setting would make us more acceptable and less threatening to the students we planned to see for treatment. With but few exceptions, we found youngsters would leave the special classroom but never get to us. They would wander the halls, hide in the lavatory, cut, or leave the school premises. At one time or another, each of the adolescents had remained in class and, at a later time, explained that he had forgotten to keep his appointment. We wanted psychotherapy to be a part of the project program, but we learned that when the decision for treatment was left to the students, our efforts were continually frustrated, and we felt helpless in knowing how to deal with the problem.

During one of our many consultations with Dr. Berlin he proposed mandatory psychotherapy as a possible solution. At the time, this idea struck me as reasonable, but I felt a discomfort about it that I was unable to understand. Later, I thought that when therapy was voluntary and an acting-out adolescent broke an appointment, that was his problem. But if it was mandatory, I had to do something active about getting him to the session. Mandatory therapy made the lack of attendance my problem. Further, if I were successful in getting the student to attend, I was the one that was boxed in a room with six bitter, hostile, resentful kids. With trepidation and faltering enthusiasm I decided it was worth a try.

The dean, teacher, social worker, and I selected six boys from the special class who were to be members of my psychotherapy group. I interviewed each of the boys individually. My purpose was to gain some experience in handling the massive resistance we knew I would encounter from the boys when mandatory attendance was introduced to them. The proposal was met with pronounced opposition, more than I ever expected, but with which I slowly, although never completely, learned to work. On occasions each of the students expressed his anger and distrust of me by being late, cutting, or absenting himself from our weekly meetings. Attendance and being on time to the sessions, I slowly learned, was part of the psychotherapeutic process that needed to be worked through.

For example, the group had assembled on time and was seated except for Bill. He arrived several minutes late. He threw open the door wide and stood framed there for a moment. His right thumb was hooked in his jeweled trouser belt. He surveyed the group of five boys and me with a contemptuous sneer. Finally he jerked the door shut and sauntered over to the head of the table where a seat had been left vacant for him.

A voice from the group said half-heartedly, "You're late!"

Another voice, directed toward me: "Yeah, you turned a slip in on me."

A third said: "Hey, look at Billy-O, he really thinks he's bad."

Bill ignored the group with scornful disdain; he sat down and tilted his chair back to a comfortable position. He was in complete possession of himself and the situation. He looked at me daringly, inviting comment.

I said, "Hi, Bill, you know when you're late it makes me mad."

He replied, "Too bad!" And then, "I'm here, ain't I?"

I said: "Yeah, I'm relieved you're here, but in another way I'm not. Because I feel glad you're here, I don't want to report you to the dean, but if I don't, I'm not doing my job."

Bill said: "Yeah, if you were a right guy you'd forget about it."

The group had been listening intently, but they were becoming restless. My experience told me that some members would enjoy a blood letting.

I said: "In a way, I'd like to forget about it, but if I did I wouldn't feel right, and you'd never learn to get here on time."

Bill looked at me in a perplexed way; it appeared that he was surprised that I could tell him the way I felt and still follow through in reporting him to the dean. I sensed that he was relieved to find out that I would.

The group settled in their seats and began talking among themselves. They appeared to me relieved, although perhaps a little disappointed that the action ended there.

There were other things about Bill's behavior besides his late arrival which disturbed me. As I reflect on his entrance to that session, I remember the first thoughts and feelings he aroused in me. They went something like this: I thought, "Look at that jerk in the doorway--he's late again--in a way it's funny. He thinks he's the bad man in a second-rate western. I'd like to toss him right out on his ear. That would teach him who's running this

show." But I knew that this impulse didn't make sense. Bill out-
weighed me fifty pounds, and he was some five inches taller than
I. A reasonable respect for physical strength helped me not to act
on such feelings. Also, I slowly learned that retaliatory and revengeful words only increased the emotional and at times physical
distance between myself and group members, as did ambivalent,
vacillating indecision on my part. Over a period of time, I realized that mandatory therapy was not meant as force to be exercised by me. Gradually my punitive and rejecting actions, which
occasionally broke through, subsided, as did behavior that reflected my need to be liked. My self-imposed demand and its concomitant burden slowly disappeared. In its place I was beginning, as
best I could, to present to the group and individual members a
firm, consistent, and scrupulously honest adult model--an adult
they could come to trust and with whom they could feel relatively
free to talk over their concerns.

As part of the therapeutic process we evolved the following procedure to limit as much as possible the students' disruptive, delinquent behavior. Each time a student was late a slip was turned
in by me to the dean for his administrative action. Cuts were
similarly handled by me; in addition, I saw students individually
to explore their reasons for cutting. When a group member was
absent, I telephoned him after the day's meeting to inquire about
him and inform him that he was missed at the group meeting.
These infractions of rules were handled by me with dogged persistence and consistency. The group members soon began to recognize it was automatic, and they began to expect it.

Obviously, mandatory therapy is not a one-man job in a school
setting. The therapist needs the support of the other two key
people in such a program--the administrator and the classroom
teacher. The teacher's support and action is no less significant
than the administrator's, but I will limit my example to my need
for administrative support and action.

It was my seventh group session. The weather was unusually warm
and the group had been complaining about being indoors. They
were restless and had trouble remaining seated. Toward the end
of the hour Bill said, "Come on, let us out early."

His beseeching command was all that was needed to set off an upsurge of group maneuvers, all designed toward early release from the session.

A youngster particularly adroit at playing one adult off against the other said, "Yeah, the teacher always lets us out of class early." "Come on, I have to meet my girl for lunch." "If you let us out early this time, teach, we'll really talk next time." "Yeah, we'll let you know everything you want to hear." "Say, remember that time we were in that hot car?" "Cut it out, this joint might be bugged." "Come on, stop begging him. You know if we want to go it's up to us; he won't give us permission." "He wants us to understand why we want to leave; it's supposed to have something to do with the way you feel." "You mean to tell me you get paid for just sitting around and listening to us guys? Boy, how did you get this job anyway? You're the one that needs your head candled."

Bill, the leader of the group, got up from his seat and moved toward the door, saying, "Come on, let's blow. Let's get out of here."

"Would you try and stop us if we walked out?"

"No, but I want you to stay."

"What would you do?"

"Report the incident to the dean."

"If he knew what was going on up here do you think he'd care?"

Bill hissed, "Sure, you're a great guy, you'd make gangsters out of all of us." "Come on, let's blow!"

The group scrambled, shoved, and pushed their way out through the open door. I sat alone at the therapy table. What a spot to be in! My whole group fleeing. Man! I can't report this to the dean. He'll probably agree with the kids that I'm the one in need of help.

Help? Yeah, I do need help! I need his administrative authority!

Let's see, I'll ask him to come up for a brief period at the beginning of next week's meeting to talk with the group. As I sat there feeling defeated and unappreciated, the door opened wide and the boys came scrambling back into the room, saying, "Ah, Mr. Kazanjian, did you think we really meant it?"

The dean spoke to the group for ten minutes at the beginning of our following meeting. When he left, I spoke about my own feelings of defeat in having to call him in and attempted to work with the subsequent expressions of the group.

Although resistance to attending sessions was high in the beginning, eventually some students were eager to come. In our opinion, mandatory psychotherapy in a school setting is possible, and can be of benefit to the acting-out adolescent when there is a willingness by the adults involved in such a program to carry out their own roles as administrator, teacher, and therapist.

I have been asked many times about how successful mandatory group therapy is. Once the mandatory principle is worked out and fought through with the youngsters and staff, the process and its results are similar to most group therapy with disturbed adolescents. However, I want to emphasize that the very effort and struggle to firmly establish mandatory group therapy is in itself a therapeutic process. It is a process that when successful welds both the adolescent group and the adult group, group therapist, teacher, and dean, into more cohesive units who have lived through some very difficult times together in the service of these youngsters.

I, therefore, want to stress that the establishment of mandatory group psychotherapy signals the achievement of an important psychotherapeutic goal for the youngsters, and certainly for the staff.

WORK WITH PARENTS

Marjorie A. Kuhl, M.S.W.

When the Special Remedial Class was being planned it was agreed that the parents would be active participants in the team effort. In the initial contact with the home to obtain parental permission to place the child in the program, the dean laid the groundwork for the follow-up by the social worker. For many of these parents this was a new experience. We asked them to share directly in a process of furthering the education of their delinquent or pre-delinquent children.

In any high school age group, parents are too often ignored. In fact it is not unusual for teachers and administrators to join with an adolescent in keeping information from his parent. It is not unusual for a student to forge his parent's signature on excuses for absences. Also, it is the practice sometimes to give the student a choice of taking his punishment at school or letting his parents know when an infraction of a rule has occurred. Thus it is possible for a high school student to reach the point of being expelled without his parents knowing the many problems and infractions of rules that occurred, step by step, to lead up to the expulsion. This is particularly true when both parents work or when there is no telephone. Parents of these children rarely came to school on their own. When they were "invited" to come it was because their child was in trouble. Many came frightened and wary. With the start of the project the parents came to school because they had to; we required it. After the initial interview we kept in touch with them quite frequently, certainly when the child was in trouble, but also when things were going well, and when the child was late or absent or whenever it seemed important to involve the parents. We invited the parents to contact the school frequently. Often, though the parents remained frightened and uneasy, they soon recognized that for the first time the school had the time and the special personnel to be actively interested in their child and in them. We not only recognized some of their parental concerns, but we were also able to show an interest in some of the family problems, and to give some of them an opportunity to experience a therapeutic relationship with a school person. Our emphasis remained on helping the students to learn and on actively engaging the parents in the process.

Gary was pretty upset when I talked with him about seeing his parents.

"Why do you have to see them? They won't come in. My mother told me not to expect her to come to school the next time I got in trouble. Besides she's working and she really gets sore when she has to take time off work on account of me."

"Are you in any new trouble?"

"No, but she'll think so when she gets a call from school. Sometimes I'm afraid to go home afterwards."

"Do you want to stay while I 'phone her? You get her on the phone and I'll talk with her." Gary relaxed as I talked with his mother about an appointment to discuss the class and the parents' part in this project. He, like other students, was initially anxious but actually quite pleased that his parents agreed to come in to see me.

Mr. and Mrs. Smith came in for an evening appointment. They were both worried and frightened. Mrs. Smith admitted later that she gets very upset when the school calls. "It always means trouble...the school never calls for any other reason. When my boss tells me the school is on the phone I get all shaky inside... but when the dean called me the other day there was something different..."

The "something different" for this parent was that for the first time in her boy's life the school had the time and the special staff to be actively interested in helping Gary learn. It was my job to involve his parents in the educational process.

To secure the participation of most parents required long and persistent effort. Many had had difficulties in their own school experiences and old dormant hurts were reactivated. Many wanted to "give" the child to the school or to the juvenile authorities. "I'm through with that child. He has caused me so much trouble. I

don't care what you do with him." Many blamed the school completely. "If he had been taught to read in the grades he wouldn't
be like he is now. You people are too easy on him." With these
troubled parents who were hostile and aggressive it was important
to hear them out so that they might be better able to listen to what
the school now had to offer.

Most parents were seen at the time their child was placed in the
class and after that mostly at the time of crisis situations only.
Gary's parents, however, came to see me every other week for a
year, with frequent telephone calls in between interviews. Time
after time I heard Mrs. Smith say, "I can't understand why he acts
like he does...he's a good boy at home...we have a happy family
life...if he brings home a good report card we'll give him the bi-
cycle he's been wanting...we've promised him a trip to New York
when he graduates...we're saving for his college education..."

At the rate Gary was going he would get none of this loot. He was
making no progress in school and I was making very little with the
parents. After about a dozen interviews I sensed that my relationship with them was such that I could tell them that somehow things
just didn't jibe, that I could be of little help to them until they were
willing to talk about some of the problems that, in the light of the
boy's behavior, must be there. With some hesitancy they began to
talk about their own tensions and their fear that Gary was involved
in delinquent gang activities. On one occasion they had even threatened to send him away to "military school." When questioned,
they stated that they never could afford to do this, they were merely trying to "scare" him.

They were helped to see that neither Gary nor they were facing the
facts as long as they dealt in unrealities. It took a long time to
help them assume their parental responsibilities on a realistic
basis. Finally, at the end of the school year they agreed to apply
at a family agency to work further on their problems. A successful referral was a rare experience with parents of these children.

Perhaps the hardest to reach parents were those who promised
complete cooperation but did nothing. These were the parents who
made appointments readily, then failed to show up. These parents
were often like their children--all promise and no follow through.
In these instances a home visit would often convince the parents of
our active interest and their fears would be somewhat allayed.

They also began to respond to our calls since they realized that we would follow through until we saw them.

Many of the parents of the project students were foreign born, spoke little English, and were not familiar with American schools. When invited to school, they were initially anxious. As the student and his parents learned that language barriers and cultural differences were not necessarily insurmountable their attitudes towards school began to shift. They soon sensed the genuine interest of the staff and that we were not blaming any family member. For example, Mrs. Lopez spoke only Spanish and many attempts were made through Maria to arrange an appointment with her mother. I learned that Mrs. Lopez would frequently get as far as the front of the school, Maria would manage to miss connections with her, and the mother would return home. It became evident that Maria did not want me to see her mother. I wondered why. Finally Maria and her mother appeared together in my office and then I realized why Maria had been stalling. Mrs. Lopez was an elderly, toothless, shawl-covered Mexican mother. She was obviously frightened. Maria was ashamed and embarrassed. Maria acted as interpreter while I explained to Mrs. Lopez why I had wanted to meet her. Mrs. Lopez' face brightened as we talked about Maria's school program, about the dean and the special teacher whose names Mrs. Lopez recognized. She seemed interested in talking further with these people and Maria agreed to take her mother to them. Maria, whose tense face had relaxed as we talked, turned around with a warm smile as she left with her mother. Shyly she asked if I thought it would be all right to take her mother upstairs to meet her Spanish teacher too.

Mrs. Lopez' visit seemed to be one of the factors in Maria's improvement. She seemed somewhat less belligerent and defensive and began to do passing work in school. She graduated a year and a half later, the first of her mother's ten children to make it. This is an example of how the students experienced that not only they but also their parents were being looked at differently as part of the total effort.

The close communication that existed within the school as well as between school and home is a factor not to be minimized. The project students and their parents soon got a sense that each school person dealing with an individual student was working as part of an integrated whole. This was a result of weekly meetings of the dean, teacher, nurse, and social worker in which each student was discussed. Thus in talking with the family each of us could talk meaningfully of the total effort and not just one segment of it.

Many times it seemed expeditious for the dean and the social worker together to see the parents--or the teacher and the social worker, or the nurse and the social worker. This joint interviewing served many useful purposes besides saving time. For one thing, it eliminated the notion that the social worker had some kind of magic in dealing with disturbed parents and students, and that with one referral to the social worker all would be well. This was also a useful learning experience for the dean, teacher, or nurse in interviewing techniques, particularly when the parent happened to be angry and defensive. One of the functions of mental health consultation is to provide a model to demonstrate what attitudes can be effective with different kinds of parents (for example, belligerent or helpless ones). Through consultation with school administrators about troubled students and their troubled parents we could help the administrators to view the parents as potentially effective rather than angry, hopeless, ineffectual, or defensive.

My efforts with the parents of these acting-out students were directed toward helping them to be more parental, to see to it that their children got to school regularly and on time, to set limits about absences, excuses for doctor's appointments that lasted all day, and to check with the school when in doubt about their child's whereabouts. Many parents were surprised that such vigilance made for better relations with their children rather than the feared increased trouble.

Many of these parents had been referred repeatedly to community agencies during their children's school life but had never gotten there. Why, then, were they able to make use of a school social worker in a school setting as part of a special project? I believe that the answer to this lies in the relationship that began to develop between the social worker and parents when the social worker helped the parents get some feeling that they could do something about their child's problems. The worker really believed they could be helped not to be as helpless and ineffectual, as perhaps they themselves and the schools, past and present, had believed. With this ego support the parents could begin to look at their child's potentials as well as his problems. They were thus slowly and persistently helped to be more effective parents.

THE PUBLIC HEALTH NURSE'S ROLE

Clara Royston, P.H.N.

I am assigned to the high school four and one half days a week by
the San Francisco Department of Public Health, which provides
the school health services. In many school systems where the
nurse is employed by the school department her primary responsibility is to care for students with physical complaints and injuries.
The San Francisco program has as its aim _prevention_ of illness
and disability through education as well as correction. This involves work with students, teachers, counselors, and administrators in the school as well as with parents, private physicians,
community agencies, and other public health workers.

Specifically, my program includes:

1. Maintenance of health records for all students. This information from various examinations, together with notations of contacts with the student and his family during his school life, is
helpful in assessing his physical and emotional health.

2. Arranging for and assisting the school physician with physical
examinations of students referred because of health problems.
Also assisting the school physician with the examination of ath-
letes who have no private medical care.

3. Organization of the yearly tuberculin testing program with
follow-up of positive reactors.

4. Follow-up on hearing and vision defects found by yearly screening programs.

5. Providing school personnel with pertinent health information
about students as requested or as health handicaps come to light
through physical examinations or the screening programs. An
example is Jim, whose audiometer test revealed a marked hearing

203

loss in his left ear. I referred him to Ear Center where he was found to have a perforated ear drum. I notified the teachers about his handicap so preferential seating could be considered, and advised the physical education department to excuse him from swimming because of the perforation.

6. Working with parents and community agencies to obtain medical and other remedial services for students. In the case of Jim, mentioned above, I visited the home and found that Jim and his mother were trying to get along on Social Security but were paying high rent for a sub-standard apartment. After making out application papers for Crippled Children's Services to provide care for Jim's ear condition, I referred his mother to the Housing Authority to apply for public housing. I also encouraged her to register at the California State Employment Service for part-time work.

This extensive and varied program brings me in contact with large numbers of students and parents and affords many and varied opportunities to observe unusual behavior or conditions. It does not provide any method for sharing information with school people or alerting them about possible trouble.

An example of this isolation of my work is Carol. Through the vision screening program, Carol was found to have a marked visual defect. Previous tests were normal. Her mother was notified but failed to reply. I sent for Carol, who came resentfully to my office. She signed the register, never once looking at me. Her sullen unhappy behavior led me to refer the case to the district nurse who reported an unhappy home situation. A brother was in trouble with the law. There were several younger children, one belonging to an older sister who was still in the home. The mother, who had more pressing worries, such as a pending cut in her welfare check, showed very little interest in Carol's problem and thought she might be malingering.

Later I contacted Carol's counselor, who said the girl had two incompletes on her report card. The teacher who gave her these grades said the girl seemed sullen and did not complete assignments. The typing teacher thought she needed help because of her withdrawn manner. Her visual problems were not of much concern to them.

The serious matter of the girl's disturbed behavior and the knowledge I had of her disruptive home situation could not be readily shared with the school people trained to help her. Without some interpretation, busy teachers are not particularly interested. I welcomed the establishment of the special class and my inclusion as one of the members of the team because it seemed to me that now a concerted effort would be made to tackle the many problems of concern to me about these youngsters.

I was sometimes involved when candidates were first being considered for the special class. Referrals often came to me from the deans because of poor attendance where illness was given as the excuse.

REFERRALS

To me two types of referrals seemed to identify candidates for the special classes. The deans referred to me usually those boys and girls who had poor attendance because of illness. Subsequent investigation would reveal no disability severe enough to account for such absences. Teachers' referrals often questioned the status of the student's health because classroom behavior such as sleeping, disinterest in work, frequent requests to see the nurse, and erratic or explosive behavior concerned them. "Does he take dope?" was asked by one teacher about a sullen, indifferent boy.

I gave a great deal of individual attention to the teacher referrals, hoping to clear up physical complaints so these students could direct their attention toward learning. Wilbert's case is an example of the help provided by the team.

This boy, a sophomore, came with a pass from math, asking to have his eyes tested. He had no special complaint and his vision was 20/20. Two days later Wilbert reappeared, this time from his English class, saying he thought he had a fever. His temperature was normal. His health record listed numerous visits to the nurse with trivial or vague complaints during his junior high school. His private doctor's letter dated one month earlier, diagnosed him "a healthy young adult." I reviewed the record with Wilbert and told him to time his visits to the nurse so important classes would not be missed. Wilbert's third visit that week was with a pass from his English class again. The English teacher had reported that Wilbert when in class was inattentive and disturbing. Wilbert's complaint that day was a pain in his left leg which shifted to his right leg while his temperature was being taken. He had no sense of humor about using a visit to the nurse to avoid class assignments.

To the teacher I suggested a referral to the special class as Wilbert seemed headed for trouble.

VALUE OF TEAM MEMBERSHIP

One advantage of this plan, in which all team members are kept informed about behavior problems and the physical condition of students, as well as remedial measures being taken in both areas, is illustrated by Louise's case.

The teacher-counselor was concerned about Louise's poor school work but hesitated to crowd her, as he felt she was in poor health. At a group meeting he reported to me that the girl had bad color and walked with a limp, which seemed to be getting worse. She appeared very fatigued.

He felt that this fatigue might be the result of home responsibilities. The social worker stated that Louise had a serious home problem with a disturbed mother, but had made friends and developed wholesome interests on the outside. I knew about Louise's health history from her health record. She had had surgery for a congenital condition involving her spine and left leg. This accounted for the postural defect and limp. She also had a malformation of her large intestine, which necessitated careful attention to diet. Adequate medical supervision was being maintained through Crippled Children's Services. Her only restriction was in gym because of the surgery done on her spine. I discussed the case with the school physician, who felt that she should be able to carry on her school program. I visited the home and learned from her mother that Louise had no home responsibilities but was active in church affairs and was out late four nights a week. She usually got up too late to eat breakfast before school. I emphasized to the mother the importance of helping the girl get proper rest and I urged the girl to improve her health habits and arranged for a rest period in gym and a hot lunch in school. My report to the group at a later meeting allayed the teacher's anxiety and helped the team focus on the girl's learning problems.

These meetings also provided an opportunity for discussion of technical details in an effort to enlist the teacher's cooperation in discouraging pupils from using minor complaints as a way out of their learning situations.

At times the group needed reassurance about what seemed to be the nurse's unfeeling attitude and the limitations of her responsibility in working with parents and children, as in Ronnie's case.

Ronnie, a restless, immature fifteen-year-old boy, had daily complaints of illnesses, toothache most often. He refused to see the nurse with the excuse that she never helped him--just sent him back to class. The boy's health record showed the same pattern of complaints since starting school. Examinations by school doctors and reports from the clinic he attended were negative, except for carious teeth. It was interesting to note that several dental cards had been issued at the parent's request, but the boy refused to cooperate at the dental clinic. Since his coming to high school, I had made arrangements twice for emergency dental care for this boy, but both appointments were broken and Ronnie's explanation to me was he "forgot." His mother told me that Ronnie never complained of toothache, or any other illness outside of school. This information enabled the teacher to deal with Ronnie's complaints more realistically as it was made clear to him the next move was up to Ronnie, not the nurse. Incidentally, as Ronnie began to learn he also for the first time began to keep dental appointments.

Besides the Ronnies who use illness to avoid a school situation I saw students with real anxieties about their health. Sally's complaints included headaches, a reddened eye, and recurrent menstrual cramps. According to her health record, vision, hearing and physical examinations were negative. In spite of her reluctance I was finally able to mention her severe acne. Then she confided to me that she also had a problem with constipation and feared it would lead to cancer.

Diet, rest, and skin care were discussed and Sally took from me pamphlets on these and on cancer, to read. The school doctor saw Sally and advised medical care. He explained to her that an underactive thyroid might be part of her trouble. The girl's visits to the nurse on class time ceased, but before school or during lunch time she would drop in to tell me what her doctor said or to ask questions. The team was kept informed about Sally. Toward the end of the term the teacher reported that her disposition had improved and she was doing above average work.

A case that caused the workers great concern because of the threat of family breakdown, was Sarah. The girl's attendance was poor, and she was usually tardy when she did come to school. Her mother was most cooperative, but seemed to have more than her share of troubles with which to cope. Bad luck seemed to plague the family. Each day brought new reports of crisis or disaster, such as an incurable illness of a younger child, the father's heart attack, and even a serious accident to a beloved pet. The responsibility for all decisions and action fell upon the mother, who suffered from ulcers and some years before had had a nervous breakdown. I made a home visit during one of Sarah's absences and observed a rather crowded household with a closely-knit and affectionate family. Neighborhood children and young people were coming and going. Sarah and her mother were preparing an evening meal. They explained that the family ate early in order to give the father, who was making a good recovery, more time to rest after his day's work. Sarah had been staying home to care for a pre-school child, while her mother attended to business matters. I urged the mother to clear all such absences and late arrivals with the dean in order to salvage part of the school day. This information reassured the dean and encouraged her to insist upon better attendance for Sarah. The issues clarified, Sarah began to spend more time in school and to do better work.

The case studies presented at the weekly conference with the psychiatric consultant were beneficial in pointing the way to improved health service in many complicated situations.

For me, the experience of consultation and the team approach to problems has developed techniques applicable to the total health program. In working with parents it has been especially helpful. I am better able to present pertinent facts and alternatives clearly, so that parents more willingly or with less procrastination will take steps to remedy a situation or follow through with a plan.

TEACHING THE EMOTIONALLY DISTURBED
HIGH SCHOOL STUDENT IN A SPECIAL CLASS

John F. Ott, B.S.

Esther graduated last semester. She came back to visit some
weeks ago with the news that her grades in junior college were
good enough that she was accepted into a nursing college. She had
been in my special class longer than any other youngster--two
years. She was the last link to the beginning months of this class,
when there were more bad days than good ones. She is a bright
girl who has more and more turned her intelligence to academic
progress, but two years ago I would not have given two cents for
her chances of lasting out the semester. As a matter of fact, the
odds on me were not much better.

I had been teaching this class of disturbed adolescents for about a
year. During lunch one of the boys told me that Esther had a
straight razor and had told him she would use it. I decided to take
it away from her after lunch. While the students were wandering
into class, half of them after the second bell, I asked Esther to
open her purse. Reluctantly she did. I took the razor and put it
into my pocket.

"Mr. Ott? You gonna give that back to me after school?"

"No."

"Man, you can't do that. I use that to clean my fingernails. It's
none of your business what I got in my purse."

"Esther, I'm giving this razor to Mrs. O'Neill. If she wants to
give it back to you that's up to her. In the meantime you're not going to have it in this class."

Before I had finished talking she was out of her seat and moving
about the room, talking loud and fast.

Maria, behind me at the board, seemingly uninterested in Esther's problem, had written "MARIA AND ANDY" about ten times. The rest of the youngsters were quietly watching Esther. After a minute or so she ran out of fast talk, and muttering under her breath she picked up her things, marched to the door, opened it, turned and said, "Man, how I hate Paddies (white people)!" and then stepped out and gave the door a resounding slam.

What could I do? Telephone the dean? I thought of the principal running into the girl in the hall. I knew he thought I was too soft with this class. I was not going to chase after her. Along with all this confusion of mind I had the heavily depressed feeling that any progress I had made with Esther was probably out the window.

And then there was the rest of the class. I turned and yelled at Maria to erase the board and sit down.

"But that's my boyfriend, Mr. Ott, you know Andy."

"I don't care who it is. Sit down and get to work."

"What am I supposed to do?"

"What were you doing yesterday? Did you finish it?"

"No."

"Then finish it."

At this point I saw Dan in the back of the room with a yardstick in his hand hunting for some chalk to hit with it. Dan had not been in the class long. He was a small, immature, but quite intelligent fifteen-year-old. He had received little control or understanding and had developed into what might be called a "wise mouth." Senseless arguments with adults, lying, exaggerating, phony self-righteousness, picking up dirty double meanings out of almost everything said in class, were characteristic of his behavior.

Dan was a leader, but he did no leading in our room when Willie was upset. Six feet two inches, 190 pounds, sometimes vile-tempered, Willie was the physical leader of the boys, and at this moment he was propped in his chair against the back wall taking it all in. Dan could have the limelight for the moment.

I had to get the class quieted down before Dan had two of his buddies jumping around and before he triggered Willie. I told Dan to sit down and put the stick away.

"How can I sit down and put the stick away at the same time?"

"What are you, a wise guy? Do I have to come back there and take it away from you?" His smile told me that he didn't want any trouble but if I wanted him to give up the yardstick I was going to have to go get it...I did.

When I turned around one of the girls was sitting in my chair digging through the top drawer of my desk.

"What are you doing in my desk? Get out of there."

"I just want some paper."

"Look! Each of you kids has his own supply of paper in his own folder in the filing cabinet. Go back there and get it."

"Don't get excited, Mr. Ott. You're gonna break a blood vein. I ran outa paper."

"You know as well as I do that the supply of paper is not kept in the drawer with the class records. Get paper from the cabinet and sit down."

All the boys were forcing raucous laughter after the "blood vein" crack and most were out of their seats. A new student, Bob, was sitting by the lab sink, daydreaming and turning the water on and off. I had to get some order. My mind was on Esther. If she did run into the principal I could expect a visit soon, and the class was just about ready to eat me alive. I had to do something. I threatened.

"Do you want me to kick you out of the room?"

A disguised voice from the back said, "Go ahead, teach, kick us all out."

Another roar of laughter. The teacher next door must have thought we were all going nuts.

Dan had picked up the yardstick again and was challenging Raymond to a duel. At this point Willie dropped his chair from the wall, got up slowly and moved toward Dan. I did not know what was going to happen. I saw that Willie was upset but I could not get to the back of the room to stop anything. I just had my mouth open the moment Willie reached Dan. Without saying a word Willie wrenched the stick from Dan's grip, went back to his chair, and used the straight-edge to draw some diagrams on a piece of paper. Dan moved to a corner seat and sulked for the rest of the period.

Maria forgot about Andy long enough to get her work out. I got the new boy, a nonreader, away from the water. I remember wondering how a human being could be alive for sixteen years and not be able to read or write. He and I had a long tough pull ahead of us.

Four girls were at the table with their scarfed heads close together talking in low voices as they snapped gum over cavities. One girl had a mirror out and was picking at an acned complexion. No work, but at least they were being quiet. I remember thinking that was okay. But my next thought was that that kind of philosophy of teaching would make me a very high-priced babysitter.

I looked at the clock and saw that I had ten minutes to go before I could relax. Maria started nagging me to get a drink of water. When she understood that I was not going to let her out she started nagging to go to the lavatory. One of the four girls at the table must have said something funny because they all broke out into loud laughter.

The class was on top of the situation. I was beaten down, tired, and disgusted, and they knew it.

With five minutes to go the door burst open and Esther came running into the room laughing and being chased by some boy I had never seen before. When he saw me he stopped and ran out of the room. Esther had run around behind me. I told her she could get out of the room. She wanted out before and now she could stay out.

Esther looked at me for a moment and then said to the class, "Let's all go. He can't do anything. Look! He's lost control." Those were her exact words and none truer were ever spoken. Some of the youngsters did leave with her running and shouting down the hall.

I think that was about my toughest hour. Sort of a humorous after-math to all of this was what happened the next day. I was terribly worried about the future of the class and what would happen the following morning. As far as the kids were concerned the afternoon had never happened. Apart from some counseling I had with Esther I do not think the incident was ever mentioned. The youngsters came into the class in good order and settled down to good work the first thing the following morning.

I had to build and strengthen Esther's academic skills. She was a poor reader. Her attention span was short. She had no success in class. My biggest job with Esther, as indeed with all these youngsters, was making her stick to a job until it was finished.

I remember the morning Esther graduated from short division to long division. The word long in long division had defeated Esther in elementary school. She had never really tried to master these problems. She was terribly afraid of failing. I had told her the day before that we were going to move on to long division. She had told me that she could not do it. Never could and never would.

She came into the room quietly, put her head down on her folded arms and closed her eyes. It took about fifteen minutes to get the rest of the class settled with questions answered and work well under way. Then I told Esther to get her work out and I was going to come back and help her.

"I got a headache, Mr. Ott. I wanna see the nurse."

"Oh! come on Esther. I just saw you playing softball last period. You're just afraid of this division."

"I can't do that old stuff."

"Come on. Get your paper and pencil and I'm going to show you that all you have to remember are three simple steps and there isn't any number you can't divide."

In the middle of my explanation we were interrupted two or three times by other kids who wanted help. I told them to be patient. They were. When she had gone through a problem once without my help I left her and went back to the other students. In two or three minutes Esther was at my desk.

"I have to get a drink of water."

"Let's see your problem. Did you finish it?"

"No. I can't do that old stuff."

"You just did one. You sit down and finish this problem and bring it up here. If you still have to have water then I'll let you go."

"That's chicken, Mr. Ott."

"Go on now. Sit down and do the best you can."

Two or three minutes and she was back. "I gotta go to the toilet."

"You haven't finished that problem?"

"No. But honest-to-god, I've gotta go bad, Mr. Ott."

"Then it's going to be too bad for all of us because I expect you to knuckle down to this work."

We went back and forth like this for a few minutes. I was chicken and a dirty rat but she finally understood that she was going to stick to that work until she whipped it. Oh, I readily admitted that there was no way I could make her work but we would not go on with anything more until we had made it up this step. This took the better part of a week, but we made it. After this there were many other steps in all her subjects but somehow with this experience behind us these others never really seemed too tough.

Unless a teacher has strong positive feelings for students he should never get involved with a class of upset youngsters, for certainly he would not survive the everyday struggle. But these strong feelings can be dangerous too.

Emily was a charter member of my special class. Her father was an alcoholic; her mother was "long suffering" and had all the answers. In the beginning, Emily did rather well in the class. From the first our program seemed made for Emily. In all her school life she had never written even the simplest composition, but she began to write in my class. More than most students, she seemed to want to talk with me about her troubles, and I encouraged this.

I liked Emily. There was the time she told me about her father's "suicide." One evening, in the midst of a violent argument between her mother and father, after the father had been drinking rather heavily for some time, Emily's father announced that he was going to kill himself. He leapt up from his chair, charged over to the window, jerked it open, and threw himself out head first. Their home was built on the side of a hill in such a manner that the first floor very soon became the second floor. Emily and her mother rushed out around the side of the house in time to see the father pick himself up out of shrubbery and soft dirt. Emily said that she had never been so frightened in all her life. This "suicide" seemed to settle the argument for awhile and the father returned to his chair. A few minutes later the argument began again and the same thing happened. The father threatened suicide and went out the window head first. At this point, Emily stopped her story and I naturally asked, "What happened?"

"Nothing happened; that's the end of the story. My mother and I just sat there in the living room doing what we were doing, and a few minutes later, my father came staggering back into the house with a bloody nose and covered with dirt. No one in my family has said anything about this since. My father just doesn't argue any more." After relating stories of this nature, Emily seemed to be put at ease. Her classwork improved and I began to feel that this "therapy" was paying off.

The girl used our class and myself as a sounding board for her troubles quite often. In the early days of the program I had not too much faith in the "manipulations," philosophies, and methods of the social worker and psychologist. I believed it was going to be almost exclusively in the classroom that these "cures" would take place. One afternoon Emily informed the class that she was really going to have a good time later on when she got home. I asked, "Why?"

"Well, I'll tell you, Mr. Ott. Yesterday, when my father and I went shopping, a box of food that someone else had bought was still sitting on the counter and nobody was around. The checker put our food in a box, and we walked out of the store. My father picked up the box that didn't belong to us, but he didn't know that it wasn't ours. When we got home, my father just took the box into the kitchen and left it up to me to put the food away. There's hotdogs, a couple of chickens, some hamburger, and some cans of tuna; and this afternoon when I get home, I'm really going to have myself a feast."

I righteously commented that Emily should return the food, and then the subject was dropped. The next day, about mid-morning during a lull in class activities, one of the students asked Emily how her feast had been. Emily's face clouded over. She said, "When I got home yesterday afternoon, I found practically all of the food had been eaten up. My father knew all the time that he was stealing that food. He just pretended because he thought I didn't know. He's a dirty thief."

It seemed to me that after each one of these sessions Emily took a new lease on life and got down to serious work. By the time of Christmas vacation she was doing math assignments regularly, writing regularly, and was showing some interest in science. Almost a year had passed since she had entered the class, and she seemed to have developed a real desire to learn. It looked like Emily was going to be a star character in a "success" story.

Early in January, when I returned to school after Christmas vacation, a note was waiting for me from Emily's mother. The note asked me to telephone her. I contacted the mother and she seemed rather upset, telling me that Emily had run away from home on the day before Christmas. She asked me to come to the house and talk about it. When I got to Emily's home, the Christmas tree was still up and Emily's presents were unopened beneath the tree. According to the mother the family had been very happy and there had been no arguments. "Emily has just been a wonderful girl, thanks to you, Mr. Ott; but the day before Christmas, she just walked out and has not been heard from or seen since." I do not recall asking the mother what the family had done about the girl's disappearance.

As it turned out I was the only person in any official capacity that the family had contacted. But let me tell you how it happened that I became too deeply involved.

I had just returned to school from a wonderful two weeks with my own family. I have twins, a boy and a girl. Emily is one of twins, a boy and a girl. After having this nice family Christmas in my own home, seeing Emily's packages unopened really got me. When I returned to school I questioned some of the other students in the class about Emily. They gave me a series of conflicting rumors.

One girl said that Emily had gone to Los Angeles. Another girl said that she had gone to Chicago. The story that seemed to make the most sense, probably because three or four youngsters told it, was that Emily had dyed her hair and was living in an apartment in the rough part of town, not too far from school.

The next day at noontime, I went hunting for Emily. I rationalized my action beautifully. I told myself that I would have lunch with a friend who taught at a school near the area where Emily had been reported seen. I never arrived at his school. About twenty minutes after I left my school, before I had any lunch, I discovered myself driving around back streets and alleys with my stomach tied up in knots worrying that something terrible had happened to the girl. It was at this moment I woke up. I asked myself just what "the hell" was I doing there worrying about Emily more than any other agency, including her parents. At that moment I realized my job was the job of teacher, and not parent.

I had been prepared for this moment but had not realized it. Driving back to school, many conversations in consultation with social workers and psychologists came to mind. It seemed that dozens of times we had discussed this very situation. I remembered the social worker saying, "John, you know if you stand on your head and turn blue in the face, you'll never never become the parent of one of these children."

My task was to do the best teaching job I could. It was our concentration on English, the value of mathematics, and science that was helping Emily in class. Oh, I am sure that some of her discussions of her problems were of value to her, but the dynamics of learning was the difference in the classroom situation. For really effective learning to take place the student must see in the person of the teacher an adult who understands just what his role is. One of the major problems that the youngsters in our class had was that most of the adults in their lives had vacillated from role to role. Their parents had just been "sometimes parents"--most of the time they were something else. It is not always easy for a teacher to avoid becoming seriously emotionally involved. The students and their parents seduce one into this role. They find pressure or need within them and they very willingly give over this responsibility to anyone who will take it on. But this responsibility is not the teacher's and, if it were officially, there is nothing a teacher as teacher can do about it.

Emily returned two or three weeks later. She had been in rather serious trouble, but she had turned herself in to the authorities. It was not long before she was back in school, and she remained with the class to the end. I know the class did her a lot of good. Certainly the experience of her runaway did me a lot of good.

Jim's father was an alcoholic. The boy's mother said of the family, "I'm sick of the whole bunch--I don't care if they all go to hell." Their legacy to Jim was a good intellect and very little love and understanding. Jim had been in trouble with school authorities and the community for as long as we had any records of him. He had been hanging on in high school by a fingernail. Only the fact that he was in my special class kept him in school through his junior year.

He had been in and out of juvenile court three or four times, each time for some bizarre act. He was first sent to Juvenile Hall for painting an automobile. As Jim told the judge, "There I was with this can of paint and a brush in my hand and there that new car was standing at the curb so I painted it." Once he put a cherry bomb into the coin return slot of a gum machine and blew the top of the machine through the plate glass window of a hardware store. One Halloween his idea of a funny prank was putting highway danger flares, lighted, into mailboxes. On top of all this, the youngster had been observed drinking or under the influence of alcohol enough times to indicate that he was well on his way to a life of alcoholism.

Jim slept in the family garage. His only heat was supplied by a small electric heater. Once when his father got mad at him, he, the father, ripped down the electric wires that led to the garage. Later, when he sobered up a bit, he called the electric company to repair them, claiming vandals had done it. All through his time in our special class, Jim's mother lied regularly for his absences. She continually protected him and covered up for him with phony notes.

When I first heard about Jim, the dean went into his special file and showed me a paper the boy had written for an English class. It was a collection of weird comments about him being God and all the rest of us better watch out, and that sort of thing. This had impressed and worried his teacher enough that she turned the paper over to the dean. I could not put my finger on it at the time, but something about the paper did not ring quite true. When Jim came into class, I told him what I tell all the youngsters, that I would accept him at face value. Except for their academic progress, I do not dig too much into their other school records. It is an attempt on our part to start afresh. When I told Jim this, he smiled and said, "Yeah, I'll bet." He didn't do any work for about two months. The first paper he turned in was a composition in English. When the youngsters in my class turn in compositions, I keep the papers for about a week, and then call them up to the desk individually and we go over the work. When it was Jim's turn to come up, I frankly had not read the composition, and we sat down together. The title of the paper went something like "Some Advice to All You Cats Down on This Rock." As I read the first line or two, I realized that it was a paper very much like the one the dean had shown me--a series of disconnected crazy thoughts. The language became very rough until by the end of the paper Jim had used just about every blasphemy and filthy word that he knew. As I read the paper, he said nothing. I could sense that he was watching me and I corrected the paper for misspelling, grammatical errors, and the like. As I finished the paper, I commented that his thoughts were very disconnected and there did not seem to be a sensible theme, but maybe he knew what he was talking about, and if he would concentrate on correcting the errors that I had indicated, he might be on his way to learning something about English. I handed his paper back. He asked me if I really knew what I was doing, giving him this paper back, and I said, "Yes, I do." I told him that it was his paper and he was entitled to it. He sort of smiled and asked me if I didn't want to show it to the dean. I said, "No," and he returned to his desk. Just before he reached his desk, I called him back and quietly asked him if he did not think he should tear up the paper and throw it away, before any of the other youngsters in the class had a chance to read it. This was quietly said, none of the other students really knew what was going on. Jim said he thought that was a pretty good idea. He tore up the paper and threw it away.

When I changed his program so that he could come into my class, Jim argued heatedly against taking algebra. He insisted that since his father had been unable to pass algebra he also was destined to fail. I told Jim what I believe and what I tell most of my disturbed students. "Jim, our tests and my information show that you are intelligent enough not only to learn algebra, but also to do rather well at it. Just because you haven't done well in school in recent years is no reason why we shouldn't try for something better."

That was in the beginning of Jim's sophomore year. The students who started algebra with him completed geometry four semesters later. Each school day I gave Jim from five to fifteen minutes individual instruction in mathematics. I invested more time and energy in him than in any other youngster in my class. When you add up our time in one-to-one teaching, it comes to better than sixty hours, and in Jim's four semesters, he completed barely ninety-five pages in the algebra text.

For the first three weeks Jim left no doubt he could master algebra. He worked well, but then he slowed down. He missed assignments. Many days while I worked with other students, and Jim should have been working, his head was down on his desk and he was apparently asleep. When I sat down with him to pick up where he had left off the previous day, he invariably had an excuse for not studying. "I can't do this stuff--it's stupid. How can I do these problems--you just try to mix me up. I told you my family couldn't do math. I wouldn't do anything for this lousy school." My answer was usually to the effect that excuses would not help him live up to his responsibilities. In that class at that time we both had one job to do and that was to advance in algebra.

Several times in these situations Jim lost his self-control. It always happened in pretty much the same way. I would just have left him to go to another student. Jim would demand more time and attention. I would tell him to wait his turn. He would loudly insist. I would tell him to sit down and be quiet, and he would stomp back to his desk muttering some vulgarity and calling me a "son of a bitch" or the like.

Depending upon how the outbreak of temper might affect the class; that is, whether or not it might trigger another of the disturbed youngsters on that particular day, I would take one of three courses of action. I might merely reprimand Jim; or I might send him to the dean for the remainder of that period; or if he was particularly upsetting, he would be sent home for the remainder of the day. But there would be no three, four, or even ten day suspensions from school. He was always welcomed back the next period or day, and we quickly tried to get back to the purpose of our classroom-- another try for academic success.

Along with the rather consistent sequence that led to Jim's outbursts of temper and loss of control, it is important to mention another interesting phenomenon. At the very moment when I was dragged out, sick and tired of Jim and his algebra, fast losing patience and ready to quit, the boy seemed to sense that I was on the verge of giving up, and he very quickly mastered the task at hand and seemed eager to get to the next lesson.

In the two years that I had Jim in my special class, there were two highspots; that is, there were two highspots in math, for he progressed fairly well in his other subjects. About midway through his junior year, Jim said he had difficulty because he had never learned his multiplication tables and asked if I would help him memorize them. It was the first time he had not blamed something or somebody else for his inability to do this work. Again, about a month before the end of his last semester with me, he said that he had a difficult time solving some equations because he did not know how to work with fractions. In a normal classroom with normal children, these simple statements might be overlooked, but with Jim these had been minor victories.

In his other two courses, the progress for Jim had been quite different. In English and U. S. History in the beginning he did little better than he was doing in math, but as time went on, his performance in these subjects had steadily improved. At first, days or weeks sometimes went by with his exerting little or no effort. But as the months passed these lapses in work grew fewer, and Jim's upset and frustration over the work in these courses became much less intense. In the beginning Jim would often say how much he hated school and wanted out. In a few months he was saying how much he hated school, but he felt it was necessary to get that diploma. During the last few days he was in our program, he said that he did not like school very much, but there are some good teachers and students and he really would like to graduate. In the beginning his work in social studies was rather sloppy when done. At the end of that year, although it was an exception when Jim did extra work, he took quite a bit of pride in turning in neat and orderly map work and reports. When he first came to the special class, he seemed always sullen and angry. After two years, except for an occasional outburst of temper during math period, he seemed rather happy and calm.

My methods are really no different from those of any teacher who is convinced that learning is important to kids' futures and who can find the time, patience, and persistence to make individual help to the student the rule rather than the exception.

These children have special problems and the teacher of the emotionally disturbed needs the help of trained specialists. As important as the help I received in understanding the problems of my students was the emotional support that helped me to recognize and work out the limits of my job and, finally, to recognize and come to terms with my own limitations. The consultation with the mental health specialists enabled me to spend more time and energy in teaching and in trying to find ways of helping these youngsters to learn.

PSYCHIATRIC CONSULTATION
ON THE ANTI-DELINQUENCY PROJECT

I. N. Berlin, M.D.

Special classes for delinquent students seemed a puny attack on a difficult and serious problem. My initial reaction to the project, based on psychotherapeutic work with delinquent youngsters and their parents, was one of grave skepticism.

As you have read, some youngsters were helped, a few considerably. To assess the factors responsible for the changes that did occur, one needs to examine carefully the methods used and the personnel involved.

The teacher chosen for the project was one of those rare persons who is secure in his own teaching ability and experienced in teaching the pre-delinquent and delinquent youth. Most important, he was not defensive in his collaboration. Thus, inevitable doubts, objections, and misunderstandings were promptly and honestly verbalized and explored again and again, rather than internalized and brooded upon with consequent increased difficulties in teaching.

In the dean of girls we found an administrator whose long experience and mature judgment were coupled with open-mindedness and willingness to experiment and to learn in the service of her students. In her, too, we found the rigorous honesty and self-scrutiny vital to the collaboration of personnel on such a project.

The other members of the team, the social workers and psychologist, were old co-workers whose skills and collaboration could be depended upon as a known baseline for operations.

Some of the unique aspects of the consultation in this project arose from the frequency of discussion about many of the same students who presented problems to the teacher in the classroom, to the ad-

ministrator, and/or to the workers in the boys' or girls' groups.
It was thus possible to have a more vivid picture of the student than
usually occurs. Also, since this class was experimental and many
faculty members looked upon it with thinly veiled hostility, the
acute problems carried an urgency for solution that is not as frequent in other settings.

Thus there was greater temptation for all of us to offer suggestions
about handling a problem rather than to do what we usually found to
be most helpful, which was to aid the teacher and administrator to
find their solutions through exploration of the problem. Perhaps
our very willingness to offer suggestions at such moments of crisis
encouraged the teacher and dean to share their concerns more
openly with us. Happily, a few suggestions were helpful and as a
result the consultation process was enhanced.

Empathy of the consultant for the feelings and difficulties of the
consultee is an essential ingredient in effective consultation. All
members of the special class team felt the pressures to help these
disturbed and disturbing youngsters and to make the project successful. Isolated from the mainstream of the school and looked on
with distrust by other faculty members, we were forced into a
more cohesive and mutually interdependent group. These factors
also contributed to the high degree of empathy that the team members felt for each other in the work, and especially for the difficult
and arduous work of the teacher and the dean. This strong empa-
thetic bond was important to all of our successful consultation.

From previous work with such students, my own growing conviction
was that any success that might occur could result only from helping these hostile, indifferent, truanting, and usually academically
retarded students to begin to learn subject matter. This conviction
was shared by the child guidance workers, it fitted the educational
philosophy of the administrator and the talents of the teacher. Because a social worker and a psychologist were available to see parents and to work individually and in groups with students we were
able to focus on classroom teaching.

My convictions were predicated on experiences with families of
such students. It had become clear that these parents had severe
personality conflicts. Their own unhappiness and dissatisfactions
made them unable to provide any model for successful, productive
living for their child. The bitter socio-economic realities under

which many of these parents lived served to increase their own feeling of failure, of being unloved, both in their own childhood and now. Each parent felt angry at the bitter reality and the inability of the other parent to make him happy and therefore had little nurturance to give to an infant. They were unable to enjoy, praise, and encourage their child's discoveries, adventures, and early joyful successes in mastery of the environment.

They could not help their children learn to experience pleasure and fun in the achievement of those satisfactions that at each age level their growth and maturation made possible. Such a simple and vital experience as being aided to persist in their learning efforts until they could master a task was <u>not</u> theirs. The parents either hastily did it for the child so as to be done with it, or left the child alone to experience continual frustration until he gave up. In either case the child felt dissatisfied, disgruntled, and finally wanted someone else to do it for him. Such a child had a valid belief that <u>someone owed him something</u>. This feeling often prevented the child from working for his own satisfaction.

Since these students have not mastered the fundamentals of many aspects of living and schooling, they usually cannot read well. Mathematics seems an insurmountable obstacle. It is hard for them to obtain any pleasure from acquiring information or discovering and exploring any fields of knowledge. All learning requires some application and since they have not experienced satisfactions that come from perseverance and the completion of tasks, they become restless and easily distracted. They also feel continually disgruntled and angry at the persons who require that they undergo such frustrations. Underlying all of this, too, is the desire to be able to do the tasks, to experience the pleasure others seem to get, and to be able to feel adequate and worthwhile in the school setting. Such students are therefore in constant conflict with themselves and with their environment.

The monumental task of helping them to begin to learn and to want to go on learning requires an endless patience. Their teacher must be able to derive his satisfaction from doing the job itself to his full capacity, since he may not see many changes in his students for a long time. Thus the teacher by his persistence through frustrations, conflicts, and trying moments provides the necessary living model for the student: a parental model who believes the student can learn and who is willing to take the time to stand by and help him learn. The youngster hopefully experiences for the first time an adult who will not react to the angry, bitter, and hostile expression of his internal conflicts and frustrations with retaliatory anger and hurt self-esteem. Such a teacher's firm insistence on what he knows must be done by the student, so that he begins to learn, results in the gradual achievement of those satisfactions that come from mastering tasks. The student under these circumstances often experiences another "first"--a person who evidences his belief in the potential of the student and in the possibility that the student might begin to find some way out of the circular, dissatisfied, angry turmoil in which he constantly finds himself.

One of the obstacles to the learning process is the student's recurrent hope that magically he will acquire the skills in which he is deficient. This wishful phantasy, that by magic rather than by hard work he will get something, he acquired from repeated experiences with his parents who themselves could only express their wishes for solutions to their own and the family's troubles and were unable to work towards their attainment. When such a student meets a teacher who has a similar hope, that is, that the teacher's transient interest and concern will magically cause the student to learn, then both student and teacher are inevitably disappointed. The teacher feels hurt, let down, and angry that his concern carried no magical cure of the student's learning problems, and the student has again encountered an adult who could not help him learn. He feels angry, hopeless, and distrustful of all adults who promise much but never come through.

The teacher and administrators of such students must undergo interminable testing until the student knows out of his own experience that these adults derive their satisfactions from the work itself and from the student's genuine achievements, growth, and self-satisfaction. These students need to experience that they are learning for themselves, not to gratify some need of their teacher.

In our consultation the teacher several times brought up the dilemma of trying to be fair to the entire class and to the needs of the individual. So many youngsters needed so much of the teacher's time, and some of them wanted to monopolize all of the teacher's attention. The teacher gradually was able to feel that there was no either-or. He became convinced that being fair to the class meant being fair to the individual and vice versa. He then found that his own conviction when he had acted fairly with a student was recognized by the youngster, often despite the student's continued half-hearted clamor that the teacher was being unfair. The teacher was later able to be helpful to some of his students by meeting unremitting efforts to monopolize his time with firmness and occasionally with guiltless, just anger.

Early the teacher was amazed that these students did not feel rejected but were relieved when limits were clearly and unanxiously set.

The predominance of Negro and Mexican students in the class brought to the attention of the teacher and dean many racial problems. Both teacher and dean felt they had few prejudiced feelings, but brought to consultation the problem of how to convince the students. It seemed to me that all one could do was to invite the students to judge the teacher and dean by their behavior. Their constant efforts to be fair and to hold all students responsible for their behavior would speak for itself. Thus some students from minority groups were helped by the teacher's and dean's increasingly clear and unambivalent firmness with these youngsters. They came to understand that they could not use their minority status and accusations of discrimination to avoid the consequences of their destructive or aggressive behavior.

The severe socio-economic and interpersonal deprivation suffered by so many of these adolescents from minority groups posed additional problems. Staff members, especially the teacher, tended to over-identify with these youngsters. The teacher felt that these students' troubles were his own to cure. He wanted to right all of the wrongs they had endured, set their topsy-turvy world aright. Only gradually, as you have read, did he learn that all he could do was to provide the kind of model and atmosphere for them that might help them begin to learn.

The team's investment in these deprived adolescents created other problems. These youngsters had endured so much discrimination and unfairness that their hate for their white teachers and other staff often seemed overwhelming. When such hate and accusations of discrimination occurred after the teacher, dean, or psychotherapist had tried to be helpful, it sometimes led to despair and hopelessness. It was necessary to remind team members how brief this integrative experience was compared to the many years of disappointment and unfair treatment and to encourage continued efforts to help these youngsters to feel differently about themselves through learning. Finally these efforts began to pay off.

In each interchange the teacher and dean needed to be aware that the student was testing the <u>authoritative</u> adult. Many invited hostile retaliatory action from authorities. It became evident that the consequences for unacceptable behavior must repetitively be spelled out for these youngsters. The teacher and dean gradually learned to use each contact resulting from a student's hostile, aggressive acting out to define the alternatives open to the student. After the consequences for antisocial behavior were repeatedly spelled out, it became necessary to help the dean and teacher with their feelings that they were being unjust and retaliatory when these consequences had to be adhered to. Of course, inherent in these feelings was the fact that these consequences sometimes spelled the failure of the program to help a student. However, in time most students came to expect a firm fairness that was neither a guilty or capricious leniency nor punitive harshness. The youngsters began to know what the certain consequences of destructive, hostile behavior were. They became convinced that the enforcement was not felt by the authorities as punitive and retaliatory but only the necessary and inevitable result of the student's actions for which he must assume responsibility. Thus in time an apparent paradox occurred; the more firm and clear the authorities, the more inevitable the consequences of destructive aggressive behavior, the more these youngsters began to see authority in a less threatening and more friendly light. As the limits were slowly and painfully delineated, it became possible for more students to accept them and to feel secure in their consistency and in their clarity.

For some students these efforts came too late and were too little for the massive emotional disturbance present. The fact that a few students have been helped attests to the evolution of these concepts and their successful implementation by members of the team.

I, too, would like to underline, in conclusion, the value of the project as a learning experience for the entire team. This was especially so for the psychiatric consultant, who experienced again and in another setting that all work with people that leads to mastery over even a very tiny bit of the environment may help to resolve conflicts and begin to reduce even severe personality disturbances.

WHAT HAPPENED AFTERWARDS

Alice C. Henry, M.A.

It is ten years now since the Commissioner first proposed disciplinary classes for junior and senior high school boys whose behavior marked them as disruptive in their regular classes, five years since the special project described in these papers came to an end.

What has happened in this period? Did the project have any lasting effects? Are there any plans for the future?

About the individual boys and girls who "went to school to Mr. Ott" unfortunately we know very little. The hurried inauguration of the project did not permit a research design to be built into it. There was no planned follow-up of students when the classes were discontinued. While the classes were operating, each year evaluations were written by administrators, project members, and other faculty members. In addition, statistical studies were made to calculate observable changes in patterns of attendance, academic achievement, and citizenship. In summary these evaluations pointed out the following:

1. Removal of these children from regular classes made the educational tasks of their teachers easier and more rewarding to other students.

2. Some students were able to remain in school, and even to graduate, who otherwise would have been dropped.

3. Some of those students who did drop did so better prepared to find their place in the larger society. Marriage, enlistment in the Armed Services, a job were common next steps, although corrective institutions did take a heavy toll.

4. The work of the deans was initially increased rather than decreased, because of the close collaboration with other members of

the team that was required. The additional knowledge about human behavior and the nature of student motivation acquired by such close working together and the new techniques evolved for handling serious behavior problems, at least in part, made this extra expenditure of time justifiable.

5. Without the assistance of the social workers and psychologists and their direct work with parents and children, the teacher could not have carried on the class. An increase in direct service to individuals and to groups might have made the program more effective.

6. Statistically:

    a) Attendance of pupils enrolled in the class did not improve. (Chronic truants were not selected after the first year.)

    b) Scholarship showed a moderate improvement.

    c) Citizenship ratings showed a slight but significant improvement.

7. The cost of the program per student was slightly more than twice that of the cost per regular student.

The special classes in San Francisco came to an end in June, 1958. But the seeds sown by this project are still bearing fruit in San Francisco and in other parts of the state. The administration at the high school was loath to give up the services provided by the social worker and rearranged its counseling schedule to keep her on the staff half-time. She has continued to work, much as she did with the project staff, seeing students and their parents in times of crisis, consulting with faculty members with the goal of trying to make the school experience as profitable as possible for each youngster. Other schools in the city have been interested in having a school social worker at the school and to date nine secondary schools now have a social worker on their counseling staff for at least half-time.

The skills that Mr. Ott developed in the project class were recognized by a neighboring school district and he has organized similar classes as a demonstration in several high schools in the district. He considers himself fortunate that he has been able to maintain personal and professional ties with the project psychologist, who, now a member of the staff of a county mental health program, serves as his consultant when problems arise in the class.

San Francisco has not been alone in being concerned about the kinds of problems presented by the boys and girls described in these papers. In 1957 the California State Legislature directed the State Department of Education to attempt to devise instruments to identify emotionally disturbed children in the classroom early in their school career. This study was followed by a series of demonstration programs of three years duration in an attempt to meet the needs of these children. Special classes such as the ones San Francisco had developed were among the programs included in the State study and were demonstrated as being of value.

The culmination of these State experimental programs came in the summer of 1963 when the State Legislature passed a bill to provide special services for the emotionally handicapped child and appropriated special funds to help defray some of the excess costs. Special classes for small groups of students who have been identified as having serious behavior or learning disorders are approved programs under this bill. At this writing San Francisco and other school districts are beginning to set up classes that are very similar to those described in these papers.

The reader who "reads between the lines" of these papers must have come to the conclusion that the participants in this project, though competent in their own professions, almost literally had to develop procedures, policies, and effective ways of working together day by day as the project developed. Though the results were fortuitous, more preplanning might have avoided some mistakes. Out of their experience and the hope of helping other school districts who may be contemplating similar projects, the participants make certain suggestions that might help the class to get off to a better start:

1. The program should not be embarked on unless it is agreed that it will run for a reasonable length of time, preferably at least five years, in order that the process continue long enough so that results can be adequately assessed.

2. One person with administrative authority should be assigned responsibility for the total operation.

3. At least one semester should be set aside for the preliminary work in setting up the class. This would provide time for the selection of staff and an opportunity for them to become acquainted with each other, agreement on the criteria for entrance to the class, preliminary selection of students, interpretation of the purposes of the class to the faculty and the general community, etc.

4. A research design and competent research staff members should be considered essential parts of the program from the outset.

5. While it is conceivable that a special class alone, under the direction of a gifted teacher, might be of some help to students with the kind of problems this group presented, the chance of success, as hopefully these papers have demonstrated, is much greater if a multidisciplinary approach can be made. We would recommend that even more psychiatric, psychological, and social work services be provided.

So much for more or less specific results of this program and the recommendations that come from these experiences. But what about the needs? In many ways the educator, especially in large cities, finds himself more hard-pressed and with more dilemmas than he did in 1953. Advances in automation have made it increasingly clear that the world of work has little or no place for the youngster who has less than a high school diploma. Increasing stress on high academic performance in school brings in its wake more and more "pushouts" of pupils who have missed out along the way and cannot make the grade. The struggles of minority groups to secure for themselves and their children the civil rights that are their due have often brought explosions of violence in school that teachers have found difficult to handle.

No single program can be expected to solve all these problems. Nor should a school system be held accountable for failures and weaknesses of our society as a whole. Yet it remains a fact that at any given time boys and girls from all walks of life will be going to school, bringing their problems with them.

It is the thesis of these papers that it is possible to make progress with "reluctant learners." Boys and girls who have missed in their early years the gratifications that come from mastery too often experience the same defeats in the classroom; they react with apathy or aggression, give up, or strike out. Their teachers, in turn, often give up in exasperation or respond with anger, especially if their well-meant efforts are not effective, and the downward spiral continues. What this project provided was a different kind of intervention by a group of significant adults by which gradually and over a long period of time these pupils began to experience that it was possible to learn. As these youngsters found that there were adults available to them who would persistently insist that with help they could stick to the tasks assigned to them, their resistance to learning began to diminish and their behavior to improve. Concomitantly their own concepts of themselves as people also changed as they could begin to take pride in their own accomplishments.

These papers have described efforts to tackle the problem presented by pre-delinquent youngsters in a senior high school. With some of them we were able to achieve at least a minimal amount of success. For many this program came much too late in their lives. Perhaps the most important message this program has is to point up the significant role that all teachers play in the lives of children. That "knowledge is power" has been said so often it is taken for granted; but for teachers to understand that helping youngsters to a position of mastery is to contribute to a strengthening of their egos gives a new importance to their position in the group of specialists who are interested in mental health. A successful experience in school is important for all children if they are to be able to move on to adulthood relatively easily. For children such as these described, handicapped by crippling experiences at home, the program provided by the public schools is perhaps their only hope. And yet it is precisely these youngsters who are the most likely to be removed from school and cut off from the help they need.

It is the hope of the authors that this project will in some small way encourage others in education to continue to make the effort to help the "reluctant learner" to learn, and to be willing to pay the necessary price. What we learn from work with the most seriously disturbed student can hopefully help us to work more successfully with his more fortunate brothers and sisters.

SECTION SIX:

THERAPEUTIC EFFORTS IN LEARNING DISTURBANCES

Introduction

A variety of therapeutic methods have been employed to help children with their problems in learning and attending school. These papers describe efforts to help emotionally disturbed children with their learning problems, using the various professional personnel who may have an opportunity to work with the disturbed child. A common theme in all of these papers is that learning of academic material is an important therapeutic experience for children with emotional disturbances of varying severity, from the phobic child and the truant student to the severely psychotic youngster.

In another volume several papers present the work of the nursing staff in helping severely regressed psychotic children to learn such ostensibly mundane tasks as toileting and dressing. Such efforts at teaching and learning are preludes to learning in school and essential to the recovery process for these severely disturbed children.

SCHOOL PHOBIA

Adelaide M. Johnson, M.D., Eugene I. Falstein, M.D.,
S. A. Szurek, M.D., and Margaret Svendsen

For years psychiatrists have recognized that there is a type of emotional disturbance in children, associated with great anxiety, that leads to serious absence from school. This is a deep-seated psychoneurotic disorder fairly sharply differentiated from the more frequent and common delinquent variety of school truancy. The syndrome, often called "school phobia," is recognizable by the intense terror associated with being at school. The child may be absent for periods of weeks or months or years, unless treatment is instituted. The children, on fleeing from school, usually go straight home to join the mother. Eventually they refuse to leave the house. When the child is superficially questioned, he cannot verbalize what he fears and the whole matter appears incomprehensible to parents and teachers. It seems to us that this syndrome is not a clean-cut entity, for one finds overlapping of the phobic tendencies with other neurotic patterns, such as those of an hysterical or obsessive nature.

Although this type of problem is seen fairly frequently in any child guidance clinic and can become very serious, there has been very little written about it. In 1932 Dr. Isra T. Broadwin (1) described this syndrome in his paper entitled, "A Contribution to the Study of Truancy." The title might suggest that it is only another article on delinquent truancy but it does attempt to describe the psychoneurotic elements in this disorder.

There are all degrees of school phobia ranging from those that are abortive and clear quickly, to those requiring intensive treatment. The severe school phobia that is left untreated may develop into a seriously crippling condition. This is well exemplified by a woman of 31 who was analyzed by one of the writers (E.I.F.). Her first acute anxiety began in the school room at 13 and soon developed into a severe school phobia that was untreated. This rapidly

spread to include phobias of many varieties from which the secondary gains were so great that after 18 years they constituted an insurmountable barrier to any very successful analytic therapy.

Fairly intensive clinical experience with eight children treated at
the Institute for Juvenile Research has resulted in a somewhat
clearer insight into the dynamics of school phobia as well as its
therapy. The group studied includes an equal number of male and
female children. The age range at time of appearance of the phobia
was from 6 to 14 years of age. The symptoms had existed from
10 days to 2 years, one 8-year-old boy never having gone to
school. There was no consistent determinant so far as ordinal position was concerned. Intelligence ranged from low average to
extremely superior--the majority of the children being in the superior group. In the eight cases studied the four boys were submissive and obedient to their mothers, whereas the girls were aggressively defiant. All of these children had a definite history
pointing to the presence of considerable anxiety in their early
years, such as night terrors that were striking, promotion anxieties, earlier short periods of phobia regarding school, severe
temper tantrums, asthma and eczema. The children came from
homes of varied economic levels.

The outstanding common factors in initiation of the school phobia
which seem to be operating in all eight cases are, first, <u>an acute
anxiety in the child</u>, which condition may be caused by organic disease, or by some emotional conflict manifested in hysterical, hypochondriacal, or compulsive symptoms precipitated by arrival of
a new sibling, promotion in school, etc. Second, and equally important, an <u>increase of anxiety in the mother</u> due to some simultaneously operating threat to her satisfactions, such as sudden
economic deprivation, marital unhappiness, illness, etc. Third,
there seems always to be a strikingly poorly resolved early dependency relationship of these children to their mothers. How these
three cardinal factors become interrelated in the production of the
school phobia will be seen most easily perhaps from study of a case
summary and excerpts from others.

SUMMARY OF CASE

Jack, age 9, the middle child in a family of three, developed school
phobia eight months before coming to the Institute. After a mild
organic illness associated with unnecessary trips to various medical clinics accompanied by his over-solicitous mother, with two or

three months of absence from school the boy refused to return to school and developed hypochondriacal complaints, temper tantrums, fears of storms, etc. Soon a full-blown school phobia was evident. Early in her clinic visits the boy's mother said, "It made me sick to see Jack so pale and anxious, angry and upset. Jack and I had such arguments about his going to school and I became so sick and upset that last spring his father decided it would be better for Jack not to go to school. Jack has always been so lovable--always worried about my illnesses--more than the other two children." The mother stated that people in her community said the boy was "working her" and she felt their view might be justified. Patient was described as "very cuddly, always needing more love than the others." The mother felt "he would have been better off had she devoted all of her time to him."

The child's maternal grandmother had been in bed for years with an hysterical disorder, and was growing increasingly demanding at this time of her younger daughter, the child's mother. The latter suffered from many somatic neurotically conditioned disorders that sent her to bed for days. She was a very dependent, hostile woman and while in a resentful mood, used her illness as a way to punish herself and her mother, to enslave her husband and this boy. Unconsciously she exploited the boy's guilt about his resentments towards her in order to bind him to herself. When treatment began at the Institute regularly once a week, she developed more severe disorders that at first were used as an excuse for not making the long trip. The family lived 250 miles from the clinic. She wrote, "I know I'm impeding Jack's progress by not coming in, for my husband can tell you nothing." Though the boy enjoyed his treatment hours from the start, his mother early used every excuse to keep him home. Finally criticism from the school and community operated to increase the mother's anxiety to the point where she came to the clinic regularly. She quickly developed a dependent transference to her psychiatrist (male) and subsequently seldom missed treatment hours. The boy was treated in a playroom by a woman psychiatrist. In this situation he lived through in play activity and verbally his conflicts with the family as brought out in relation to the therapist. Relationship interpretations were given to the child as seemed necessary to the resolution of his conflicts.

In the five months of regular weekly treatment hours the patient worked through a great deal of his ambivalence and rivalries toward both parents and siblings. Especially was he concerned early with rage and guilt against the mother because of her demands upon him for obedience and attention, and because of her resentment of any independent strivings. After he had been in treatment for some time he sent her a rather expensive present to cover both Mother's Day and her birthday. The mother complained bitterly to her therapist that Jack was "no longer her dear little Jack who had always given her two separate presents before." There were periods of fearfulness, especially when his mother would be very sick, and, as these were worked through, the patient brought out clearly at times his intense hateful wishes against her. As he asserted himself with the mother and turned more to outside interests, the mother interpreted this behavior as a real rejection. Often during treatment it was obvious that the boy felt very unhappy regarding his absence from school, recognized the crippling to himself, and felt keenly the blow to his self-esteem when children became critical of him.

The mother discussed with her therapist her own unresolved dependence on her mother, her sister, and the therapist. She discussed also her bulimia when left alone, her longing for love, her feeling of inability to give it to her children, and her competition with Jack for attention, e.g., she often complained that her headaches were worse than his. Her "pride was cut to the quick by Jack's not going to school" and she saw his refusal to go as defiance of her. This led to discussion of her wish to dominate the boy as she was being dominated by her neurotic bedridden mother. Early in the treatment she vacillated in her wish to have Jack home, developed guilt as a result, and tried to put the responsibility for forcing him to go to school on Jack's therapist. She also tried to prove that Jack's therapist was inadequate, and she exploited every opportunity to keep the boy near her. As she worked through her own frustrated, dependent needs with her therapist and felt indulged without criticism, she became much more giving with her children and husband and demanded less appreciation and nursing care. She became able to assert herself with her own mother, to side-step the mother's attempts to make her guilty, and to feel far better physically. After five or six months of treatment the boy returned to school, and a year later a detailed letter stated that there was no more trouble with the boy and that the mother was feeling better than she had for years.

DYNAMICS

Consideration of the dynamics of this case with a few illustrative excerpts from the others seemed to point to the following impressions.

Jack suffered from acute anxiety associated with organic illness, and this created a tendency to regress to a greater dependency on the mother for the moment. This is the first crucial step in the cycle to follow. The mother herself had been recently more hostile and frustrated because of the increasing demands made by her neurotic mother. This is an equally important factor in the genesis of the disorder.

Study of the early life situations of these mothers always shows an inadequately resolved dependency relationship to their mothers with intense repressed resentments. One recalls that Jack's mother felt she could never give him enough love--that she should have been free to devote all her time to him as a little boy. This with many other similar comments suggests strongly the dependency relationship of Jack to his mother was never well resolved. What happens when Jack's mother, herself recently deprived and needing new satisfactions, begins to renew over-indulgence to her child for the gratification it affords him and her? Though gratified to some extent because of the child's revived dependence on her, she feels aroused within her at the same time great resentment about granting to anyone that which she was not given. Thus Jack's mother reacted to his bid for renewed dependence with indulgence first and then with hostile envy. She clearly indicated her envy and resentment by competing with him in the sphere of illnesses; her headaches became worse, she felt that he should serve her refreshment in bed, etc. She felt guilty about her resentment, however, and sensing his rage at her none too subtle frustrations and begrudging, she began to vacillate in firmness in all situations. Furthermore, his rage aroused in her a recognition of a mirror image of her own reaction to her mother's dependent, infantile demands and begrudgings, and this in turn led to even further guilt and vacillation in firmness on her part. "When he looks so wild and angry and pale," said the mother, "I cannot stand it--it scares me and I give in. I can't make him go to school."

Occurring concomitantly is the ever-present conflict over the child's efforts at independence. The mother of one boy said, "I can't stand to see Bob such a sissy. I want him to stand his own ground like other boys," and a few minutes later commented, "I told him to go to bed at nine o'clock and at nine-thirty he walked into my bedroom fully dressed, hands in pockets and whistling-- just defying me--a mother should be considered an authority."

In treatment Jack felt less dependent on his mother and gave her one gift to cover Mother's Day and a birthday which were one day apart. She was angry and complained bitterly. On the one hand, tired and resentful of the child's dependence she urges him to stand on his own feet, but on the other, when he tries this, she resents it as rejection and affront to her authority. In countless subtle ways these mothers create intense guilt in the children for their independent strivings.

What does the child do in these various situations? Sensing his mother's wish to have him dependent again, he at once exploits it. One girl utilized her asthma attacks with the anxiety they aroused in her mother to exploit indulgence to a great degree. One child early inveigled his mother into taking him to Florida to rest, "He looked so sick and pale." When the mother becomes angry at the degree to which she is asked to give, the child is furious and more demanding. The same rage appears when the child's attempts at independence are thwarted. All these reactions lead the child to wish to punish the mother in various ways, particularly by not going to school. Sooner or later all these mothers were humiliated and miserable with the criticism leveled at them from the community and relatives. As one mother put it, "It is like a knife through my heart." Also the child punishes himself for his hostile rages in a typically self-destructive way by falling behind in school and crippling himself for life, if not treated. All of the children show fears and sensitiveness regarding this. Frequently they will stay indoors all day and be seen on the streets only after children are home from school. Furthermore, being home permits the child to reassure himself and check up to be sure his hostile destructive wishes against the parents, particularly the mother, do not ensue. One boy frequently said to his mother with real venom, "You're so old and haggard looking I doubt if you will live long and I want to be with you."

A fundamental step in this vicious circle is finally that of mutual restitution which involves loving, giving, over-solicitousness regarding one another's comforts, with the need to be near each other. This constitutes the end and beginning of the circle and they begin again with mutual indulgence of dependence and of all that we now know follows this first step.

Very early in this chain of events there enters as a factor the school itself. When the teacher, as a more consistent disciplinarian, frustrates the child, she arouses his rage. Being less dependent on the teacher, who is a diluted form of the mother, the child's rage inhibited toward the mother can now find expression through displacement, and the teacher in her milieu becomes the phobic object. To avoid the teacher and school is now the defense against being placed in the situation in which the overwhelming anxiety is aroused. Often a child early complains that the teacher dislikes him.

It must be emphasized that in any clinic dealing with children we encounter countless histories of abortive school phobias and all gradations of transient anxieties with reference to going to school. These constitute the so-called "self-cures" which possibly were brought about by sufficient shift in the balance of life situations to offset anything more serious. A word should be said about the relation of this acute and deep anxiety which produces absence from school and the common form of truancy where the child often absents himself from school and dallies here and there about the neighborhood. He does not rush home as the phobic children do. In the cases of phobia where the child hurries home, the reaction seems to be part of a crystallized circle of mutually partially inhibited rages and need to make restitution where dependence and guilt of the child is far greater with respect to the mother. In school phobias the mother is, in her vacillating moments, more affectionate, and therefore guilt is greater in the child, whereas in common truancy the child senses far less genuine love from the parent.

TREATMENT

Because of the vicious circle of guilt already indicated to be operating, it was believed that this circle could best be broken into by a therapy that involved a collaborative dynamic approach to mother and child--treatment carried out by two therapists who co-incidentally attempted to relieve the guilt and tension in both patients. The aim in each was to foster a positive dependent transference in which each patient was permitted indulgence of his or her dependent needs and at the same time the expression of hostilities as lived out with the therapist. The particular conflicts that led to the acute anxiety in both at the onset of the disorder, as well as the basic neurotic dependence problem, had to be resolved. This led to ultimate release of tension and anxiety in both. Treatment of the mother led to a calmer and more secure firmness in her attitude toward the child. The child recognized in her a new firmness and this, plus his own treatment, led to a resolution of the previous conflict. It cannot be over-emphasized that the mother needs and is given treatment as intensively as is the child, and by treatment we do not mean advice.

Six children were treated in a playroom where their conflicts, reflected in behavior toward the therapist, were dynamically understood and interpreted to them. One preadolescent and one adolescent child were treated in the usual interview situation as were the mothers in each case. Of the eight children, seven have returned to school and seem to be well along in their adjustment. One boy is still in treatment and only in the past three months was it seen that nothing fundamental could be accomplished unless his mother received regular treatment by another psychiatrist for her neurotic role.

Early in our studies the mothers were frequently treated by the social worker and the child by the psychiatrist, but it soon became clear that the most difficult problem had been given to the social worker, and to treat mother and child adequately in most instances two psychiatrists had to work collaboratively treating mother and child equally intensively. The duration of regular once a week treatment was from five months to over a year. In considering the factors operating in effective treatment one must recognize not only the depth to which the therapists are able to go with both patients, but also those community attitudes that are frequently vital to the mother and operative in bringing her to the clinic before she has developed any transference. Other factors are the relative secondary gains of child and mother from the existent phobia, for if at any time the balance of secondary gain moves too much to one or the other, such an imbalance becomes an asset in breaking the vicious circle. The history of earlier neurotic episodes in mother and child, length of time the phobia has existed, and especially present life satisfactions of the mother, are important criteria of the prognosis. Treatment of the child alone might be all that is necessary if the child is older (preadolescent), and if he has not been ill too long. With younger children especially, a collaborative type of treatment seems to us more efficacious because such a child is more dependent upon the mother and the latter will not free the child without intensive treatment herself. Such collaborative treatment by two psychiatrists has been used by this clinic in treating a number of deeply crystallized intra-familial neurotic disorders, but this is a matter for elaboration in a subsequent paper.

Little has been said of the role of the father and treatment of him, but in several cases fathers have been seen many times. The impression has always been gained, however, that though he and his neurosis played into the mother's difficulties and led to greater disturbance and frustration in her, and thus indirectly to greater conflict in the child, still, treatment of the mother with clarification of her feelings about the father has seemed the more direct route to a resolution of the conflicts for the child. Fortunately, from a practical point of view, the mother is freer to come for treatment than would be the average father.

DISCUSSION AND CONCLUSION

Just how is this neurosis differentiated from other childhood neuroses? The syndrome of school phobia does not seem to us to be a qualitatively new and specific entity. It is a symptom developing under definite circumstances. First, it appears to us that there is present a history of a poorly resolved dependency relationship between the child and its mother. With this background, two specific factors now enter to initiate the phobia. There always occurs in the child at the outset some acute anxiety, produced either by organic disease or some external situation that arouses conflict, and manifested in hysterical or compulsive symptoms. Simultaneously, the mother suffers from some new threat to her security--marital unhappiness, economic deprivation, or demands that she resents. Newly frustrated in her satisfactions, she needs to exploit the child's acute anxiety and his wish for dependence. On the basis of an early poorly resolved dependency relationship, both readily regress to that earlier period of mutual satisfaction. Now the cycle begins that soon results in the school phobia if the child is of school age, with the teacher, in her milieu, made the phobic object.

REFERENCES

1. BROADWIN, Isra T. A contribution to the study of truancy. <u>American Journal of Orthopsychiatry</u>, 2:3, 1932.

Reprinted by permission from <u>American Journal of Orthopsychiatry</u>, 11:702-708, 1941.

THE SCHOOL COUNSELOR:
HIS UNIQUE MENTAL HEALTH FUNCTION

I. N. Berlin, M.D.

It may be somewhat presumptuous of a psychiatrist to try to clarify and define the particular function of colleagues in an allied professional group. However, it has become clear to me from my
almost 12 years of work as a psychiatric consultant to several
school systems that among the most troubled, overburdened, and
perhaps most unappreciated group of people in a school are its
counselors. One of the plaints I've heard repeatedly is that as a
group, counselors are expected to be all things to all people within the school, and of all the professional people in the school system their jobs are the most poorly defined and most subject to repeated change in emphasis, depending upon the pressures then
current in a particular school system.

I have encountered such wide and varied ideas and concepts of the
counselor's job as at one extreme being held strictly responsible
for the disciplinary control of the antisocial, delinquent youngsters
assigned to them, and on the other extreme the surveying of large
groups of youngsters, spending only a few moments with each, di-
agnostically, in order to "spot" potential problems, so that the
administrator could say he had his counselors in touch with every
child in his school. In addition to these duties, counselors are
expected to possess a particular brand of magic so that after one
interview with an antisocial, hostile youngster, or a frightened,
withdrawn one these students should return to the classroom completely changed in attitude and behavior.

It should be evident that I am talking about the "personal problems"
counselor, and his "primary" job of helping disturbed youngsters,
not the counselor whose job is essentially one of program evaluation and planning with students. I am aware that the personal
problems counselor is expected and is often trained to do voca-

tional counseling, aptitude testing, etc., and often has administrative duties as well.

The counselor's job is usually so ill defined and at the mercy of the fates because of the demands placed on schools by the increased number of problems due to ever larger numbers of disturbed students. These conditions have followed the Second World War with resulting population shifts and increases. The schools, in an effort to deal with the, in many instances, overwhelming number of difficult youngsters, usually have appointed as counselors teachers with sensitivity and greater than usual concern about children. Sometimes these are designated as full-time jobs, more frequently as part-time functions, and in some instances as a duty in addition to their regular teaching assignments.

Despite the increasing number of specialized curricula in counseling and guidance, and the increased number of trained personnel, most counselors have not had much specific training for their jobs. Most counselors conscientiously have taken courses in psychology and in counseling and guidance. Rarely have they had an opportunity once they began to function as counselors to learn about counseling through a formal course of didactic lectures and seminars and supervised field work experience. I have been amazed repeatedly at the outstanding work as a group that counselors do, despite all the above problems and pressures.

THE OUTSIDE VANTAGE POINT

I would like to discuss several aspects of the counselor's job from the vantage point of an outsider, one who, while concerned with the ways in which people, especially children, can be helped with their problems, is not subject to the pressures that beset the counselor who may try to define his job. I hope that any discussion that helps make the counselor's job progressively clearer to him and encourages him to define it more and more precisely for himself may help him to help others in the school setting and in the community to recognize his unique function.

Thus I would like to try to describe my impressions of the kinds of work the counselors I have known have been involved in, the kinds of expectations the school administrators and community have of school counselors, and the realistic functions school counselors can have in which they might function with maximal effectiveness for the benefit of the school. I would like to attempt one other kind of clarification from my particular vantage point, that is, to describe what I have felt to be the unique function of the school counselor. Over and over I have heard counselors ask with some discomfort, "How is what I do different from what the social worker or psychologist does in the school department or community agency?" It seems to the counselor that the expectations are often the same. The confusion may be greater when such expectations of the counselor carry no added training or remuneration as part of the job. Inherent in this question also is how counseling differs from casework and psychotherapy as practiced by others. It has been my increasing feeling and belief that the school counselor's job is a unique one. It is a unique function requiring clearly describable techniques that borrow from dynamic psychology and psychotherapy, but is distinct from these in practice. As I think of the task I have just outlined for myself, I have some qualms about how clearly and succinctly I can complete it. I am aware that what I will say is not especially new, but I hope it will put various familiar elements into a different context that might stimulate critical evaluation and assessment of what I am trying to say.

The counselor's job as I now know it seems to center primarily around trying to help those youngsters who are disturbing to their teachers or to the school. Thus, most youngsters come for counseling usually after prolonged difficulties with various classroom teachers, or repeated truancy and hostile, defiant behavior which disturbs the administration. The counselor is thus often faced with an enraged, distraught teacher or administrator on the one hand and a disturbed, angry, hostile, defensive student on the other. Under these "auspicious" circumstances, he is frequently asked to do several things: first to understand the child's problems and explain them to others, second to secure the cooperation of the parents, and third and above all to use a few talks with the youngster to help him become a good citizen of the school. In other instances the counselor is asked to deal with the learning problems of a youngster who is failing in his academic work and is beyond whatever remedial help the classroom teacher can offer. In this case also he is expected to diagnose and "cure" a problem of many years' duration with a few interviews. More rarely the withdrawn, socially isolated, schizoid youngster is referred for counseling. Usually the expectations are not so great with those youngsters because this type of student is not as troublesome to the teacher as is the hostile, defiant, or sullen, nonlearning student.

THE UNWARRANTED DEMANDS

In addition to the expectations of teachers and administrators that such problem children will be quickly "cured," there are other expectations that make the already difficult job even more difficult. These expectations are in part at least the result of an ever growing demand by communities that schools assume more and more parental functions in addition to or often instead of their prime function of educating children. To the extent that administrators accede to these demands and expectations, they expect the counselor to be parent to the disturbed child, i.e., to discipline him. The counselor is sometimes required to accept responsibility for the student's behavior, and above all he must keep him out of the administrator's hair. In a few schools the counselor has actually had to face the wrath of administrators for "allowing" a youngster to continue to get into trouble. Perhaps the most difficult expectation the counselor has to deal with from fellow teachers, administrators, and community is that of the magic effect. When a parent, teacher, administrator, or other adult human being has failed to solve the disturbance of a youngster with whom he is related as a parent, teacher, etc., and when he finally turns to someone else for help, there are rather ambivalent feelings involved. On the one hand he hopes the other fellow has some magic that he does not have since there really should be some easy answer to the problem with the child. On the other hand, if someone else does succeed where parent or teacher has failed, it means that he is not very effective and there is a half hope that the other fellow will not be successful. Thus the emphasis on the magic change that should occur carries with it a great deal of feeling. Sometimes the counselor accepts such assigned expectations. He hopes that he can effect a magical cure or change to prove his worth and his abilities. Such unrealistic self-expectations make things even more difficult for the counselor and counselee. When the hoped-for magic does not occur, the teacher, parent, administrator, etc., are angry overtly or covertly with the counselor since the problems are still theirs to cope with and they often do not know where else to turn for help. Also the youngster may have been led to expect an easy solution to his problem and when this does not occur he feels again let down and even more angry with the unhelpful adults.

Where does the counselor fit into the mental health team? What is unique about his function? What special methods can he use and how may his particular competence be best used by the school?

The counselor, by virtue of his being a teacher, brings to his work not only his understanding of children and techniques of education, but also an experience that no other mental health worker can have. In his work as a teacher usually he has come to recognize the important integrative and even healing function that learning can, and often does, have for many children. He has often observed that for many children from deprived and/or conflict-ridden homes, school may be a haven, and that learning, i.e., the mastery of the techniques for acquiring knowledge, may be an important help to the child in making him feel better able to cope with the world. When he can at least adequately cope with and master the skills necessary for learning and achieving in school he feels less at the mercy of forces he cannot master in his environment.

Thus learning and mastery of academic material may give some youngsters a sense of self-worth, a glimpse of their own abilities, and a feeling that they need not be stuck in the same circular impasses in which they see their parents and other adults mired. Out of just such experiences, the counselor may get a feeling of how important learning and mastery of skills are to a youngster and may recognize that often the hostile, antisocial, truant youngster is one who has never learned. Such a youngster feels incompetent as a student among his peers and angry at the insistence of teachers that he perform school work that his parents have never felt was important. In fact, the child has experienced that he was not important enough to be helped with school work and encouraged to learn. Each succeeding year of failure in academic mastery increases the frustrated, hopeless, angry feeling and the sense that the future holds little for him. He can see for himself only a future full of the problems and miseries with which he sees his parents vainly trying to cope. He thus turns his anger against the adult world and tries to get his satisfactions (kicks) from any short-term respite from tension through alcohol, drugs, stealing, sex, etc.

Thus the counselor has a particular point of view, the educator's, about why and how the school setting may help or increase the child's difficulties, and he may often have a sense of at least a partial solution to the youngster's aggressive, defiant behavior via learning.

It may not be surprising to many readers to know that in psychoses of childhood one of the more recent important therapeutic tools has been the use of educative techniques. The mastery first of skills of self-care and then of academic skills is important in the recovery from this most serious mental illness (1-3).

Similarly, recent experiences in an anti-delinquency project revealed that helping delinquent adolescents to learn was vital to their improvement and their relinquishing their delinquent ways (4). How then can the counselor use his unique vantage point to help his counselee? It seems to me that with the use of insights from recent developments in ego psychology and of certain psychotherapeutic techniques the counselor can be of some help to the disturbed student.

A DEPENDABLE REALIST

First the counselor tries to develop a relationship of some trust and dependability with the troubled student. Since most of these students are angry, hostile, defiant, and unable to trust any adult, much less rely upon him, the job of showing some interest in the student without over-identification with him and thus being regarded as a sucker is important. Perhaps the most important aspect of developing such a relationship is regular interviews and careful follow-up of the student's behavior and activities in school. I can recall instances when hostile, defiant students have accused counselors of being stool pigeons or spying on them and have felt relieved when the counselor has been able to say, nondefensively, "Look, my job is to help you. I know you're going to try to con me and avoid telling me the truth if you can, so I'm getting all the facts I need to help me help you with or without your help." Also helpful is the effort to define for the youngster the clear alternatives to continuous destructive, antisocial behavior without its being either a punitive "behave or we'll kick you out," or a seductive "We wouldn't want this to happen to you, so please be a good boy," but a realistic "I want you to know where we stand and what may happen if we aren't able to work together successfully."

It also becomes important that the counselor use his task-oriented attitudes to help cement his relationship with the student. That is, if he can spend the required time with the student, first assessing his learning problems realistically, spelling out what his current academic status is, and helping him make plans for the next steps he must take to begin to achieve and feel better about himself, then learning can begin. It's also important to be quite truthful and yet to extend one's help in overcoming the difficulties. If in the face of the student's feeling of overwhelming hopelessness and dread of beginning the monumental task the counselor can help him take but one tiny step, much has been accomplished. No false hopes, unrealistic formulas, or dreams of glory without the inevitable attendant drudgery must be subscribed to by the counselor. Often after prolonged backing and filling, equivocating and avoidance, when the youngster really knows the counselor will hold firm a beginning is made, and the student grudgingly and warily will make the attempt to work. The counselor helps by being clear within himself and with the counselee that it will not be a straight path and that there will be may false starts. With each small step forward, such a youngster will often try to quit and try to avoid the next step up and will have to be encouraged with more frequent interviews for a short time. At such times the student can use the personal relationship and beginning trust in the counselor as an aid in reducing the anxiety attendant on learning.

In this work, the counselor's enlistment of the student's teacher is vital. As teachers begin to understand the problems and the difficulties of the undertaking, their help with the learning by special attention and encouragement may spell the difference between success and failure. Here the counselor uses his insights into the particular teacher-pupil relationship. He can help the teacher by being available to him at moments of discouragement and anger about the impossible task. He also needs to remind the teacher to send him regular reports of the student's work in the classroom, so that the counselor is always informed about the counselee's current status. When the counselor clarifies for the classroom teachers the therapeutic value of learning for the youngster, he makes of them important allies in a mutual undertaking. It is helpful to clarify with each teacher how long, slow, gradual, and frustrating the process will be, but also how important it is.

Another aspect of this task-oriented psychotherapeutic work is that the counselor's work with the parents also has as its focus the academic achievement of the youngster rather than control of antisocial behavior, which implies blame of the parent for his failure as a parent. It is thus sometimes easier for the parents to help encourage their child to be interested in his school work when this is made part of their task than to exercise control that they long ago relinquished. Interestingly enough, such an emphasis has in many instances brought child and parents together for the first time.

Obviously what I have tried to describe for the hostile, antisocial youngster applies equally to the sullen, indifferent nonlearner. The help of the counselor to teachers in assessing the child's academic status accurately and then the firm and steady help in beginning the learning of fundamentals is here also essential and often very effective.

In addition to the core therapeutic task of the counselor, he also needs to follow his usual practice of assessing the teacher's role in the particular child's problems and planning how these may be worked out. Further, it is informative to try to understand the particular disturbing behavior of a counselee as a request for some counter action of an integrative kind from some adult. Thus the insolent but not destructive youngster is often asking for an adult to look beneath his insolent words and attend to his actions, an adult who is concerned with the youngster, rather than with his own hurt, pride, and self-esteem. Much hostile, insolent, aggressive behavior is aimed at unmasking the phony attitudes of adults who say they care about youngsters. These young people seem to be looking for honesty, firmness, and security in the adult with which to identify and emulate since such patterns were absent in the adults at home.

Often the counselor's contacts with the child's family will give him clues to the student's behavior as he assesses the emotional deficiencies in the family situation.

An important therapeutic agent is the student's relationship with his counselor whom he begins to see as an honest adult who believes in the student's human potential for growth, who does not deceive himself about the gravity and difficulty of the situation, and who is willing to expend the time and energy to help the student toward self-realization. It is especially important that the counselor do his task because it is his job and he wants to do it well, and not out of any unclear altruistic love of the student. Such love the student knows from bitter experience could not withstand the frustrations and disappointments that this work brings. The firm expectations of teachers and counselor that a student can learn, and their willingness to stand by until he does may be the necessary reliving of an important part of the parent-infant relationship which these youngsters have not yet experienced, and may provide an important model for the youngster, a model he has never encountered.

The counselor continues his help when he responds to the inevitable crises with spot appointments and clear, consistent presentation of the two roads open to the youngster. The student can persist at his learning tasks or he can give up and revert to his usual pattern of running away from work. Slowly, as the alternatives are presented, his usual pattern of behavior becomes clear to the youngster and he is encouraged to try a different solution this time.

As elsewhere described, there is no more rewarding experience than having lived through such difficult times with a youngster (4). It is especially gratifying to recognize how much differently the student sees himself and the world around him and how differently he functions.

I can hear as I have described the counselor's therapeutic task the cry of counselors everywhere. It sounds interesting and even promising, but where can we find the time to do such a job? It is impossible. It is for this reason that a definition of the professional job to be done is so vital, because then and only then can one begin to clarify the task, plan for, and get others to help in getting recognition of the job to be done, and finally discover the means to do it.

I have tried to emphasize that the school counselor's job is a unique one. His experience as a teacher permits him to focus on the mental health aspects of learning in helping his counselees. He uses techniques from ego psychology that focus on the here and the now, that is, the task to be mastered in the present, rather than past experiences. Such therapeutic activities borrow from psychotherapeutic techniques common to social work, psychological counseling, and psychiatry in their use of the developing relationship between counselor and counselee and the conscious use of the process of identification (providing a model) to help the counselee to accomplish his task -- beginning to learn. In this light no one outside of a school setting is in the position to help the counselee as fully from his knowledge of the teachers, the school, and learning theory as the school counselor. Personal problems counseling is thus a mental health profession, distinct and unique, with much promise if time to practice it and time to acquire training in it are provided.

REFERENCES

1. BERLIN, I. N.; HENRY, A.; et al. Improving learning conditions for delinquent and predelinquent adolescents. California Journal of Secondary Education, 35:175-202, 1960.

2. BOATMAN, Maleta J., and SZUREK, S. A. A clinical study of childhood schizophrenia. In Don D. Jackson (Ed.), The Etiology of Schizophrenia. New York: Basic Books, 1960.

3. SZUREK, S. A. Childhood schizophrenia: psychotic episodes and psychotic maldevelopment. American Journal of Orthopsychiatry, 26:519-543, 1956.

4. SZUREK, S. A., and BERLIN, I. N. Elements of psychotherapeutics with the schizophrenic child and his parents. Psychiatry, 19:1-9, 1956.

Reprinted by permission from Personnel and Guidance Journal, pp. 409-414, January 1963.

WORKING WITH CHILDREN
WHO WON'T GO TO SCHOOL

I. N. Berlin, M.D.

The attendance officer of 30 or 40 years ago would have trouble
identifying his job today. At that time he had a rather simple,
well-defined function: to get truants back to school. And truants
in those days seemed also to be less complicated individuals. They
truanted because they wanted to go hunting or fishing, needed to
work to earn extra money by harvesting crops, or just did not like
school and preferred to learn a trade. By and large, truants were
not very hostile toward school and authority, and truanting even
had its own ground rules, which both truant and truant officer observed.

In contrast, the attendance worker of today, who in some school
systems is the school social worker, has a complex job requiring
him to deal with a wide variety of chronic and severe social and
emotional problems.

At its simplest, the job involves dealing with youngsters whose
families are economically and socially deprived and more concerned with keeping food in their stomachs than with schooling.
Many of these children have severe learning problems because education is neither valued at home nor presented to them in their
overcrowded classrooms in such a way as to give them the experience early in life of some of the fun and satisfaction derived from
achievements in learning.

Many of these children live in broken homes or with parents who
have been terribly defeated by the difficulties of living and so have
given them little of the vital ingredients of nurturing. Such youngsters learn at very early ages to fend for themselves and to grab
the pleasures of the moment because only the moment counts in
such drab and joyless existences. They resent and even hate any
adult authority figure who interferes with their pleasures.

School for many such children provokes anxiety. Learning requires effort, patience, and perseverance, especially to learn enough to begin to get some pleasure out of the process. Early in their school experience, these youngsters react to the teacher's insistence on learning with increased restlessness. They escape into daydreaming or loud, provocative, hostile behavior. Removal from the classroom via disturbing behavior may become an escape mechanism. In high school they are among the nonreaders and nonlearners who can find no interest or purpose in school. Many turn to delinquent activities. They truant to get their "kicks" with age mates outside of school. Since they see no future ahead, no job, no security, no real purpose in living, today only is important.

EMOTIONALLY DISTURBED CHILDREN

Another group of children encountered by schools with increasing frequency today are the emotionally disturbed children whose disturbance is manifested through psychosomatic illnesses that keep them out of school, or by school phobia. In either case, their parents are usually intimately involved with the children's difficulties. This is perhaps most evident in cases of school phobia. In such cases, the mother usually feels great anxiety about separation from her child, who has provided most of her emotional satisfactions--satisfactions she cannot get with her husband. The child in turn reacts to the separation with marked anxiety, fears, and somatic complaints. The father generally is either passive and not very concerned about the child, or resents the child-mother duo that freezes him out. His hostility or indifference often tends to further cement the neurotic, symbiotic mother-child relationship.

The child with severe psychosomatic illness--asthma, allergies, colitis, ulcer, or even rheumatic fever--may be reacting to rather severe emotional problems in and between his parents, problems that have deprived him of important love and attention. The present illness gains for him at least a good deal of attention and concern, however ambivalent that concern may be.

In all of these instances, the worker is confronted with disturbed and often hostile parents who unconsciously feel attacked by any discussion of their relationship to the child. These parents usually resist the worker's efforts to get the child back to school. Yet another kind of child is the schizoid, the lonely, introverted day-

dreamer who tends to leave school because it is frightening to him.
He often wanders the streets alone or sits alone near the school.
He is clearly not delinquent or involved with gangs. The parents
of such children are often severely disturbed people who feel rather
helpless and hopeless in dealing with their child, as well as guilty
about their disturbed relationship with him. They frequently deny
that the child presents a problem.

HELPING THE PARENTS

The worker's efforts to help youngsters stay in school involve not
only conferences and work with the child, but also, and increasingly, efforts to help parents. It is these efforts especially that
result in referrals to social agencies and consultation with mental
health professionals.

Of what value are short-term efforts to help disturbed, defensive,
concerned parents? The most hostile parents are those whose
troubles have been so great that they have felt defeated in most
areas of living. They have been unable to concern themselves
much with their children and are disturbed, distraught, and helpless in the face of the child's anger and demands, or his predelinquent and delinquent activities. They want others, especially the
school teacher or administrator, to act as a parent to their child
and to change him into a useful, cooperative citizen.

Any demand upon them to deal with their child more effectively as
parents, to be more responsible and more firm, results either in
greater helplessness and anger with school personnel or hostile,
retaliatory, punitive, often sadistic action toward the child, without much change in his behavior. It is difficult to help such a parent, even with prolonged psychotherapeutic work. What then can
a few interviews do?

Surprisingly, the worker who can openly recognize what a difficult
spot the parent is in with such a child--a child who responds to
neither cajoling nor punishment--may be able to get the parent to
understand how important education is for his child's future, how
important for helping the child from becoming as stuck and helpless as the parent himself now feels. This realization may come
from a discussion of the opportunities that may be lost to the child
who cannot read or who cannot sustain interest in tasks long enough
to complete them.

An emphasis on the importance of the parents' interest in the child's schooling sometimes gives the parents a new sense of their worth and importance to their youngster. Joint interviews held by the worker with the defiant, sullen adolescent and his hopeless, angry parents sometimes give each a different view of the other and their underlying, usually unexpressed concern for each other. After such an interview, I have heard both adolescent and parents say that they really had not known that the other really cared at all. Thus, occasionally, one may help in even the seemingly hopeless parent-child relationships.

The parents of the phobic or psychosomatically ill child are tied by a conflictful bond to the child. It is important to support their efforts to understand and recognize what is best for their child, so they can feel like good and effective parents. Thus when the worker does not blame the parents for the child's absences from school (which usually arouses parental resistance and hostility) but outlines the parental task necessary to help the child, he begins to reduce the parents' feeling of guilt. Then the worker can help the parents understand why going to school is important to the child's sense of mastery over his fears.

The emphasis on gentle firmness and continued persistence may help parents not to be punitive out of their own sense of helplessness and guilt. Often such help requires a step-by-step analysis of what the parent needs to do, and how the child may react to each of his moves, so the parent can understand and anticipate the child's reactions to the efforts to return him to school. Parents who are warned that the child may react with increased illness or hysterical outbursts may be better able to withstand these difficult moments and to stand pat on their insistence that the child go to school. The worker's readiness to meet with the parents at moments of impasse is often critical to a successful outcome. With parents who deny the presence of disturbance in a schizoid child, there is a serious impediment to communication. Often it takes repeated efforts by many people who know and express their concern about the child's illness to get through to them. Sometimes only court action ordering a period of hospital observation for the child will activate the parents to seek help.

USE OF AUTHORITY

Often, frequent interviews over a long period of time are necessary to help children with school attendance problems. However, even when the contact is brief, the worker has to help the parents to get to know him not as an authoritarian and hostile authority, but as a concerned and understanding professional person who uses his lawful authority in a benign but firm way to help both child and parents with their mutual problem.

The worker's authoritative role, his efforts to enforce the compulsory attendance law, and his potential use of a court hearing can in many instances be helpful and therapeutic. Frequently, parents of children who truant or suffer from school phobia are unable to behave toward their children with any consistent parental authority. They permit their child to cajole them into overlooking serious misdeeds and then, feeling guilty, punish him for trifling infractions. Or they seem to let their whim decide the issues. Or, needing desperately to be liked by their child, with whom they have a strained relationship, they excuse his truanting or other unacceptable behavior. Some parents seem to feel that being lenient about recurring misdeeds may make the child appreciate their kindness and so give them a hold over him. Occasionally, parents identify so closely with their child's defiance of authority that they are unable to be authoritative themselves.

The effectiveness of the worker's authority can come only from its judicious and consistent use. The worker must not give the child or the parent another experience of the kind of ambivalent, capricious use of authority the parents have exhibited. Such a use of authority ends in exasperation and the imposition of vindictive measures and makes impossible any real respect for authority. Through the methods he uses to enforce the law, the attendance worker may present an example of how authority may be used with firmness and kindness to accomplish the task of returning the child to school.

PSYCHIATRIC CONSULTATION

The ever-increasing caseload and severity of the problems presented have in many instances led attendance workers to try to use psychiatric consultation as one way of helping them cope with problems. However, the worker's relationship with mental health consultants can sometimes be rather strained. The worker may be expected by the school to deal effectively with all of these difficult problems although he knows that even the mental health expert is often not successful with them. Thus he may feel that to call in a consultant may mean to others that he has failed or lacks competence. When regular consultation is not available to help in the treatment plan, the consultant is apt to be called in only in a last-ditch effort to solve a problem.

As also happens in medical consultation, the mental health consultant is then expected to have the expert knowledge and special magic to solve the problem. Often, however, he has no magic, and his suggestions are not new to the worker who has already considered them. Therefore, the worker sometimes feels angry and disappointed because he has not been helped, while at the same time he may feel secretly pleased that the expert has not come up with much more than he did. His anger is always partly justified if the consultant has not been able to help him see that one value of consultation is the sharing of responsibility about difficult problems so that the worker will not feel alone and burdened by them.

As workers gain experience as participants in consultation, they learn that although the consultant's ideas and suggestions are often not new or even very effective, they tend to help the worker clarify his own thoughts and encourage him to try out ideas he has entertained but has been wary of attempting.

The consultant can be helpful to the worker when it is necessary to refer the child and his parents to another community resource for service. He can help not only in determining what the appropriate resource is, but also in assessing the probable length of time it would take to bring about the desired change. This latter assessment can be helpful to the worker in dealing with school personnel who are apt to expect altered behavior in the child promptly after referral and are disappointed and angry when it is not forthcoming. School personnel frequently need help in understanding the gradualness of change and how the attitudes of the schoolteacher and administrator toward the child's need to learn can help bring it about.

PREVENTIVE ROLE

How can the worker be a more effective member of the school mental health team? This is a touchy problem. The worker tends to be used in a variety of roles in the school. Sometimes he is a leg man for the administrator. Often, referring a long-term truant to him is a last-shot effort before an expulsion or suspension already predetermined in the administrator's mind, and the worker has little opportunity to work with the child and his parents. In some instances, the worker is told to take the case to court without having had any contact with the child or parents.

The preventive function of the worker is rarely called upon. He is not often included as part of the school team of administrator, teacher, and school nurse which evaluates children whose behavior and learning difficulties indicate they may be potential truants. He is rarely asked to work with such children and their parents early in the difficulty or early in the child's school experience.

Thus, in each case he works with, the worker has a job to do to apprise the school personnel of what might have been done had the child been referred to him earlier, and to demonstrate how the teacher may help keep a youngster in school by giving more attention to his learning problems and calling on the school social worker to work with his parents.

ADULT MODELS

In working with truants, the worker must keep in mind the kind of models these youngsters need in the adults around them--grownups who are neither punitive nor patsies, whose understanding of children leads them to be firm, fair, and consistent in their attitudes, realistic in their evaluations of the child and his situations, and hopeful about a human being's ability to change. These youngsters need to experience adults who, unlike their parents, neither fool themselves nor are conned by a child's false promises. They need a person who is convinced of the importance of the child's remaining in school and who at the same time realizes the difficulties for the child and teacher in getting any learning started because of the obstacles in the child's home environment and the grim realities of today's crowded classrooms. Such conviction and reality assessment when communicated to children and teachers sometimes begin to help them to try it again, and perhaps again, and to stick to it a bit longer each time.

With the phobic or psychosomatically ill child, the worker needs to adopt a determined persistence with child, parent, and school so that the child will begin to feel in his bones that he has to go to school, that if necessary he will be taken to school. Only consistent authoritative efforts help both the child and the parent who has abandoned the authoritative parental role.

The prepsychotic, schizoid youngster desperately needs psychiatric help. Sometimes the worker's awareness of the problem and his sensitivity to the youngster's needs provides the child with valuable stopgap attention until his parents are able to seek aid from a clinic.

IN CONCLUSION

For a worker to use a mental health consultant is not a sign of inadequacy and incompetence. On the contrary, it reveals mature thinking designed to make a difficult job more manageable.

The consultant's function is not only to supply some insights from his particular field of work, but also, and most important, to provide a noninvolved, fairly objective perspective toward problems. Often solutions can be found by the worker once the problems are discussed from a new vantage point.

The worker, in turn, has certain obligations to the consultant: (1) to educate the consultant about the worker's job so that he understands what and how the worker functions and what pressures the worker is under and from whom; (2) to help the consultant understand the school setting more fully, the people involved, and what they contribute to the child's, parents', and worker's problems; (3) to learn to use the consultant well--to assess the kinds of problems the consultant is most helpful with, and to see if together worker and consultant can learn to collaborate more effectively on the others. If the worker carries out these obligations, he will be helping the consultant to grow into a more helpful colleague in this important joint venture of keeping children in school.

Reprinted by permission from Children, May-June 1965, U. S. Department of Health Education, and Welfare, Welfare Administration, Children's Bureau.

FUNCTIONS OF THE EDUCATIONAL PSYCHOLOGIST
IN A PSYCHIATRIC SETTING FOR CHILDREN

Dale D. Miller, M.A., and
Irving Philips, M.D.

This paper describes the functions of an educational psychologist
in a psychiatric treatment center for children. This center, the
Children's Service of the Langley Porter Neuropsychiatric Institute,
provides inpatient and outpatient psychiatric services for emotionally disturbed and some mentally retarded children (Szurek, 1952).
During the past decade and a half, the clinical program of this
service has been directed toward a better understanding of the nature of severe emotional disturbances in children, toward developing more effective means of treating such disorders, and toward
the improvement of training for clinical personnel in the field of
child psychiatry.

In its effort to provide training in all aspects of child psychiatry,
the Children's Service has maintained a continued interest in the
field of mental retardation. Four years ago it applied for and was
awarded a grant from the National Institute of Mental Health to provide additional faculty to augment its teaching and training program
in this field. Although the focus of this additional faculty was on
the special problem of mental retardation, each member of the
group continued to participate in the broad spectrum of the work
of the Children's Service (Philips, et al., 1962).

Included in the grant was a provision for an educational psychologist. He was expected to have training and experience in education
and psychology as well as an understanding of the rehabilitative and
therapeutic aspects of education. In addition to his contribution to
the work of the mental retardation training project, the staff felt
the educational psychologist might begin to explore other areas in
the clinical program where his special knowledge and skills might
be utilized.

Although the staff had some general notions about how the position of the educational psychologist might be developed, the specific functions he should perform were unclear. After he joined the staff and began to work, further questions were raised. Staff psychiatrists wondered how and what he might contribute to their work. Staff psychologists were concerned with his relationship to them and the department of psychology. The schoolteacher wondered if he would be critical of her teaching efforts with inpatient children, and the nurses questioned whether he had a role on the ward at all. The educational psychologist was concerned about working in an ill-defined position, felt isolated from the rest of the staff, and wondered if he could contribute anything of significance to a psychiatric program that seemed already well organized in its approach to the problems of the individual child.

Despite these initial misgivings, the educational psychologist during the past three years has made an effort to define functions appropriate to his position, to carry them out effectively, and to become a member of the clinical staff working toward the common goals of the Children's Service. The task of integrating such a position into the on-going program has not been easy. Many problems developed in the course of the work. Nevertheless, this experience has demonstrated that the employment in a psychiatric service for children of an individual trained in education and psychology can help in a variety of ways to bridge the gaps between education, psychology, and psychiatry as these disciplines coalesce in the study and treatment of the disturbed child. It should also be mentioned that in addition to his dual training, the educational psychologist brought to the Children's Service experience as a classroom teacher of both normal and atypical children at various age and grade levels in the public education system. This experience was found to be particularly valuable to the educational psychologist and placed him in a unique position to participate in the treatment, training, and research program of the service.

It is evident that there are contributions that an educational psychologist can make to this psychiatric program for children. These contributions will be discussed in terms of the specific functions of the educational psychologist as they have been defined up to the present time. It is hoped that the discussion will be applicable to similar psychiatric programs elsewhere.

EDUCATIONAL TESTING AND EVALUATION

Many children who are referred to the Children's Service for study or treatment are handicapped in their ability and/or capacity to function adequately in school. Their difficulties may be manifested in conduct disorders, partial or gross failures in learning, or both. Frequently, children are seen whose behavior is so disorganized, whose ability to learn is so impaired, that school attendance has never been possible. A number of children show varying degrees of mental retardation. Often it is difficult to determine whether the child is psychotic or mentally defective, or whether both conditions contribute to the child's difficulties.

Among many other questions, the psychiatrist may want to know how the child's present functioning compares with that of his peers, what difficulties the child may be having at school, and under what circumstances his abilities might best be realized. In the diagnostic study of disturbed children with learning disorder, the assessment and evaluation of the child's educational capacity and actual level of achievement may contribute to the diagnostic impressions as well as to the treatment, planning, and remedial work.

In some ways the educational and psychological evaluations may overlap. The educational psychologist as well as the clinical psychologist often is concerned with the child's level of achievement and capacity for schoolwork and the extent to which emotional conflict may be interfering with his ability to learn. However, there are distinct differences in their contributions to the understanding of a child. These are related to the kinds of problems attended to, the materials used, and the training and experience of the respective examiners.

The educational psychologist attempts to assess the child's achievement in the basic school subjects. This includes an evaluation of his proficiency in various skills, specific areas of ability or disability, and attitudes toward school and learning in general. Whenever possible, appropriate standardized tests of school achievement are used in the evaluation. Some of the commonly used tests are the Stanford Achievement Tests, the Metropolitan Achievement Tests, the Wide-Range Achievement Test, and the Gray Oral Reading Paragraphs Test.

If the child does not respond to formal tests of this kind, the educational psychologist employs a variety of informal procedures. In these instances, as in all testing situations, he relies on his ability to observe the child's methods of, particular difficulties in, and attitudes toward problem solving. Close attention to all aspects of the child's behavior--his body posture and tone, his affect, his voice and his remarks--during his approach to various tasks may offer valuable clues. A child's secret counting on his fingers in solving an arithmetic problem below his known capacity, giving up without effort, inconsistencies in performance, and nervous chatter and giggles that succeed in postponing problem solving for fear of failure, or even success, may indicate the degree of anxiety generated by the test situation.

The nonresponsive child may be capable of performing if it is possible to stimulate curiosity and interest through friendly talk or mutual participation in familiar school activities such as blackboard games, recitation, and free play. This kind of quasi-teaching interaction with a child may reveal data not obtainable on formal tests. In addition, the child may even begin to feel free enough to respond to formal test materials. To illustrate:

A girl of seven was referred to the Children's Service for study because of her slow progress in school. The school and parents were considering her placement in a special class for the retarded. Her teacher reported that she was socially immature, easily distracted, almost never uttered a sound, and had learned little in her school experience. Her parents considered her to be shy, withdrawn, and fearful; both they and the school wondered whether she was mentally defective. In the course of the psychiatric study, an educational evaluation was requested.

While waiting for the child to be brought to his office, the educational psychologist prepared some paper-cutting and pasting materials. He was in the process of making a paper spyglass when the girl entered. He held it up for her to see and invited her to come and help him finish it. For a number of minutes the child silently ignored his requests. As he gently continued his efforts to interest her, she suddenly approached and helped him apply the last touches. She took the spyglass and with obvious pleasure followed his directions to focus on various objects in the room. Afterwards, she continued to follow instructions and was able to perform adequately on most sections of a formal reading readiness test. The educational psychologist responded with much enthusiasm and encouragement to each task she completed. Her performance was much higher than expected from past reports. She still was not talking. As he continued, she was surprisingly co-operative on a section of the test which required verbal responses. Toward the end of the session she was counting aloud as she wrote numbers on the blackboard. It was soon obvious that she could do first-grade work and that her capacity was essentially normal. This was subsequently corroborated by other parts of the study.

When a child seems incapable of performing on a standardized achievement test that is appropriate to his age and grade, the educational psychologist spends time with the child drawing pictures, working at the blackboard, modeling clay, or looking at colorful books. During this informal play with a variety of readiness materials, some simple learning tasks may be introduced. For example:

One thirteen-year-old severely retarded boy, totally incapable of dealing with a formal test of achievement, found some picture vocabulary cards as he explored some of the readiness games and materials in the office. Noting his enjoyment in looking at and naming these cards, the educational psychologist selected several and paired them with their associated words. On one attempt this boy was able to identify all eight words when they were presented a second time without picture cues. This brief experience suggested that this child, despite his evident severe defect, had some capacity for learning which had not been reflected in his test performance or in his functioning at school.

The educational psychologist also has available to him information about the child's school achievement obtained from interviews with the parents, interviews with the child, reports by the clinical psychologist, and school reports based on current and cumulative records. His own work with the child contributes additional information about the child's educational status that may be interpreted in the light of, and either substantiate or qualify, the data obtained from these sources. All of these factors are considered in making the educational evaluation.

REMEDIAL TEACHING WITH EMOTIONALLY
DISTURBED CHILDREN

The children's inpatient ward is composed of from twelve to four-
teen preadolescent boys and girls, most of whom have been diagnosed as schizophrenic reactions of childhood. Both the children
and the inpatient program have been described in previous publications (Boatman and Szurek, 1960; Szurek, 1952, 1956; Szurek and
Berlin, 1956). It is important, however, in order to understand
the setting into which the educational psychologist came, to describe briefly the already-existing school program.

School activities have always been considered an integral part of
the treatment program for these hospitalized children. One ward
teacher, provided by the San Francisco Unified School District,
has conducted classroom activities for individual children as well
as for small groups. Since many of the children are severely disturbed, the ward nurses accompany them to school in order to help
the teacher and children with difficult aspects of their work.

In its recognition of the potential value of the ward school program
as an adjunct to the therapy of the hospitalized child, the staff has
always looked forward to any opportunity to further its development. The arrival of the educational psychologist afforded the opportunity to explore ways in which this wish might be realized. Before the educational psychologist could participate in the already-
existing school activities or become more effective in the over-all
Children's Service program, it was felt that he should have some
experience teaching psychotic children on an individual basis.

His beginning work with several inpatient children provided the
educational psychologist an opportunity to learn what others already knew about problems of teaching the psychotic child, how
the educational effort was related to the whole treatment program,
and what part he might play in its further development. He also
became familiar with the inpatient staff and their methods and problems of working with severely disturbed children. Over the past
two years he has continued intensive educational work with two of
the children.

The educational psychologist was immediately confronted with the
difficulties involved in teaching these children. Nevertheless, it
eventually became clear that these children learned in much the
same way as any child learns. For the most part, they required

the same methods, materials, and activities that any child needs in order to master basic skills. At the same time, their behavior in the learning situation was often so unresponsive, so disruptive, or so filled with apparent paradox that it was difficult to evaluate their progress from moment to moment. As a result of the wide range of behavior exhibited by psychotic children in the learning situation, the educational psychologist found it hard to maintain system or continuity in the work, whatever method or approach was employed. Shifts in the learning behavior of the children were often so subtle or paradoxical that it was difficult to describe accurately all the nuances of a single individual tutoring session, to develop notions about, or even to identify consistent principles upon which continued work should be based. Nevertheless, two elements in the process seem important:

First, it is essential for the teaching person to be aware of the disturbed child's ambivalence or fearfulness about learning basic skills and to help the child reduce his conflict at a given moment or over a given activity (or step therein). At the same time the teacher should not allow the child to lose sight of the educational effort. The child so fearful of learning may express his anxiety by inhibition, negativism, or aggressive behavior. At these moments no amount of reasoning, persuasion, firmness, or insistence can make him attend to his learning materials. At such times the interaction between the child and the teaching person becomes the major focus of the tutoring session. The child may be encouraged to express his feelings of ambivalence, dependency, love, and hate. There may even ensue a mutual engagement in some activities which may be remote from academic learning. The teaching person in such ways tries to help the child reduce his conflict in an effort to help him <u>return to the learning task</u>. To illustrate:

An attempt was made to teach a mute, self-absorbed, and self-destructive ten-year-old girl to read in a variety of ways, including that of writing. At first, she seemed unable even to hold a pencil. When gently and persistently persuaded to try, the child would bite the pencil in half, tear the paper to shreds, or attempt to injure herself or the educational psychologist. In time the child began to trace over faintly outlined letters. Later on she even began to write independently, but, as had repeatedly happened in the past, her interest and performance began to decline just at the point of mastery.

Later, in the course of her hospitalization, she became more acutely disturbed for reasons beyond the scope of this illustration. She began to pull out her hair and in the course of a few weeks several large bald patches were visible on her head. She would dig at her skin with her fingernails to the point of bleeding. She persistently refused overtures of help from anyone and became increasingly assaultive at one moment and withdrawn at the next. The educational psychologist continued to meet with her daily, but any effort to continue the remedial reading seemed impossible without, first, some reduction in her rage and despair. Often, she would indicate a wish to be carried from the ward to his office, an overture he gratefully accepted as a token that there was at least something she would permit him to do for her. Once in his office, however, her chaotic behavior continued whenever he introduced any material even remotely related to reading. He tried repeatedly to help her. On one occasion after many weeks, he carried her to his office and noticed a change in her behavior when he, for the first time, felt fully able to accept the child's wish to remain cuddled in his lap. After almost an entire session of relaxed closeness, he told her he was getting tired of holding her and suggested that they look at her word book together. She left his lap, got the book, and freely pointed to the words she had "learned" in previous sessions.

Another element of importance is the necessity for the teaching person to become aware of his feelings and to understand his own conflicts and anxieties as they arise in the ebb and flow of the work with the child. The "success" of the teaching person, for example, may all too readily be felt to hinge upon concrete progress in the child. When failure due to some impasse threatens the personal worth of the teaching person, his subsequent efforts with the child may be futile. Whenever feelings such as helplessness, disappointment, anger with the child's hostile rejection, or a feeling of isolation occur in the work, they interfere seriously with establishing an effective working relationship with the child. To illustrate:

When the educational psychologist moved into a new office, the anxiety of one of the children became centered on a large water pipe. With each succeeding visit the child's anxiety mounted. Finally, he could no longer attend to the learning materials and retreated to sitting on a window ledge where he screamed or repeated echolalic phrases over and over. He would often spit and kick at the educational psychologist when any attempt was made to reduce his fear to focus his attention on the learning materials.

The educational psychologist felt at a loss to help in any way, and began to feel that any expectation was too much of a demand for this child. As this feeling increased, he became more ambivalent about encouraging the child to attend to the learning materials. He found it more difficult than before to cope with the child's spitting and biting behavior. He became discouraged with his inability to reduce the child's fear, furious with his unending negativism, and doubted whether he could ever learn anything. As the educational psychologist expressed these feelings in consultation with a staff psychiatrist, he began to think of alternate ways of encouraging the child's participation in learning tasks. Finally, in a later teaching session with the child, he took some materials into the corner where the child sat perched in terror and gently insisted that he look at them. The child suddenly relaxed, got down from his perch, and tentatively fingered the materials in the corner of the room. In the next session the fear of the pipe had largely disappeared. The child was able to remain seated at the desk for the entire hour as he became engaged in some new learning activities.

Through the experience of working with individual children and other staff engaged in the program, the educational psychologist gained a better understanding of the psychotherapeutic endeavor and the relation of education to it. As a result, he was able to develop other functions and through them to define his position more clearly. He began to help other staff members apply educational methods in their work with children in the ward classroom and in other phases of the ward program. He began to consult regularly with the classroom teacher planning group activities, discussing general problems and methods of teaching inpatient children, and helping her work more effectively with the nursing staff.

This experience with the inpatient children also led to the beginning of individual work with an outpatient child with a severe learning disorder. This work provided experience for psychiatric fellows in collaborating with educational personnel and led to increased interest in the use of remedial education with other outpatient children as an adjunct to psychotherapy. Finally, the remedial work contributed to the treatment program by providing, in treatment reviews and staff conferences, evaluations of a child's specific progress in learning.

HELPING INPATIENT STAFF LEARN ABOUT EDUCATIONAL METHODS AND THEIR APPLICABILITY OUTSIDE THE SCHOOL PROGRAM

The children on the inpatient ward are cared for by nurses and psychiatric technicians. This staff provides twenty-four hour care and supervision of each child in the necessary daily routines of ward living such as dressing, toileting, eating, playing, sleeping, and attending various planned programs in recreation, occupational therapy, and school. The effectiveness of the ward care program depends primarily on the skill of the nursing staff in helping each child participate in these experiences and activities and at the same time helping to reduce the conflict or anxiety that may arise in a child in the course of or, indeed, about such participation.

In order to familiarize himself with the nature and problems of the ward care program, the educational psychologist initially spent considerable time observing the inpatient staff work with the children. The magnitude of difficulty faced by the nursing staff in the moment-to-moment management of such disturbed children and their skill in doing so was apparent. As a result, the educational psychologist felt that it was presumptuous for him to think that he had anything to contribute that could in any way implement the work and competence of this staff. For some time, this feeling that his own field had little to offer to an unfamiliar discipline impeded his fuller participation in the ward program.

Eventually, however, it became evident that the nursing staff had almost no training in techniques and methods of developing learning and play activities with children. Intuitively, the staff were for the most part effective with the children; but it seemed that if they had a better understanding of basic educational practices and procedures, they could offer the children even more.

During those hours in the day when the children were not involved in organized activities such as outings, occupational therapy, or school, many of the children at times became increasingly withdrawn and absorbed in solitary pursuits. Frequently, children could be observed spending long periods of time isolated on a bed or in a corner, rocking back and forth in a chair, posturing strangely or in frozen contemplation of some part of their own bodies. At such times it seemed particularly important to the educational psychologist that (unless contraindicated for some special reason) the nursing staff be able to initiate, encourage, and join the children in appropriate play, self-care, or learning experiences.

The opportunity for the educational psychologist to assist the nursing staff in the selection, planning, and utilization of appropriate materials and activities in their work with the children was finally provided by the nurses themselves. The educational psychologist had been working with the ward classroom teacher in an effort to develop a nursery school program for a group of younger inpatient children. Shortly after the nursery school began, the number of nursing personnel on the ward was increased in order to staff a special research project emphasizing intensive work with individual children. Two of these new nurses expressed an interest in observing and participating in the nursery school program. They felt they could help and at the same time learn something that might be useful in their hours alone with the children throughout the day.

Although the nurses were pleased with the program and functioned well in it, they complained after a time that their participation had been largely on an imitative basis. They felt they had not gained an adequate understanding of the basic concepts underlying the activities carried on with the children in the nursery school situation. Such an understanding, they felt, would serve them in working creatively with the children individually and in small groups during those hours in the day when the children were not engaged in planned activities.

Reviews of what had gone on in a particular nursery school session and planning for the next one had been limited to a brief discussion period at the end of each hourly meeting with the children. There was rarely enough time to deal adequately with all the questions that were raised. Therefore, it was decided that the educational psychologist would hold for the nurses a biweekly seminar in educational methods and principles. Along with the presentation of basic educational concepts, the seminar focused on a discussion of problems that were continually arising in the ongoing nursery school program.

As the seminar progressed, arrangements were made for the nurses to observe nursery school programs for normal children in the community. They were astonished to see the similarities between normal and disturbed children as they function in a nursery school setting. Their observations stimulated provocative questions that when related to their ongoing experiences in the ward nursery school seemed to increase their understanding of basic concepts as well as their effectiveness in the group.

As more children were included in the nursery school program, the nurses of these new children also asked to attend the seminar. Before long, the nurses were not only able to carry on the nursery school program during the absences of the teacher, but they began to experiment with new activities on the ward. One outcome of the work was the gradual development of a project in which two of the nurses continued working with several children as a group at critical hours during the day. Perhaps no specific activity developed as a direct result of the seminar, but it was evident that the nurses learned something that helped them function effectively in the ward situation.

These efforts to help nursing personnel learn about educational methods and their applicability to situations outside as well as inside the school program seemed to carry over to other staff and promoted further development and utilization of individual skill in working with each child.

COLLABORATION AND CONSULTATION
WITH CLINIC STAFF

Collaboration of all disciplines engaged in the clinical work is a necessity for the best understanding and attainment of the clinical goal--the resolution of conflict in the child. The educational psychologist collaborates on a regular basis with all staff members engaged in clinical work with each child (or his parents) he sees. This collaboration facilitates his educational effort with the child and aids him, the nurses, and the psychotherapists in further understanding the child's difficulties and areas of conflict.

The educational psychologist also attends ward rounds, intake meetings, diagnostic study reviews, staff conferences, and ward administrative meetings in order to keep informed of ongoing problems in all phases of the therapeutic program and to contribute his own observations and suggestions.

As he became integrated into the staff, the educational psychologist became involved in assisting the ward teacher with the school program. In the enthusiasm to provide as much as possible for the children, this educational planning occasionally lost sight of the stress that new or different programs might create for other members of the staff. Although the children seemed to benefit, some of the innovations created additional demands upon the nursing staff that made it difficult, if not impossible, for them to continue working effectively with the children in other important areas of development. Such experience demonstrated that obviously worthwhile innovations may actually interfere with an ongoing program unless careful planning results in a coordination of the new developments with the existing services and resources. New ideas, approaches, and activities can be developed, but only within the realistic limits of the time, interest, and staff available in the ongoing program.

CONSULTATION WITH COMMUNITY RESOURCES

Close collaboration between the Children's Service, referring persons or agencies, and potential community resources for the child and his family is part of the study and treatment of each child seen at the clinic. When learning problems are associated with the child's general behavioral disturbances, the school may become involved in the continuing work of the Service with the child and his family. Collaborative conferences between school personnel and members of the clinic staff are arranged upon the completion of many evaluations of this type of child. The school may request information about the child's capacity, specific difficulties, and limitations. The educational psychologist attends these conferences and contributes to them what he has learned about the child and what he considers would be helpful to the school in its further planning.

The educational psychologist has participated in the total evaluation of the child as described above. Throughout the course of the study he has collaborated periodically with all other staff members who have been involved in the assessment of the child's strengths and special disabilities and in the formulation of plans for proceeding in the most helpful way for the child and his family. His knowledge of the limitations and potentialities of the public schools for providing some form of individualization in the program for a particular child can assist the clinical staff in its collaborative conference with school personnel. When there is some reason to doubt the feasibility of public school placement for a child, the educational psychologist may contribute suggestions about alternate educational facilities in the community that might be available and appropriate for him.

The fact that education, in the person of an educational psychologist, is represented on the Children's Service staff and that someone who is familiar with school problems has participated in the clinical evaluation of a particular child may facilitate communication between school personnel and members of the clinic staff during the school conference. For the representatives of the school, the presence of the educational psychologist in the conference means that someone is at hand who "talks their language" and who is familiar with the problems they may face in working with emotionally disturbed children. His findings in terms of school achievement are reassuringly familiar and readily understood. They can assist the school in deciding whether it can effectively continue to work with a child and begin to formulate a program that their school setting can offer. While these impressions of the child's abilities may confirm or be at variance with those of the school, the sharing of such impressions in the light of other clinical information can be of help to school personnel.

SUMMARY

The value of appropriate educational experience for emotionally disturbed children in residential centers and the teacher's role in providing such experiences in the total treatment process for such children has been well documented (Alt, 1960; Krug, 1953; Robinson, 1953; Witmer, 1920). This paper has described some of the functions of an educational psychologist in a particular psychiatric treatment center for children. The educational psychologist, although primarily interested in the educational problems of children seen at the psychiatric clinic, also may be involved in other areas of the clinical program. His skills may be utilized to broaden the efforts of all engaged in the therapeutic task.

The integration of such a person into the ongoing program of a psychiatric center for children and the development of his position so that he can function for the benefit of the program take time, patience, and understanding on the part of the staff and the individual. It is important that the educational psychologist be familiar with the aims, methods, and purpose of the clinical work in order to utilize effectively the skills of his own discipline. The psychiatric staff, too, must be aware of what education has to offer to the clinical program to help the educational psychologist become an integral part of the clinical team working toward a common goal.

REFERENCES

ALT, H. (1960). Residential Treatment for the Disturbed Child. New York: International Universities Press.

BOATMAN, M., and SZUREK, S. (1960). A clinical study of childhood schizophrenia. In D. D. Jackson (Ed.), The Etiology of Schizophrenia. New York: Basic Books.

KRUG, O. (1953). A concept of education in the residential treatment of emotionally disturbed children. Amer. J. Orthopsychiat., 23:691-696.

PHILIPS, I.; JEFFRESS, M.; KOCH, E.; and BOATMAN, M. (1962). The application of psychiatric clinic services for the retarded child and his family. J. Amer. Acad. Child Psychiat., 1:297-313.

ROBINSON, J. F. (1953). Educational procedures in a residential setting. Amer. J. Orthopsychiat., 23:697-704.

SZUREK, S. A. (1952). A descriptive study of the program of the Langley Porter Clinic Children's Inpatient Service. In J. Reid and H. Hagen (Eds.), Residential Treatment of Emotionally Disturbed Children. New York: The Child Welfare League of America, Inc.

SZUREK, S. A. (1956). Childhood schizophrenia: psychotic episodes and psychotic maldevelopment. Amer. J. Orthopsychiat., 26:519-543.

SZUREK, S. A., and BERLIN, I. (1956). Elements of psychotherapeutics with the schizophrenic child and his parents. Psychiatry, 19:1-9.

WITMER, L. (1920). Orthogenic cases XIV, Don: a curable case of arrested development due to a fear psychosis the result of shock in a three-year-old-infant. Psychol. Clin., 13:97-111.

Reprinted by permission from the Journal of the American Academy of Child Psychiatry, 3:536-550, 1964.

THE TEACHING OF SCHIZOPHRENIC CHILDREN

Shirley E. Forbing

I am just completing my fourth year as a teacher on the Children's Ward at the Langley Porter Neuropsychiatric Institute in San Francisco, California. My job is an unusual one, as my pupils are all severely emotionally disturbed children up to 12 years of age. Many are diagnosed as having childhood schizophrenia, a severe mental disorder. The Langley Porter Neuropsychiatric Institute, supported by the State of California Department of Mental Hygiene, is a teaching and research center. This article relates my teaching experiences on the Children's Ward, and is not intended to be a description of how all psychotic children should be taught.

The teaching position on the Children's Ward of the Institute is under the jurisdiction of the San Francisco Unified School District and its program for the physically handicapped. Since there is no special credential available in California for teaching emotionally disturbed children, a California General Elementary Credential is all that is required for this position. At present it seems that experience at the primary and kindergarten level is the best preparation for the job. This is true because many of the children have never attended school, or attended only minimally, because of the severity of their emotional illness.

The nursing staff regularly gives valuable aid in the classroom by caring for special problems that arise. They sit by a child to see that he performs his tasks, guide those children's hands who otherwise would not attempt to work, see that noses are wiped, shoes tied, curb destruction of school materials, see that paint goes on the paper instead of in the mouth, remind children to pay attention. Without this assistance, I could not begin to handle such a classroom except by doing individual tutoring.

The school calendar and schedules are the same as for the rest of the schools in the district. In addition to the regular school year, there are two five-week summer sessions. During the summer, the school day is cut to four hours, and these hours are arranged by agreement of the teacher and the ward staff.

I have often been asked why I decided to go into this field of teaching, as if I had special reasons for doing so. The matter was simple enough--I needed a teaching job and this position was the only one available at the time! Up until this time, like many other teachers I was not aware that any attempt was being made to educate emotionally disturbed children. My acquaintances seemed to think I was making a drastic mistake even to consider teaching psychotic children. I felt that it would be a learning experience, and if I did not enjoy it, I could transfer back to a regular classroom. By the end of the first school year, I had just begun to understand and enjoy my special pupils and so I decided to stay on to explore my new frontier.

Another question that is often asked of me is whether or not the work is depressing and whether I might not be so sorry for these children that I would be unable to work with them. The answer is that I am so busy trying to find new ways to help the children learn that I never think of being depressed. Of course there are times when I am discouraged, as I would be in any other position. While I am working, I do whatever I can as a teacher to help the children. After I leave work, I am quite occupied with my own family, and I do not think of my job until the next day. I am informed by the psychiatric staff that a person who is able to find satisfaction in his personal life and who enjoys helping children learn is better able to succeed in this type of work than one who channels all of his efforts day and night into his job, in an effort to achieve all of his satisfactions from his work.

One of the things that was most helpful to me when I came to work with emotionally disturbed children was the formulation of a certain attitude about what I hoped to accomplish in my work. I learned that only about 10 per cent of the children would ever be "cured." And what of the others? I felt that whatever learning they could accomplish, even though minimal, might help them be a little more self-sufficient and less frightened of the learning process.

Our experience is that a teacher, even though she may not have had psychiatric training, may be successful if she is versatile and can vary her approach to meet individual needs. While a psychiatrist's primary job is to try to understand a child's fears and to try to help him solve his emotional problems, a teacher must try to help a child learn; and, although learning has a therapeutic effect on the child, the teacher's aim is not to do therapy. Some of my friends who are teachers have said that they would be afraid to attempt working with a disturbed child for fear of doing or saying the wrong thing. I have found that these children, while in school, can be treated as normally as possible and can be expected to conform within their individual limits.

There are 15 in-patients on the Children's Ward, with one bed for a study case. With one exception, the children stay on the ward throughout the week, and go home, if possible, on weekends. One child stays during the days only and goes home with his mother at night, this being a satisfactory arrangement for her.

Besides his school program, each child participates in occupational therapy activities, where he has an opportunity to learn arts and crafts. He also spends three hours a week in play therapy with his psychiatrist, and he goes on special outings with the nurses. Some of these outings may include such activities as picnics, a trip to the zoo, the aquarium, the dimestore, the beach, or a movie.

I regularly attend various staff meetings on the ward such as treatment reviews (presentation of case studies and treatment), rounds (where current work with individual children is discussed by psychiatrists, nurses, occupational therapists, social worker, psychologist and teacher) and another meeting where the ward staff discusses ward activities. These meetings are beneficial to the teacher as well as to the other staff by providing an opportunity to exchange ideas, to air problems, and to know what is happening to the child in other areas. The teacher's observations about what the child is doing in school contribute materially to the overall picture of the child, and sometimes may offer clues about the child's readiness to move ahead in other areas.

The classroom schedule changes with the needs of the ward, but generally it is as follows: During the first session in the morning, one group of children will be in occupational therapy, and the remaining group usually has some type of musical activity. This is one activity in which the children participate as a group. Next, the class meets as a whole for the flag salute, the daily news (the children love to see their names in print), a discussion of the daily activities, and a story. If, for some reason, we are not able to have these opening exercises, the children seem to feel that the day has not started right. In fact, some of the children may get the flag and have their own private salute. Routine seems important to these children, even more than it is for normal children. We break up into groups after that, and while I am working with one group, the nurses take care of the others. I have one group that is doing first grade reading and simple arithmetic. Another group has just finished some pre-reading material and is enthusiastically starting on the first pre-primer. In a group of four, I have a nurse to assist in keeping the children's attention on the book. Some of the children are unable to do any kind of work in a group, and these I take individually.

Some of the other activities consist of simple art projects, planting gardens, learning to use simple rhythm instruments, writing group stories. Music is the one area in which almost all the children respond. They are especially attentive to classical music. Even such simple things as learning to color and cutting on a line require a great deal of individual attention, and many children will not even try to do these unless a member of the staff is right beside them, either giving verbal encouragement or actually guiding their hands.

Our school, like other schools in the district, is on a budget. Since the children are quite destructive to materials, they do not last very long and are supplemented by other funds. Attempts are made to help the children be less destructive and many of them have responded to our insistence that they take better care of their things. For some, this is the first step in learning. Once in a while, the ward receives donations of toys and records. Among the materials we have acquired for school room use are a piano, an autoharp, records and record player (one of our most popular items), a blackboard, and a bulletin board.

When working with normal children, a teacher expects her class to go through a testing period at the beginning of each new year. This means that the child tries to see how far he can go; he wants to know where the limits will be set for him and what is expected of him. I have found that the emotionally disturbed child reacts in much the same manner as the normal child, except that the testing is more rigorous and reoccurs frequently. His methods of testing are seemingly bizarre at times. They may take the form of dripping saliva in odd places, eating crayons, depositing feces, pulling and tugging, screeching, destroying completed lessons, tantalizing by doing a tiny bit of the assigned task perfectly and then refusing to complete it.

In dealing with this problem, consistent firmness pays off. Anticipating a child's behavior and being attentive to the first clues he gives of his moods helps to prevent a lot of difficulty. If the child is successful in provoking me, he will continue his testing. In the early months of working together, there seems to be a great deal of this kind of behavior, and as a good relationship is established as a result of consistent and kindly firmness the testing diminishes and sometimes subsides altogether. Some children, however, seem to need to do at least a slight bit of testing each time they are asked to do a task. The more quickly this is handled, the faster the child settles down to work. Establishing rapport seems to take less time as my experience increases, and the period of testing seems to get shorter for each new child that enters the group.

The attitude toward learning varies with each child, but, for the most part, an emotionally disturbed child approaches it with varying degrees of resistance. For instance, a child may try to convince you that he is totally unaware of what is being taught by not hearing, not seeing, not comprehending. This attitude can be handled in various ways, according to the child. One can learn by trial and error which method to use with a child. The child who is openly negative is much easier to handle than the one who is quietly negative. For example, when a child flings her pencil across the room and throws her paper away, I quietly pick up the paper and pencil and assure the child that she has to do the work, even if I have to help her for a while by guiding her hand. It is more difficult to help another child who, given the same lesson as the first one described, will pretend not to hear. If I try to guide his hand, he will let his hand go limp. It is difficult not to ignore a child of the second type when the child of the first type demands attention in such a way that disastrous things will occur if the situation is not immediately handled.

When teaching these children to read, I employ many of the techniques used with normal children. The main difference is that I must simplify much of the material to adjust to their short attention spans. I may read to the mute children while they follow with their eyes. I must use a lot of repetition in the lessons as the children seem to learn more easily by rote than by the reasoning process. Many children have difficulty in applying what they have learned in one situation to another situation. The ability to use reasoning in problem-solving seems to increase when a child is more relaxed and less concerned about his personal problems.

With disturbed, as with normal children, learning seems to follow a pattern. For instance, in learning to write, a child may insist that he cannot use his hands unless I place mine over his to guide him. After guiding him in this manner for several months, I may loosen my grip on his hand so that he is doing the guiding. If I stop using the pressure of my hand before I feel his hands are ready to take over, the child may stop entirely, or if he is ready to go ahead, he may trace over letters that I have made. After this he may try to make letters by himself. The writing may be large, shaky, and done with very light pressure. As the child's confidence increases, the writing improves until it is fairly normal.

Once a child experiences success in learning, he seems to learn more things at a faster rate; if he is being helped in other areas then everything moves smoothly. As an example of this I recall one bright boy, who was mute, on a psychological basis, who, when invited to school, would throw a big temper tantrum. I told him that he would come to school even if he could only stay ten minutes a day at first. So, when I wanted him, I had to pry him loose from his bed, and carry him (while he screamed and kicked) to school. At first the tantrums were violent, but gradually they changed quality so that, finally, they seemed to be a device for "saving face." If he thought I was not going to notice that he was under his covers on his bed, he would let out a little screech to attract my attention. Once he started accomplishing his tasks in school and experiencing success in them, he moved ahead rapidly. In fact, I found it difficult to keep up with him. Instead of my having to come and get him for school, I found him waiting for me, and the moment I opened the door in the morning, he would rush me down to the cloak room and pull my coat off and then take me to the classroom. A short while after he became interested in learning to read, he preferred to read out of encyclopedias, medical and scientific books.

Psychological muteness is common among severely emotionally disturbed children. However, although I found this a handicap at first, I soon discovered that there are many ways of communicating with these children. One day when I was completely mute from laryngitis, I was surprised to find that I could communicate almost better than usual with the children. There are ways that I am able to know whether or not a child is learning anything, even if he will not speak or write. The boy I mentioned in the above paragraph developed his own sign language. Once the nurse assigned to him brought him into the classroom and very excitedly wanted to show me that he could comprehend the meaning of pictures in a magazine. She then drew a picture of a bar of soap on the blackboard and stood back, waiting for him to make the motions of washing his hands. It was a surprise to both of us when he picked up the chalk and wrote "Ivory" inside the picture of the soap. It was doubly amazing since he had never before written anything!

Quite often a child, while pretending extreme indifference, will absorb the lessons and then reveal his knowledge at a much later time outside the school setting. I am working with a child at present who refuses to write at all unless I guide her hand. The lessons I present to her appear afterwards on the chalk board, on scraps of paper, and occasionally on the walls. Still another child who will not read from her pre-primer will use the words that are presented as new vocabulary in her social patter. For instance, if I present the word "run" and ask her to identify it, she will be quite negative, but a moment later might say, "Mike is running past my chair," which is actually not true.

Another example of belated response is a girl who had difficulty referring to herself in the first person. If she wanted a piece of candy, she would say, "You want a piece of candy." After correcting her many times with "Not YOU, but I want a piece of candy," we realized she had learned the right way to say it. One day she went riding in the park. One of the nurses pointed to a tree and said, "Jane, see that tree over there? That's a eucalyptus tree." She countered with, "No not EUcalyptus--I-calyptus."

There are some subjects such as music and rhythmic activities in which the whole class can participate effectively. The flag salute and sharing of the daily news is another. Play activities such as clay, tinker toys, puzzles, and blocks can be done as a group. In these experiences, children learn to share and take turns. Their playing is, for the most part, parallel play rather than interpersonal. Games such as enacting "Jack-Be-Nimble" in which a child or the group recites the rhyme while the children take turns jumping over the candlestick is more successful than "Drop the Handkerchief." In the first instance, the action and result are completed without the interaction of the other children. If the child who is running with the handkerchief decides to use it as a scarf instead, then the game is lost.

Subjects such as reading, writing and arithmetic are best taught either individually or in small groups of not more than four. Children who cannot tolerate being taught in a group are first tutored individually and, when ready, are transferred to the group. These subjects require great effort and concentration on the part of the child. I have found that it does not work out to have other children present in the room when these are being taught, since almost none of the children are able to work alone and they end up vying for my attention. When one child is being settled, the others start acting up, and vice-versa. There is a tremendous difference in the quality of work that is supervised and work that is given to the child to complete by himself. If someone sits quietly but attentively by, a child may put forth a certain amount of effort, while left alone he may destroy the paper or write on the desks, or may simply daydream. Because these children require so much individual attention, each of them ends up receiving only a little bit of schooling. Some of them could tolerate no more than this meager amount, but others definitely could use more school time. The only solution to this would be to have more teachers in such a classroom.

Sometimes a child moves so slowly that his progress is not discernible except over a period of time. Some children make very little progress in school work. Grade placement as such is impossible. A teacher's knowledge of the norm in scholastic attainment is beneficial when a comparison is to be made between the level of a disturbed child and what he should accomplish at his age. By the time a child approaches what should be his normal achievement he is usually ready to be discharged.

A child may be making steady progress and then, because of emotional disturbances, he may hit a plateau or regress. Such was one boy who was promised by his parents that he would go home if he improved. The child worked diligently and was making progress in practically every area. The parents, who were in therapy, did not improve as fast as the boy did, and by the time he was ready, they decided they were not. The boy's regression was immediate, especially in his reading and writing. His writing reverted to a shaky, illegible scrawl, and finally he made very little attempt to do any school work.

Another boy, once he became interested in school, began to make rapid progress in reading. One day his therapist happened by as the child was reading. When the doctor praised the boy for his efforts, the child was all smiles and full of enthusiasm about reading. I made the mistake of asking the boy if he would like to read for his mother that afternoon, to which he responded willingly. Upon hearing her son read, the mother froze, and she stared disbelievingly. Shortly after this episode, the boy's therapist completed his training and left the Institute. The child's interest in reading suddenly waned, and it has taken me two years to get him back to the level at which he originally read.

During the four years I have worked with emotionally disturbed children, four have gone on to public school. One of these had been in school before coming to the clinic, and one had had a certain amount of schooling at Sonoma State Hospital. Another was dropped from school a short time after she entered. The fourth child had never been to school before and from our clinic went to the third grade in a regular public school. He entered at the mid-term and was promoted to the 4th grade the next year. This is a child who had just begun to talk at about the age of eight years and was barely intelligible when I first started teaching on the ward. He now speaks very well when he wishes and has quite a sense of humor.

When a child is ready to go on to public school, conferences may be arranged between the school (teacher, principal, school psychologist) and our staff (which usually includes the teacher, the child's therapist, our psychologist, the social worker, and the child's nurse). Evaluation is made of the child's scholastic ability and how he would adjust emotionally to the new school. In some cases a summary letter to the interested school is all that is required. In any case, our staff is willing to meet with the school if necessary or when special problems arise. The child generally continues his therapy with the outpatient department.

There are several ways a child may fit into the public school program. He may, as were several of our patients, be accepted into the regular classroom. Or, he may have a home teacher or may attend school for just an hour a day and gradually increase this until he is going to school full time. Another possibility is for the child to enroll in an adjustment class in the public schools. These classes usually emphasize remedial work.

Some schools, especially in the larger cities, have what are called Point I and Point II programs. The Point II program is for mentally retarded children who are trainable but not teachable, and whose I.Q.'s are under 50. The Point I program is for children with I.Q.'s from 50 to 75, and it is usually set up so that half of the time is spent in learning crafts and the other part is for academic subjects. In this program, children are at different levels within the same class, and it is flexible so that children who make good progress may be placed back in the normal classroom. One of our patients may be enrolled shortly in the Point II program, even though it is felt that her I.Q. is average. There are, as far as I know, few special classes for emotionally disturbed children in the public schools. However, there are some school districts that are cognizant of the problem and are exploring the possibilities of adding such classrooms to their schools.

I have thoroughly enjoyed my work with emotionally disturbed children. They have both provoked and elated me, but no moment was ever a dull one. Once I was asked which child was my favorite, and to my utter surprise I could not single out one!

Index